The Sky Dr

Victory Lap

The Sky Dragon Slayers: Victory Lap

Other books by The Sky Dragon Slayers:

Slaying the Sky Dragon: Death of the Greenhouse Gas Theory
The Deliberate Corruption of Climate Science—Tim Ball
Human-Caused Global Warming—Tim Ball
Buffoon: One Man's Cheerful Interaction with the Harbingers of
Global Warming Doom—Ken Coffman
Black Dragon: Breaking the Frizzle Frazzle of THE BIG LIE of
Climate Change Science—Geraint Hughes

STAIRWAY PRESS—Apache Junction

Cover Design by Guy Corp
www.GrafixCorp.com

STAIRWAY≡PRESS

www.StairwayPress.com
1000 West Apache Trail, Suite 126
Apache Junction, AZ 85120

Dedication

We dedicate this book to the memory of Dr. Martin Hertzberg
(1930-2018)
'Marty' began his career as a U.S. Navy meteorologist.
Holder of a Fulbright Professorship, he obtained his PhD in Physical
Chemistry from Stanford University.
A stalwart empirical scientist and inspiration to many, upon Marty's
shoulders others now stand.

Foreword

I WROTE A foreword for the first edition of *Slaying the Sky Dragon*. I did not think I would write such a foreword again because all the issues, problems, and limitations of climate science and climate change were identified, which, supposedly, means they were halfway to solution. The problem is—for the mainstream—neither the foreword nor the book changed much. It proves, once again, that a big lie has a mass and momentum that truth struggles to overcome. This book examines and tries to explain that struggle to reach a mass audience.

It is hard to believe that such false information as that created and perpetuated by the UN Intergovernmental Panel on Climate Change (IPCC) continues to exist. Worse, it goes almost unquestioned and is the prevailing view with the dominance and certainty of previous religious views. The more critical points that underpin the completely incorrect view of climate and climate change include the following.

1. CO_2 is only 4% of the greenhouse gases.
2. Every record from any time or over any period shows temperature increasing before CO_2.
3. All computer models are programmed so that a CO_2 increase causes a temperature increase.
4. All global predictions of temperature are made using General Circulation Models (GCM) of the IPCC.
5. Every prediction of global temperature made by the IPCC

was wrong.

6. During the Ordovician Ice Age (~430 million years ago) atmospheric CO_2 levels were 4500PPM.

A simple but powerful definition of science is the ability to predict. If the prediction is wrong, the science is wrong. If the science of weather and climate was accurate, all weather and climate forecasts would be correct. This book identifies most of the reasons why they are not correct. However, in the bizarre world of weather and climate, the IPCC tells us specifically why they cannot be correct.

In the Science Report of the Third Assessment Report (TAR) they note:

> *In climate research and modeling, we should recognize that we are dealing with a coupled non-linear chaotic system, and therefore that the long-term prediction of future climate states is not possible.*

But one other thing guarantees the failure of all the official work on climate and climate change. It is the fact that 99% of the public think that the IPCC work includes studies of global climate and climate change.

However, in fact, they only look at human causes of climate and climate change. This serious restriction was imposed on them in order to predetermine the political outcome, which was the isolation and demonization of CO_2. Despite its enormous benefits to all life on Earth, environmentalists attacked it because it was the byproduct of industry, development, progress, and wealth, all things anathema to their beliefs.

The facts don't support the case for climate and climate change, but neither does the theory. Science advances through positing and testing hypotheses—some call this the "scientific method." A hypothesis is proposed based on a series of assumptions. Others then try to disprove the hypothesis by challenging the assumptions. For example, Einstein's Theory of Relativity assumes nothing can travel faster than the speed of light. Find something that does, and the entire theory is in jeopardy. The global warming hypothesis assumes that a CO_2 increase causes a temperature increase. Since that is a core assumption and incorrect, then the hypothesis cannot stand.

The question posed and answered in this book is why the hypothesis is incorrect. This foreword suggests why such a situation exists, namely that it was accepted as proven from the start. Indeed, anything that disproved or contradicted the hypothesis was glossed over, actively rejected with misinformation or completely ignored.

As a result, an untested, unproven, hypothesis continues to exist and even flourish.

Usually, it is a death knell for an idea to cite, quote, or even refer to something from the Nazi era, but, as Shakespeare observed, even the Devil can quote the scriptures in his arguments. An idea that has continuing logic and application, whether we like it or not, was Joseph Goebbels' concept of the Big Lie. Most reject the concept because of the source, but in reality, it exists. The idea that human CO_2 causes climate change is a classic example. As Adolf Hitler explained in chapter X of *Mein Kampf:*

> *All this was inspired by the principle—which is quite true in itself—that in the big lie there is always a certain force of credibility; because the broad masses of a nation are always more easily corrupted in the deeper strata of their emotional nature than consciously or voluntarily.*

That quote, disquieting as it is, applies very much to the creation, underpinning and acceptance of environmentalism by people who don't know that environmentalism assumes humans are not a part of nature. It is why environmentalists assume every change is unnatural and therefore caused by humans. They are conflicted by the belief that we are part of nature, but superior to nature.

In fact, we are the most successful species because, as Darwin observed, adaptability is the most important attribute for survival and no other species comes close to human levels of adaptability.

—Dr. Tim Ball

Those who promise us paradise on earth never produced anything but a hell.
—Sir Karl Raimund Popper

Introduction

BY READING AND sharing the information you will find in this book, you will be part of a growing army of unpaid skeptics and climate realists across many different forums and mediums. Join us in refusing to be cowed by the lie that there is a "97% consensus" supporting the greenhouse gas theory of climate change.

Hopefully, like us, you are motivated to be a truth-seeker and devote your time to doing that which the post-modern mainstream media will not—question dogma, appeals to authority and the preferred wisdom of the day. Your weapons will be empirical data, common sense and reason.

We must all be vigilant and also understand that science, like any profession, is prone to the human failings of bias and corruption, misconduct and criminality.

We wish you success in your shared journey of discovery into the truly astonishing potential of science and human technological advancement. Let the wise words of science philosopher Karl Popper be your guide.

Please keep in mind that Natural science is empirical. Empiricism says knowledge is derived from what we can sense or observe. Knowledge is gained by passive observation of natural occurrences or by active and controlled experiments.

As long as good people with honest intentions defend Popper's ideas of objectivity, transparency and reproducibility in scientific research, humanity will be rewarded with a brighter future.

Our enduring mission is to encourage open, honest debate as a counterfoil to mainstream misinformation, propaganda and false narratives. Please join us.

For further information, additional publications, articles and resources, please visit prinicipia-scientific.org

If you have further queries, please contact us at: info@principia-scientific.org

Principia Scientific International CIC is legally registered in the UK as a company incorporated for charitable purposes.

Head Office:

27 Old Gloucester Street, London WC1N 3AX

There is nothing so powerful as an idea whose time has come.
—Victor Hugo

Courage and confidence are practical necessities...courage is the practical form of being true to existence, of being true to truth, and confidence is the practical form of being true to one's own consciousness.
—Ayn Rand

Publisher's Note

PROJECTING MYSELF BACK in time, I remember preparing the *Slaying the Sky Dragon: Death of the Greenhouse Gas Theory* manuscript for publication. It took intestinal fortitude and a certain amount of foolhardy courage to publish this controversial, against-the-grain work. I knew we Slayers would be eviscerated by bad-tempered activists. I was acutely aware they would heap insults and threats on us, and they did, in spades. They are small in number, but very powerful, an aggressive, manipulative mob that can—and do—ruin lives.

As a word of caution, a mob might be wrong when they kill you, you're still dead.

But, here we are, all these years later, celebrating with a figurative Victory Lap. The battle rages on, but mostly, we won and earned the right to gloat a little.

What is my basis for saying we won?

Here's data from a 2015 poll which asked Americans to name

the top-15 things they are worried about.[1]

54% —The availability and affordability of healthcare
53% — The economy
51% — The possibility of future terrorist attacks in the U.S.
46% — The Social Security system
46% — The size and power of the federal government
46% — The way income and wealth are distributed in the U.S.
43% — Hunger and homelessness
43% — Crime and violence
39% — Illegal immigration
38% — Drug use
37% — Unemployment
34% — The quality of the environment
28% — The availability and affordability of energy
28% — Race relations
25% — Climate change

If this poll was taken among creepy climate activists like Michael Mann, Gavin Schmidt, David Kent, Al Gore, James Hansen, David Archer, Ray Pierrehumbert, Alexandria Ocasio-Cortez, John Cook, Katharine Hayhoe, Andrew Weaver, David, Suzuki, Greta Thunberg or the many others, climate change would be much closer to the top of the list if not at the very top. After all, according to them, we only have ten more years before a self-inflicted, existential climate catastrophe happens.

Look at another Gallup poll.[2] It shows that a mere six percent of the sample population think Environment/Pollution/Climate change is our top concern.

Six percent.

Despite endless outreach and overwrought media exposure, the public, mostly, does not buy into the overheated hyperbole. However small, I am proud of the role the Slayers played in the

---

[1] https://abcnews.go.com/Politics/top-15-issues-americans-worried/story?id=29758744

[2] https://news.gallup.com/poll/1675/most-important-problem.aspx

grand debate.

That said, this battle will not be fully won in my lifetime. Until deep into the next ice age, there will be rabid, self-hating activists trolling on the Internet and sucking up government money. Don't misread me. I am happy there is disagreement. If there wasn't, humble, independent Stairway Press would not sell as many books. The marketplace doesn't need more books covering topics everyone agrees on. Controversy sells. As a side note, generally, people don't buy books they disagree with—they buy books that will help them win arguments with the corrupt and clueless. That is a need we are happy to fill. I hope we can continue to do it for a long, long time.

History will judge us. It takes a long time for popularized, but fake, science to be flushed down the toilet of history. If we Slayers are wrong, our ancestors will judge us harshly and we'll be rightfully categorized as hucksters and lunatics.

However, as an engineer and minor league expert in applied thermodynamics, I am certain we are right. There are scores of theories about physics, but the surest and quickest way to discard an idea is to test it for absurdities like perpetual motion or free energy from nothing. If you propose a mechanism that, in the final analysis, moves forever without outside force or does something equivalent like reflect heat back on itself and get itself hotter, then it's nonsense. And remember, when an idea is wrong or absurd, it can be wrong or absurd in an infinite number of ways. There is no limit to the ways a bad theory can be false.

You think I like the reality that CO_2 has no great power?

I don't.

I'd love to have cheaper and cleaner sources of energy. In fact, I think that is all that will save us from real existential threats like ice ages, earthquakes, extreme volcanic activity and asteroid impacts.

Sadly, unlike the progressive activists, I don't get to invent my own post-modern form of physics and profit from government grants. As an engineer with a role in promoting public safety and an official code of ethics,[3] I don't have the luxury of creating a heater by

---

[3] As a member of the Institute of Electrical and Electronics Engineers, among other things, I am bound to be *honest and realistic in stating claims or estimates based on available data.* Is there a

manipulating numbers, playing with computer models or contorting statistics. If CO_2 really acted like an extraordinary insulating or exothermic gas, it would give me another tool for heating and cooling electronics. Then, the aircraft and vehicles using the technology I touch would be smaller, lighter, more efficient and safer. I wish God had given us this gift—among the others we're granted. But, He didn't.

And yes, I'm sure.

I love being wrong. It means there are still things I can learn. It would be sad if I knew everything. My quest for knowledge would be over. Fortunately, we're far from that. My ignorance abounds and so does yours. However, when it comes to heating and cooling, I am an engineer with decades of experience. I know the basics of how conduction, convection and radiation work. If I didn't, I would not have navigated a long, fruitful career working on hundreds of successful products.

Perhaps you know more than you realize about practical thermodynamics. If not, it doesn't take much equipment, time or brainpower to enhance your intuition.

A Basic Exploration of Heat Transfer

Equipment Needed: A candle, a match, a metal spoon and a hand (ether left or right—if you don't have a hand, borrow one from a friend).

Process: Light the candle. Hold your hand off to the side and move it close enough to feel the heat. Off to the side, your skin senses thermal radiation, mostly infrared. Move your hand close enough to experience discomfort. An uncomfortable skin temperature begins when the air is around 50°C, give or take. Make a mental note about how effective the hot (something like 800°C) flame is at heating your hand via radiation.

With your hand held a couple of feet *above* the flame, lower your hand until the heat is uncomfortable. Make a mental note about how effective the flame is at heating your hand via convection and

---

similar code for post-modern climate scientists? I don't think so.
https://www.ieee.org/about/corporate/governance/p7-8.html

estimate how much of what you feel *above* the flame, which is mostly heated and therefore rising, convected air, is caused by omnidirectional radiation. Not much, right? You feel mostly the power of radiation by holding your hand off to the side. You feel mostly the power of convection by holding your hand over the flame.

Now, let's explore the trump card of heat transfer, conduction. Hold the handle of the metal spoon and put the spoon's bowl into the flame. Make a mental note about how effective the flame is at heating via conduction.

Did you burn yourself?

Good. Stupidity should hurt. Estimate how much of what you experienced was due to the spoon's conduction as compared to convection and radiation.

Now you have a general sense about the relative effectiveness of heat transfer via radiation, convection and conduction.

Meditate for a minute and think about how likely it is that passive, back or downwelling radiation from cool, rarefied gases can increase the Earth's average surface temperature by about 10% or 33°C.

Fundamentals of the GHE

When we dig into the GHE theory, it's not that complicated. You don't need to be an engineer to understand the fundamentals and to tell when wool is being pulled over your eyes. With no extraordinary effort, the average person can grasp the GHE theory's violation of basic concepts in minutes.

We have to give credit to the manipulators—they achieved a lot based on nearly nothing. The human-caused global warming hoax was destructive, wrong and stupid, but masterful use of hyperbole and fear mongering. Sadly, it distracted us from real world problems and wasted a lot of cash. So goes the battle.

What are we talking about?

Here is the composition of our atmosphere.[4]

---

[4] http://ossfoundation.us/projects/environment/global-warming/atmospheric-composition

Note: Volume is by percentage and PPM is Parts Per Million.

Gas Name	Chemical Formula	Volume	PPM
Nitrogen	N_2	78.084%	780,840PPM
Oxygen	O_2	20.95%	209,500PPM
Water	H_2O	2.5%	25,000PPM
Argon	Ar	0.93%	9,300PPM
Carbon Dioxide	CO_2	0.0397%	399PPM
Neon	Ne	0.0018%	18PPM
Helium	He	0.000524%	5.24PPM
Methane	CH_4	0.000179%	1.79PPM
Krypton	Kr	0.000114%	1.14PPM
Hydrogen	H_2	0.000055%	0.55PPM
Nitrous Oxide	N_2O	0.0000325%	0.325PPM
Carbon Monoxide	CO	0.00001%	0.1PPM
Xenon	Xe	0.000009%	0.09PPM
Ozone	O_3	0.000007%	0.07PPM
Nitrous Dioxide	NO_2	0.000002%	0.02PPM
Iodine	I_2	0.000001%	0.01PPM
Ammonia	NH_3	trace	trace

What jumps out at you? CO_2 is a tiny percentage of our atmosphere. Really tiny. Activists will tell you that snake venom can be deadly in tiny doses (for example, 0.5PPM of Pakistani Saw Tailed Viper (Echis Carinatus) can be deadly). You'll have to ask them what snake venom has to do with a benign, life-giving gas we exhale in proportions like 40,000PPM. When they mention snake venom, that seems like the very definition of a non sequitur to me.

If the proportion of CO_2 is tiny, then it must have great power. Sadly, though, it doesn't.

We all know and agree that CO_2 is an excellent absorber of IR radiation at some narrow wavelengths. It does nothing measurable to the other 1,000,000 PPM (close enough) of the atmosphere. The idea of atmospheric CO_2 heating violates one of my religious beliefs—if something cannot be measured, then it does not exist.

Keep in mind that infrared radiation is not heat. It can cause heating and it can convey thermal energy, but it's not heat. Heat is a mechanism for equalizing temperatures. Temperature is a property of matter. Infrared photons are not matter.

Let's establish a definition. If x causes the average temperature of y to increase by 33°C, then let's call x a heater. You have experience with heaters in your home, even if you heat your yurt by burning yak dung.

Here's the general case.

There's something hot. It conducts thermal energy to air. The air is moved via convection around the living space where its energy is conducted to your skin. If there was a way to increase the temperature of air by 33°C without moving parts—no compressor, no fans, no ducting, no condensing and evaporating fluid, what a miracle that would be. And, with only cool, rarefied gases to work with? Thank you, Gaia.

Believe it or not, that's the Anthropogenic (human-caused) Global Warming claim. Water vapor and CO_2 absorb thermal energy and reflect part of it back toward the Earth to make the Earth 33°C hotter.

They say, sorry, we can't make it work in your living room, but believe us anyway.

How I wish there was a cheap way to increase the temperature of anything by 33°C. Gleefully, I'd double it to get a 66°C increase. Or, I'd block it to get a 33°C decrease and freeze water and cool things.

Unfortunately, the activists say the Greenhouse Effect does not work that way. They're right. It doesn't work that way. It doesn't work in any way. It doesn't work, period.

I will compose a picture for you.

This picture represents a two-dimensional sample of the air in front of your face.

This picture has 2,000 dots with blue representing the relative proportion of N_2 molecules, green representing the relative proportion of O_2 molecules, violet representing the relative proportion of H_2O molecules and the one red dot representing the relative proportion of CO_2 molecules. The two missing dots are Argon, they don't do much of anything.

I wanted to create a more accurate image with 2,500 dots, but the 2,000 as illustrated has the correct proportion of atmospheric constituents, so it will do.

Study this illustration and think about it.

N_2 and O_2 absorb and re-emit IR, but far, far less than H_2O and CO_2. However, for the one CO_2 molecule to have any influence on the other 1,999 molecules, it must have amazing power.

Breathtaking power.

Incredible power.

I invented a pithy theory about this imaginary power called *Little Carbon Dioxide Suns.* Interested readers can read about it in detail in my book, *Buffoon.*

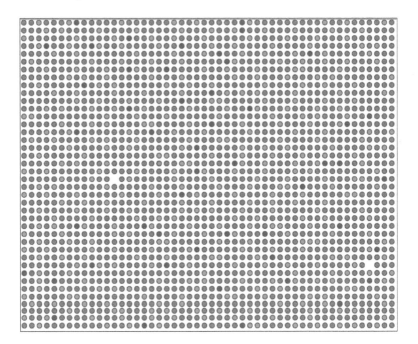

I truly wish CO_2 had the ability to block, trap and store disproportionate amounts of thermal energy, but it doesn't. In the sample illustrated above, the blue and green dots have a temperature, but that temperature has nothing to do with the puny amount of CO_2.

Near sea level, this array of molecules is coupled—sharing energy via molecular collision, physical collision. Remember, temperature is a property of matter. The CO_2 molecules have a temperature, but, near sea level, achieved this temperature via collision from the N_2 and O_2 which were heated via conduction from the Earth's water and soil.

That should be as obvious as the dots in front of your face. The people who don't get this really don't want to.

Sometimes people hold a core belief that is very strong. When they are presented with evidence that works against that belief, the new evidence cannot be accepted. It would create a feeling that is extremely uncomfortable, called cognitive dissonance. And because it is so important to protect the core belief, they will rationalize, ignore and even deny anything that does not fit in with the core belief.

—Franz Fanon

We are the Sky Dragon Slayers. We urge you to think for yourself and draw your own conclusions.

We tell you clearly and openly what we think—and why— and don't demand that you believe us.

We hope you don't because we love to argue.

With calm confidence, we await judgment from the objective lens of history.

May the best ideas win. Inevitably, they always will.

—Ken Coffman, Publisher, Stairway Press

Table of Contents

Preface—The Three-Sided Debate

You see, one thing is, I can live with doubt, and uncertainty, and not knowing. I think it's much more interesting to live, not knowing, than to have answers which might be wrong.
—Richard Feynman

Why are the Climate Debates so Complicated?

FROM THE OUTSIDE looking in, climate science debates appear to be heated, confusing, technical, and all too often, emotional. The debate spectrum varies between the extreme positions of those who claim we must act immediately save the planet to those who claim there is no real problem.

This leads one to ask:

> *How many sides are there in the debates; what are the sides; who are the goodies; who are the baddies?*

One could easily wonder, given the ferocity of some of the

debates, "Are there baddies pretending to be goodies?" This can be very, very confusing. However, there is a very simple viewpoint that instantly illuminates sides of the current climate science debates.

Although it may not be immediately apparent, there are three "sides" or groups in the current climate science debates. The first two sides define the acceptable limits of debate. The sides are:

- Mainstream, orthodox and politically correct academics and activists—widely known as *Alarmists*—propagate pseudo-science. Examples include Dr. James Hansen, Dr. Gavin Schmidt, Dr. Michael Mann, Al Gore, billionaire Maurice Strong, Greta Thunberg and the United Nations who promulgate propaganda and a unified, global, bureaucratic framework to tax and control all countries.

- Mainstream skeptics, who ONLY question within certain bounds (we call them *Lukewarmists*) who concede that some warming is due to human emissions. These mainstream skeptics define the limits of what can and cannot be discussed. Examples include Roger Pielke, Jr., Arthur Rorsch, Dr. Roy Spencer, Anthony Watts, Joanne Nova, CFACT, The Heartland Institute, Christopher Monckton, conservative and libertarian bloggers, columnists, radio, TV and film personalities.

- The politically incorrect skeptics who question everything as a matter of course. This group includes The Sky Dragon Slayers and Principia Scientific International (PSI). These outcasts rigorously follow the scientific method to decide what is true and what is false.

This is clearly demonstrated when one questions the Radiative Greenhouse Effect (GHE) theory, which academics, activists and Lukewarmers accept as an unquestionable given. The GHE theory fails the scientific method and its tenacious defence exposes this theory as dogma, not science.

The GHE is held rigidly as settled science because it is a key mechanism for securing funding and accumulating power. Its use as doctrine reveals it to be despicable pseudo-science. GHE adherents and defenders are dismissive of outsiders; they belittle, threaten and pursue baseless lawsuits to silence critics—those who demand actual evidence to support a theory.

Especially targeted for attack have been the Sky Dragon Slayers and PSI[1] associates who openly and directly challenge the GHE theory. Those most attacked for their work include Hans Schroeder (for an early determination that overall, carbon dioxide actually cools the atmosphere); Alan Siddons (for showing the basic physics used to explain human-caused global warming are applied incorrectly); Joseph E. Postma (demonstrating the Earth is incorrectly modelled and advancing a more realistic modelling approach); Professor Nasif Nahle (empirically demonstrating atmospheric back radiation has no warming effect at Earth's surface); Carl Brehmer (showing water vapor is a negative feedback not a positive one as modelled); and Dr. Pierre R. Latour (inarguably demonstrating carbon dioxide is proven to be only a cooling gas).

Further information in regard to the details, calculations and methodologies of these examples can be found on the PSI website.

The motivation for the polarization of these three "sides" or groups is illustrated clearly in the quote below by Noam Chomsky:

> *The smart way to keep people passive and obedient is to strictly limit the spectrum of acceptable opinion, but allow very lively debate*

---

[1] principia-scientific.org

7

within that spectrum.[2]

Why is the strict application of the scientific method so troublesome for academics, activists and Lukewarmers, but not for the GHE skeptics? A closer look at the scientific method may well shed light upon the matter. Many people do not realise that the scientific method is not just for scientists, it is much more than that.

As a simple, logical and nearly incorruptible approach to science, it is a useful strategy for all who reason. In short, it can verify that what the so-called experts say is so, actually is. It's simple, practical, open, honest and easily remembered, but that does not mean it is weak. In fact, its strength resides in its simplicity.

The scientific method is:

Observation » Hypothesis » Experiment » Theory » Law

First, something is observed. From repeated observations, sense is made of the phenomena and likely outcomes are hypothesized. Hypotheses are tested by replicable experiments. If results can be predictably repeated, then a summarizing theory can be embraced—though testing continues. When the theory proves reliable and is not falsified over time, it can acquire the status of a scientific law.

Please do not just accept, believe, or take-on-trust a single word so far, or any that follows—from us or anyone else. Accepting things on faith is NOT following the scientific method. We can all play a part in upholding the scientific method and advancing civilization by skepticism—testing hypotheses and theories. An honest proponent of a hypothesis or theory should not dismiss or ignore contrary facts or reasoned criticism.

Science must be performed in an open manner challenged

---

[2] https://chomsky.info/commongood01/

by skeptical others. If a theory's raw data, assumptions or methods are not clearly and openly revealed, how can it be proved?

It cannot.

Used intelligently, the scientific method empowers us all— it is not solely the domain of scientists. We can all use the scientific method in our investigations—that is what this method is for and is its most powerful attribute. We can see, check, question and verify data, methods, assumptions and the resulting conclusions. If this cannot be done, at best, results can only be taken on trust. But, science is not about trust. It is about openness and verifiability.

The scientific method can be expressed by the following six points:

- Observe empirical data.

- Hypothesis. Explain the observations and propose an explanation.

- Experiment. Test the explanation by an experiment (i.e. evaluate a prediction from the hypothesis).

- Note: an experiment should include information which would confirm or deny the hypothesis. This is common in subjects such as climatology and cosmology because climates and stars cannot be altered to conduct a test.

- Analyse the experimental results and draw a conclusion.

- The hypothesis is supported if the experiment confirms the prediction. It will be on its way to being accepted as a scientific theory if others are able to independently duplicate the experimental results.

- The hypothesis is rejected if the experiment demonstrates

that the prediction was incorrect. In this case it is necessary to return to steps 2), 3) and 4). This loop is repeated until a hypothesis is obtained which is supported by experimental results.

- Openly publish the experimental methodology, results and data. Publication should include discussion and evaluation of all known possible problems and reservations. Openly, honestly and fully publish everything and ask if anyone can find anything wrong with any part, from observation to conclusion.

If a hypothesis is confirmed by experiment, the hypothesis can be proven.

If, over time, a theory is not falsified, it can become a Law. A Law, according to the scientific method, is a theory that has never been disproved, and cannot be broken or violated, unless the Law is first shown to be wrong. For example, the 2nd Law of Thermodynamics states colder cannot heat hotter—this has never been shown to be wrong.

The reason the scientific method as described above is empowering is that it enables non-experts to discern when experts are mistaken. This power was clearly expressed by Thomas Huxley, an English biologist also known as "Darwin's Bulldog" for his advocacy of Darwin's theory of evolution, who said:

The deepest sin of the human mind is to believe things without evidence.

Further, he famously stated:

Science is organized common sense where many a beautiful theory was killed by an ugly fact.

10

Importantly, it should always be kept in mind that all presented hypotheses could be wrong, so an 'ugly fact' that defeats one understanding of an issue is not evidence that another understanding is correct.

One of the cornerstones of Greenhouse Effect theory is that atmospheric back radiation warms Earth's surface. Here's a summry of that claim:

> *Global warming occurs when carbon dioxide (CO_2) and other air pollutants and greenhouse gases collect in the atmosphere and absorb sunlight and solar radiation that have bounced off the Earth's surface. Normally, this radiation would escape into space—but these pollutants, which can last for years to centuries in the atmosphere, trap the heat and cause the planet to get hotter. That's what's known as the greenhouse effect.*[3]

The GHE theory depends on a violation of the 2nd Law of Thermodynamics—in that the colder atmosphere further warms the Earth's surface via atmospheric back radiation.

Therefore, according to the scientific method, the GHE theory is wrong unless the 2nd Law of Thermodynamics is wrong, which it is not. Sky Dragon Slayers, using the scientific method, believe the GHE theory is wrong and will not accept it or anything based on it.

Computer climate modelling is based upon the GHE theory, therefore GIGO (Garbage In, Garbage Out) software is incorrect too. Why do activists, academics and Lukewarmers accept and defend the GHE theory? Put simply, they have to—it is necessary to support their apocalyptic worldview.

Richard Phillips Feynman was an American theoretical physicist—one of the best-known scientists in the world. In a 1999 poll of 130 leading physicists worldwide by the British

---

[3] https://www.nrdc.org/stories/global-warming-101

journal "Physics World", he was ranked as one of the ten greatest physicists of all time.

Feynman was a keen populariser of physics through both books and lectures, for example the three-volume publication of his undergraduate lectures, *The Feynman Lectures on Physics*. He is often quoted as having said:

> *I would rather have questions which can't be answered than answers that can't be questioned.*

It would appear Huxley, Chomsky and Feynman may well have agreed about the three sides in climate pseudo-science debates.

How and why has this arisen? In very short form:

Politically Correct (PC) funding-PC approval » Teachings » Sick Unicorns » Preferred Solutions » Taxes and Controls

In the world today, politics is everything. It is also a sad fact that science, particularly the natural sciences, lost out to politics many, many aeons ago. It has been said many times—if you pay a scientist enough he/she will prove whatever you want proving. Plainly, such a person is quite prepared to be a pseudo scientist if it benefits them. It is an inherent weakness of human nature and the current political/social system that funding, particularly government funding, can skew what is accepted as science.

Henry Louis Mencken was an American journalist, satirist, cultural critic and scholar of American English. Known as the "Sage of Baltimore", he is regarded as one of the most influential American writers and prose stylists of the first half of the twentieth century. He famously stated:

> *The whole aim of practical politics is to keep the populace alarmed—and hence clamorous to be led to safety—by menacing it with an endless series of hobgoblins, all of them imaginary.*

Hobgoblins (or sick unicorns) must be invented so politicians and bureaucrats can reward themselves and their cronies with expensive, nonsensical solutions. How do you cure a sick unicorn? Any way you want to—because a unicorn is imaginary. The purpose of pseudo-science is to make the public believe a problem exists (their unicorn is sick) and that the self-serving solution is the correct answer to the problem (it will cure the unicorn's ills). However, the problem does not exist in reality, and the preferred solution will have no effect, other than to tax and control people who believe in unicorns (and pseudo-science). In effect, there is little protection built into the system. Science needs protecting. The fact that the GHE theory still has such global political significance after being rejected so many times plainly shows this. One could often be forgiven for thinking Anthropogenic Global Warming (AGW) is almost a religion, such is the fervor of some of its advocates. AGW believers accept without question what they are told by higher authorities.

Professors, for example, are higher authorities most people believe should be taken at their word. However, education might not be such an unbiased source of information as it may appear, given that it is Government funded. Mike Haseler, who describes himself as a climate scientist and blogger, shed light on our situation in a Citizen Scientist article. Here is an excerpt:

> *Originally many Universities were set up as religious institutions in order to support the arguments to enforce orthodoxy in the Catholic Church. We find this religious origin in words such as dean (from Late Latin decanus "head of a group of 10 monks in a monastery"), rector and doctor ("Church father," from Medieval Latin doctor "religious teacher, adviser, scholar,"). We also see this in the dual meaning of "Professor" as also one who professes a religion, and "lecturer" which is also a junior member of the clergy in the*

Church of England.

So, supporting the orthodoxy and "repressing heretics" from outside has always been part of the culture of academia. In light of this history, it should not be surprising that science, particularly British Science, and particularly those "upper-class" echelons like the Royal Society, have a culture of being hostile to anything that is "not invented here."

It therefore becomes somewhat obvious that Professors have to profess the PC (funded) line only and dismiss/belittle/destroy all others, otherwise they will not have jobs or careers.[4]

It is, with a little thought, obvious that a pseudo-science has to define the limits of debate to avoid exposure. Given the political and bureaucrat importance the green/environmentalist agenda has become, our opponents are very powerful, well-funded and have many friends in high places. The skeptics consist mostly of unpaid amateurs or the retired. Our political/social system does not fund us.

At present, there are no effectual, or arguably any, system protections in place to stop PC pseudo-science and the imaginary hobgoblins or sick unicorns thus created, for which the people are being made to pay dearly.

Attacking the GHE theory, taught as settled science to schoolchildren around the world, was never in the minds of any of this book's researchers and writers when they first gave serious thought to the hot topic of man-made global warming. For us, like most people, the issues revolved around how much warming were humans (by their activities) inadvertently causing to Earth's climate system. Before any of us had enough data to formalize our collective efforts into coherent and publishable

---

[4] http://scottishskeptic.co.uk/2013/12/19/the-citizen-scientist/

criticisms of GHE science, we recognized a clear abuse of science *per se*. Fundamental to all our arguments over human impacts on climate is the shocking abuse and misuse of the primary evidence (raw data) and the flaws in the methodology and the science which are relied upon to form conclusions by policymakers who spend trillions of tax dollars on the "climate problem."

As concerned citizens, we, diversely and separately, worried about the more prosaic, non-technical, issues. For example, the unethical removal of thousands of ground weather stations from official data gathering; the unjustifiable refusal of government climate researchers to answer lawful Freedom of Information (FOIA) requests on their secret science; and the unscientific assertion that our complex, non-linear, chaotic climate system was so well understood by governments that they could declare their science as "settled."

This raises the question: can an infant science such as climate science, and in particular the modelling of Earth's climate system, be described as "settled"? Such a description is premature. In fact, the "best" climate science evidence, which we are to trust comes from the UN/IPCC computer climate modelling, has this to say:

> In climate research and modelling, we should recognize that we are dealing with a coupled non-linear chaotic system, **and therefore that the long-term prediction of future climate states is not possible.**[5] [emphasis added]

According to the UN/IPCC's own published report (TAR3) of 2001, describing the science as "settled" is plainly and simply wrong. The science is not "settled" and the modelling and predicting of climate into the long term future, is not actually

---

[5] IPCC Third Assessment Report (TAR3 - 2001) Section: 14.2.2.2, *Balancing the Need for Finer Scales and the Need for Ensembles*, p274. https://www.ipcc.ch/ipccreports/tar/wg1/505.htm

possible.

The closer we looked, the less settled was the science. Through our eyes, as experienced, well-educated researchers, independent scientists, mathematicians and engineers, it became apparent that we were being fed propaganda couched in selective, scientific-sounding terms. In other words, we were being fed nonsensical pseudo-science.

Science is supposed to be impartial, ethical and above reproach, because it adheres to the scientific method which openly invites questioning by all. Perhaps that ideal had meaning for previous generations. It doesn't now. Against skeptics, there is an army of paid government scientists serving their employer's agenda via pseudo-science. Sadly it must be recognised that many have a vested interest in the environmental agenda.

As a perfect example, take the venerated environmentalist James Lovelock, who famously gave the world the 'Gaia Hypotheses.' Here was a true green guru from the 1990's and he turned against those ideas later in life. In a recent interview with *The Guardian* newspaper he said:

> *CO_2 is going up, but nowhere near as fast as they thought it would. The computer models just weren't reliable. In fact, I'm not sure the whole thing isn't crazy, this climate change.*[6]

Believers in global warming hold to what is commonly called the Anthropogenic Global Warming hypothesis (AGW) with includes many claims:

- anomalous global warming is occurring;

- this warming is the result of anthropogenic (man-made) greenhouse gas emissions;

---

[6] Decca Aitkenhead, James Lovelock: Before the End of this Century, Robots Will Have Taken Over, The Guardian; September 30, 2016

- unnatural levels of global warming will occur during this century;

- the consequences of this warming will be disastrous; and

- specific, immediate public policy actions are necessary to mitigate this coming disaster.

While the story goes that the scientific community agrees with these claims, in reality, scientists come to a variety of conclusions on all five claims. It has been the experience of many PSI members that academics teaching the sciences in government-funded universities mostly agree with the five aforementioned claims, while applied scientists and engineers outside of academia (those not dependent on governments' grants) are usually those who reject most of the above claims. So, when you are told "scientists say...[insert chosen alarmist claim here]" the 'they' making the claims tend to have their incomes, careers, reputations, etc., dependent on you believing the AGW premise.

In their self-serving narrative, carbon dioxide was targeted and characterized as a dangerous toxin. The United Nations chose the Intergovernmental Panel on Climate Change (IPCC) as the final arbiter of Scientific Truth. Yet all the while, biologists and food producers know CO_2 to be an essential atmospheric nutrient for plant growth. Anyone can see something is seriously amiss.

As Canadian climatologist, Dr. Tim Ball, so concisely shows in his book *The Deliberate Corruption of Climate Science*, the UN had been looking for some means of bringing about a global government. Readers can look at this and other evidence and decide for themselves whether climate science serves that goal.

So, what is it? Conspiracy or innocent group think? Intentional misdirection, or just another example of the rise and fall of a scientific theory? Readers are invited to make up their own minds about whether this is more about thousands of scientists colluding in a 'Big Lie' to serve the political goals of a wealthy and influential elite, or being simply (and naively) swept along on a wave of environmentalist good intentions to protect our precious (and seemingly threatened) planet.

Our book is intended as a statement of the scientific evidence rather than concern itself with the ideological and political forces underpinning the motives and values of some scientists. Nonetheless, we need some context and will supply it where it explains what is happening in the science or pseudoscience.

For example, a reader of this book could benefit from reading Michael Crichton's *State of Fear* which illustrates Crichton's belief that environmentalism is a form of imperialism used by the West to suppress industrialization in the developing world. To his critics, Crichton is off the mark. Those who have studied *State of Fear* (e.g. William Kay), argue that the environmental movement's primary target for economic suppression is North America. As Kay tells us:

> *Case in point, and Crichton's main focus, is the Kyoto Accord which does not apply to the newly industrializing world and was designed to inflict grievous harm to the economies of Canada, Australia and the United States (i.e. the "West"). A concept of European cultural-political imperialism does not reside in Crichton's mind.*
>
> *Crichton compares environmentalism to the eugenics movement of the first half of the 20th century. Both movements were junk science and both were embraced by the Establishment. Crichton's point that—just because a large number of scientists are paid to say something is true does not make it true—is a valid point, but he is missing something when he claims eugenics vanished after WWII. To his credit he does say:*

18

"Eugenics ceased to be a subject for college classrooms, although some argue that its ideas continue to have currency in a disguised form."[7]

The eugenics movement is vastly larger now than it was in the pre-WWII era. As Kay tells us, the American Eugenics Society is now the Society for the Study of Social Biology. Socio-biologists like E.O. Wilson exert a profound influence on both the U.S. scientific and environmental movements. Of course, this book is not about eugenics, but about climate science. But we include mention of it here to show readers just how insidious and all-encompassing are the dangers when science is in the service of evil. Outspoken eugenicists like Margaret Sanger (whom Crichton disapprovingly quotes) went on to help found Planned Parenthood which is now a vast multinational enterprise.

Rockefeller-financed population control programs strode over the middle of the twentieth century without a hitch and continue on. By their shared goals, the population control movement is inextricably linked to the environmentalist movement. By some estimates the world would have an additional billion humans if not for the pro-active efforts of this social movement. The populations targeted for suppression are largely from the same general social classes and ethnic groups which the eugenicists focused on in the pre-WWII era.

The current world population is approximately 7.4 billion people, yet some AGW believers suggest that figure should be between 0.5 billion to 1 billion.[8] It is, sadly, all too easy with a quick Internet search to find quotes such as:

The present vast overpopulation, now far beyond the world carrying capacity, cannot be answered by future reductions in the birth rate due to contraception, sterilization and abortion, but must

---

[7] http://www.ecofascism.com/review6.html
[8] Eco-92 Earth Charter

be met in the present by the reduction of numbers presently existing. This must be done by whatever means necessary.

The resultant ideal sustainable population is hence more than 500 million but less than one billion.[9]

and..

In order to stabilize world population, we must eliminate 350,000 people per day. It is a horrible thing to say, but it is just as bad not to say it.

I believe that human overpopulation is the fundamental problem on Earth Today...[10]

and...

We humans have become a disease, the Humanpox.[11]

Sadly, using Internet searches, it is all too easy to find numerous references to the United Nations' Agenda 21 describing what it is trying to do and how. The UN is closely associated with Agenda 21 and working to bring about the intentions expressed in the above quotes. The green, environmental and sustainable movements are all justified, at least in part, by computer climate modelling of the GHE theory and the supposed effects human emissions of CO_2 are projected as going to have.

It should be noted that criticism of the GHE theory, and debunking of current climate models, will undermine, if not completely remove, the main basis and justification for the UN's Agenda 21. Thus, as stated earlier, progressive activists and rent-

---

[9] Club of Rome, Goals for Mankind
[10] Jacques Cousteau, 1991 explorer and UNESCO courier
[11] Dave Foreman, Sierra Club, co-founder of Earth First!

seeking academics have powerful friends in high places and many small but vociferous radical environmentalist groups that wholeheartedly support it with religious zeal, who do not want to see the greenhouse effect 'theory' questioned.

There are many who will stop at almost nothing to suppress questioning of their theory, because, simply, it is far too valuable to their cause, or rather agenda. This goes a long way to explain why often the climate (pseudo) science debates become heated, abusive and emotional. AGW believers and many of the human-caused climate change advocates, supporters and believers are not interested in the science, only their radical agenda.

Literally, to them, saving the planet from an imaginary problem is far more important than the fact that it has been proven there is no greenhouse effect. They simply do not want to know. They will not discuss it. They do not want their unicorn—which with all their heart they think is real—slain. Currently, climate pseudo-science is mired in vitriolic debates which are easy to find on the Internet. The current state of climate science is encapsulated by Jonathan Swift:

> *Reasoning will never make a Man correct an ill Opinion, which by Reasoning he never acquired.* [12]

Here's an answer...

> *Men, it has been well said, think in herds; it will be seen that they go mad in herds, while they only recover their senses slowly, one by one.* [13]

For those seeking an escape from herd-like groupthink, this book is for you.

---

[12] A Letter to a Young Gentleman, Lately Enter'd Into Holy Orders by a Person of Quality, Jonathan Swift, 1721

[13] Extraordinary Popular Delusions and the Madness of Crowds, Charles MacKay, 1841

Chapter 1—Using Karl Popper to Overcome Post-Normalism

It's the scientists, not the science, that's determining how much it's going to warm.

—Pat Michaels

BACK IN 2013, PSI co-founder and project coordinator, John O'Sullivan summed the situation aptly when declaring:

> *We never have and never will get a detailed scientific explanation of the 'greenhouse gas' effect (GHE) because for climatologists to seek one would require them to dissect it, thus exposing the truth; it hangs on nothing of any substance.*[14]

At the time of writing, a slow paradigm shift in climate science is inevitable. Western society moves inexorably towards radical political change.

---

[14] https://johnosullivan.wordpress.com/2013/02/04/the-tragic-tautology-of-the-greenhouse-gas-effect/

It now seems fair to say that climate realists, along with traditionalist thinkers (mostly conservative leaning) sense a watershed moment in history. The more optimistic among us say we have earned a hopeful 21st century. It is ironic then that hope for a better future comes at a time when public trust in the opinions of experts has collapsed.

Cronyism in corporate culture and government is under assault in the Age of Trump. A shift towards a classical liberal openness and mistrust of consensus-approved experts gathers pace.

Isaac Asimov, the Russian-born American author and professor of biochemistry at Boston University. summed up our situation perfectly:

> *There is a cult of ignorance in the United States, and there always has been. The strain of anti-intellectualism has been a constant thread winding its way through our political and cultural life, nurtured by the false notion that democracy means that 'my ignorance is just as good as your knowledge.'*

Is humanity waking up to the need to question authority and be better informed?

It behooves us all to beware of those who are guided less by principle and more by profit and prestige. Take no one's word for anything any more.

> *It is very difficult to get a man to understand something, when his salary depends on not understanding it.*
> —Upton Sinclair

While modern life is based on technology and the advancement of scientific ideals, we need to be alert at all times and filter good science from bad. This task will not get easier any time soon.

Objectivity in data collection, sharing and communications is the means by which, generation-to-generation, we build on past achievements such that, as Newton said, we stand on the shoulders of giants in our accumulation of knowledge. But modern living makes us covet our free time and too often we are disinclined to spending time fact checking.

But, at minimum, we must wear a skeptical hat in all matters and apply due diligence on the big issues impacting our daily lives.

Thanks to Sir Isaac Newton and others, science became standardized and testable because it was objective. It demanded skepticism of new findings. We tested the new stuff empirically—in the laboratory or by trial and error—building things that either broke or worked.

Skeptics trust no one's opinion on anything. The best way to do science and advance society is to seek answers from hard empirical evidence versus opinion of so-called experts.

The collapse in the acceptance of expert opinion, in whatever field, was never more exposed than in the two popular national votes cast in the United Kingdom (2016 Brexit referendum) and in the United States (2016 election of President Trump). In each case, experts failed to foresee the outcome—despite their much-hyped skills.

But this is not a book about politics. Our contributing authors and editors represent no political party. But we note the rise in disaffection with politicians and governments among the masses has been matched with a loss of faith in mainstream science and academics.

To us, it seems the great error has been made, in no small part, by a drift towards post-normalism, which is addressed in other parts of this book (post-normalism is the antithesis of Karl Popper's conception of the traditional scientific method).

For more than three centuries, a focus on observation and replication of experiment paved a glorious new road with nonpartisan truth. Regrettably the endeavor was eroded in recent decades by corrupt and self-interested entities. It's as though we are back in the days of Giordarno Bruno—who was burned alive by the Papists AD 1600.

We are witnessing the winds of change in global politics. Perhaps future historians will delineate this not as a time of conventional world war earmarked by nation versus nation, but where the ideologies of globalism versus nationalism were bitterly conflicted.

We believe the cozy Establishment and their cohort of experts are losing the war of ideas. Their undoing is fueled by the sentient elements of our societies studying on the Internet, rather than blindly accepting information and self-serving nonsense from the approved authorities.

The emergence of wholesale, grassroots-level, self-directed learning via knowledge and data from the world wide web undermined the hallowed, traditional institutions. Increasingly, those institutions are exposed as shills for a self-serving elite.

The authors of this volume, as with most of Principia Scientific International's members and supporters, are avid researchers, despite most of us being middle-aged and stereotypically less tech-savvy than Millennials. But we are not political animals and we do not promote any party politics. Our motivation is derived from a long-standing, festering disaffection with the politicization of academia, particularly in Earth sciences.

In the past three decades, our trust in mainstream science journals and their corrupt peer-review process (which is little more than gatekeeping for vested interests) has diminished. Perhaps perspective over time gives us an advantage over our younger selves. Experience is a great teacher. Many of us recall when state education was less centralized and prescriptive.

Our teachers did not follow a national curriculum—nor did they conform to centralized, government-approved standards. Schools and universities once placed a high value on analytical, critical reasoning skills. The teachings of Karl Popper were observed, as were the warnings of George Orwell in *Animal Farm* and *1984*.

Popper, Orwell and other visionaries gave us books defending democratic liberalism as a social and political philosophy. They also presented extensive critiques of the philosophical presuppositions underpinning all forms of totalitarianism.

But we became complacent with each generation getting lazier and less apt to challenge norms. Today, independent thought is ridiculed and discouraged while identity politics and conformism abound.

As western nations allowed their public education systems to become politicized, the distinctions between fact and opinion became blurred. Free-thinkers, young and old, must learn not to rely on what they are told, only on what can be proved.

Choosing a path towards individualism over conformism, we set on a journey—a quest for truth when so much of what we have been told is untrustworthy. As a consequence, we are keenly aware that we must engage in a continuous reassessment of our position in the Big Picture.

We urge readers to take no one's word for anything—don't blindly trust our book, or any book. Do your own investigations and draw your own conclusions. PSI and the Slayers make no apology for exalting Karl Popper's work—we believe it is the best guidance for finding the truth in science.

Our innate sentience, ability for self-reflection and re-evaluation earns us insight and understanding. This is what Karl Popper enshrined in his description of the scientific method. It is humanity's best tool for finding truth in the chaos that surrounds us.

According to Professor Popper, one of the most influential philosophers of science in the past millennium:

> *In so far as a scientific statement speaks about reality, it must be falsifiable; and in so far as it is*

not falsifiable, it does not speak about reality.

To us, the emergence of post-normal science is a threat to the utility of the traditional scientific method. We have identified two opposing methodologies in conflict:

- **Traditional Scientific Method**: The key driver of our Age of Enlightenment which gave rise to the technological advances of the industrial revolution.

- **Post-Normalism**: Pre-deterministic approach where policy and outcome dictate the science. Governments, NGO's and big corporations are culpable purveyors of this modern malaise.

Post-Normal Science is a concept developed by Silvio Funtowicz and Jerome Ravetz who characterize a methodology of inquiry that is appropriate for cases where...

> *...facts are uncertain, values in dispute, stakes high and decisions urgent...*[15]

It is primarily applied in the context of long-term (politicized) issues where there is less available information than is desired by stakeholders (the social elite).

In our universities, post-normalism first infected the humanities, then the social sciences. It then invaded environmental sciences, and as we have shown elsewhere, even attempts to subvert the hard sciences of physics, chemistry, medicine and mathematics. Fortunately, it is not so easy to pollute rigorous disciplines, for, as Karl Popper advocated, any hypothesis that does not make testable predictions is simply not science. Such hypotheses might be useful or valuable, but without verification and proof, they are not science.

---

[15] Funtowicz and Ravetz, 1991

In Popper's view, the advance of scientific knowledge is an evolutionary process characterized by his formula: [16]

$$PS_1 \rightarrow TT_1 \rightarrow EE_1 \rightarrow PS_2$$

In response to a given Problem Situation PS_1, a number of competing conjectures, or Tentative Theories (TT), are systematically subjected to the most rigorous attempts at falsification possible. This process, Error Elimination (EE), performs a similar function for science that natural selection performs for biological evolution. Theories that better survive the process of refutation are not more true, but rather, more "fit"—in other words, more applicable to the Problem Situation at hand PS_1.

Consequently, just as a species' biological fitness does not ensure continued survival, neither does rigorous testing protect a scientific theory from refutation in the future. Yet, as it appears that the engine of biological evolution has produced, over time, adaptive traits equipped to deal with more and more complex problems of survival, likewise, the evolution of theories through the scientific method may, in Popper's view, reflect a certain type of progress: toward more and more interesting problems (PS_2).

For Popper, it is in the interplay between the tentative theories (conjectures) and error elimination (refutation) that scientific knowledge advances toward greater and greater problems; in

---

[16] This and the following four paragraphs are taken from Wikipedia, https://en.wikipedia.org/wiki/Karl_Popper

a process very much akin to the interplay between genetic variation and natural selection.

Where does the 'untruth' of post-normal scientist take us? Here is a clue:

> *Self-evidently dangerous climate change will not emerge from a normal scientific process of truth seeking, although science will gain some insights into the question if it recognises the socially contingent dimensions of a post-normal science. But to proffer such insights, scientists—and politicians—must trade (normal) truth for influence.*
> —Mike Hulme, British Climate Scientist

We are emerging as not only the dominant species, but also as a species with the power to alter fundamentally all life on Earth. Whether we do this for good or ill, only time will tell. It is axiomatic than that no sentient being should want to intentionally destroy his or her environment. We say this as climate realists (skeptics of the alarmist mainstream). Unlike alarmist (Establishment) bedwetters, we realists wish to symbiotically give and take from Nature what can be replenished.

Learning to adapt to change is what life is about. One of the conundrums brought about by the new Information Age is how we process and act upon the data we now have at our fingertips.

We see in the evolution of homo sapiens that we succeeded by overcoming practical challenges—surviving the hardships of climate change, severe weather, war, famine, disease, etc. These were existential challenges.

Today our problems are more cerebral and spiritual due to our success in mastering our environment.

To all the school kids going on strike for climate

change, you are the first generation who require air conditioning in every classroom. You want TV in every room and your classes are all computerized. You spend all day and night on electronic devices. More than ever, you don't walk or ride bikes to school, but you'll ride in caravans of private cars that choke suburban roads and worsen rush hour traffic. You are the biggest consumers of manufactured goods ever, and update perfectly good, expensive luxury items to stay trendy. Your entertainment comes from electric devices. Furthermore, the people driving your protests are the same people who insist on actually inflating the population growth through immigration which increases the need for energy, manufacturing and transport. The more people we have, the more forest and bush land we clear. The more of the environment that is destroyed. How about this? Tell your teachers to switch off the air con. Walk or ride to school. Switch off your devices and read a book. Make a sandwich instead of buying manufactured fast food.

None of this will happen—because you are selfish, badly educated, virtue-signaling little turds inspired by the adults around you who crave a feeling of having a noble cause while they indulge themselves in western luxury and unprecedented quality of life.

Wake up, grow up and shut up until you are sure of the facts before protesting. [17]

---

[17] Author unknown, https://caldronpool.com/alan-jones-brutally-schools-child-climate-protesters-youre-the-first-generation-to-require-air-conditioning-and-televisions-in-every-classroom/

Some scientists say a new ice age is emerging. What if it does? Will we, as a species, suffer the utter devastation we endured during so-called "Little Ice Age" when the population of Europe fell by 30-50 percent? Are we likely to again witness the virulence and death toll of the 1348 AD plague? It is totally unmatched by modern examples. Further, the world mega-famine of 1315 AD, due to both weather and pestilence, was truly catastrophic. Relentless temperature drops combined with erratic weather are nearly impossible to explain, but mankind had no hand in its inception.

We climate realists are entirely unperturbed by alleged recent global warming of around 1°C. We find it quite pleasant compared to what we know happened in relatively recent history. We understand how benign our climate is compared to bygone eras. The wealthier and more technologically sophisticated we have become, the more we have increased our efforts to preserve and cherish our environment.

And let us be very clear. Alarmists are hypocrites who willfully refuse to think through the logic of their catastrophism. Because, as Progressives, they love evolutionary theory until it comes to climate. Then, survival of the fit and adaptation-to-change gets thrown out the window. When it comes to climate, they want us to believe a modest rise in global temperature of one or two degrees will decimate life and adaptation would be out of the question.

Really?

With confidence, we assert that mankind will suffer far fewer deaths and real tragedy from natural disasters, famine and mass pandemics as long as we continue to invest in science, research and common-sense policies. We should feel good about our progress, not ashamed. While innovators and entrepreneurs move technology forward and help us exploit the enormous increase in our leisure time, what we do with our minds becomes a bigger question than what we do with our bodies.

Thanks to computers and the world wide web, we have so

much data and shared information to raise cognizance and informed analysis and planning. This is just as well, because our scientific communities can barely keep pace with the explosion of information.

But there has been a downside: no longer can the lone inventor easily compete with the monolithic force of the military-industrial complex President Eisenhower warned us about in 1961.[18]

Despite our great enrichment in knowledge, we realize an increasing inability—as individuals—to truly absorb so much data; to comprehend, analyze and determine what is useful and good. The more data we have, the more we struggle to make sense of it all. This is the new paradox.

Of course, for millennia, successful communities embraced division of labor, shared responsibility and specialization. From the very first conscious division of labor, we chose simple and practical solutions to life's challenges: hunters hunted meat and gatherers foraged for fruits and berries. This is nothing new. From the Stone Age we implicitly surrendered some of our individualism in return for the benefits living in groups with shared responsibilities and rewards gave us.

We saw, during the rise of the Industrial Revolution which began in England in the early 1800s that people moved away from subsistence living on the land and migrated to cities where they found employment as factory workers, or if they were lucky, entered a trade or profession. The rise of the professional classes was necessary to sustain our increasingly complex lives because we relied on the skills and expertise of others.

We saw industrialized nations flourish. To fulfill ourselves as individuals, we worked collectively for the greater good. We lived by sets of rules (laws and ethics) and understood the need to give up some behaviors that impacted others. This was the

---

[18] see: *Military-Industrial Complex Speech*, Dwight D. Eisenhower, 1961, Public Papers of the Presidents, Dwight D. Eisenhower, 1960, p. 1035-1040

social contract.

Among all the people the social contract provides legitimacy of the authority of the state over the individual. As individuals we consent, either explicitly or tacitly, to surrender some of our freedoms and submit to the authority of laws and to the decisions of a majority. We do this in exchange for protection of our remaining rights. We trust our governments to act on the best available evidence to make decisions to shape our future.

The heyday of the social contract was the mid-17th to early 19th centuries. Historians refer to this period as the Age of Enlightenment. This was also the period when the traditional scientific method taught us to test and verify our ideas via empiricism borne of experimental proofs.

As a result, we saw science, technology and industrial manufacturing free many tens of millions from agrarian hardships and shortened life expectancy. We became better educated, valued our teachers and began to trust experts who sounded rational and made logical-sounding arguments.

Today we look back and understand the benefits of technological advancements from generation to generation. But there exists a paradox: as our lives became easier, the systems that sustain them have become very complex. Modern life requires societies to move towards ever-increasing specialization in new, technical fields.

The never-ending growth in the number of scientists and experts making new scientific discoveries brings with it concomitant mass accumulation of knowledge and expertise. It appears essential to possess a university degree to do anything. Anyone aspiring to careers in the professional classes now are compelled to accept a lifetime of continuous education and re-training to keep up with the changes.

It is more than just a truism that the more we learn, the more we have to learn and decide what is safe, what is morally right and what impacts our decisions. We must be vigilant with checks and balances for ourselves and those who govern.

We are browbeaten as individuals and as groups by 'experts' in the media from either corporations or governments to follow a course of action said to enhance our lifestyles or to be for the greater good. This has run in tandem with the rise of the Politically Correct (PC) culture where everyone has to be 'woke' to every nuance of societal change.

To us, this is why the global warming industry has been so successful for 30 years. It exploited our inherent desires to improve ourselves, everyone and everything around us (including our environment).

When someone persuades you they have the science on their side, it provides the rational and moral imperative to get you to pursue a course of action.

Governments have been proven to have selected scientists willing to add their support to a pre-determined agenda. And let's be real here: scientists are no different from anyone else with bills to pay. Alongside our modern moral imperatives, the bait of career and financial inducements served well as the *modus operandi* for policymakers to win over scientists in need of job opportunities, better pay and the promise of secure careers and prestige.

Because of the increased complexity that comes with this growth in sophistication lone inventors, researchers and pioneers are met with the challenge of needing to collaborate with others.

The need to collaborate for the benefit of the creative process—such as technology and science—behooves us to collaborate on the checks and balances of what technology and science we rely on.

Collaboration requires communication and participation. As life becomes more complex, we need not just better access to more information but greater skill in weighing that information. This we *must* do to determine the merits of our decision-making and what we permit governments to do in our name.

At the grassroots level on the Internet, a mass consciousness is expanding and benefits from the freer access to information sharing. This is where hope resides.

The discredited peer-review system in academia and science publishing, foisted on researchers and innovators about a century ago, was a tool for the Establishment to control and censor ideas that threatened the status quo. Thankfully, online communities now engage in their own peer-to-peer review. So successful has this open access exchange of ideas and review been that even the most prestigious national academies are being exposed.

The shambles of academic 'peer review' is becoming more widely recognized. Dr. Duane Thresher, a former NASA expert in computer climate modeling, tells us his own experience:

> *No one ever peer reviews the program code that makes up so much of science these days, particularly climate science. Additionally, there's a well-known but unwritten rule among scientists for giving talks: never show program code. Usually only one person, the IT incompetent scientist who programmed it, knows what's in the program. A large program like a climate model may be written by many IT incompetent scientists, but each of these usually only programs part of it—one or a few subroutines—and by themselves. Having never been double-checked, the programs are almost certainly full of bugs and their results are questionable.*[19]

With more whistleblowers like Dr. Thresher coming forward, we hope the days of 'appeal to authority'—reliance on the words of an elite with supposed superior insight and knowledge—are on the wane. Also, absurd, post-normal science is likely to perish if the new renaissance of the scientific method continues.

---

[19]

http://realclimatologists.org/Articles/2019/01/03/Climate_of_Incompetence/index.html

Principia Scientific International has been a champion of exposing this cancer in modern intellectual thinking. We have posted extensively on the subject.[20]

Post-normal science has been used by policymakers to create the scientific case to make anti-science policy into law. Post-normal science is predicated on the precautionary principle and delves into 'what ifs' applied as propaganda to coerce changes in our behavior and restricting freedoms that we would not otherwise consent to absent the 'evidence' of government-funded fake-science.

Sadly, in 2016, American legislators missed a good opportunity to enact into law rules to limit the misuse of concocted evidence.[21]

Michael Halpern, program manager of the Center for Science and Democracy at the Union of Concerned Scientists and many others say it should be required of government agencies to accord "greatest weight to information that is based on experimental, empirical, quantifiable, and reproducible data."

Halpern et al. said:

> *The decision about how to weigh different types of information should be a scientific decision, not a political mandate.*[22]

In this challenge we must overcome the reckless and the extreme pessimists (the Malthusians).

---

[20] https://principia-scientific.org/?s=post+normal+science

[21] https://www.washingtonpost.com/news/energy-environment/wp/2016/12/20/these-two-sentences-could-hint-at-the-next-threat-to-climate-science-under-trump/?postshare=2601482289897266&tid=ss_tw&utm_term=.669a853679d1

[22] https://www.washingtonpost.com/news/energy-environment/wp/2016/12/20/these-two-sentences-could-hint-at-the-next-threat-to-climate-science-under-trump/

Malthusians are the save-the-planet brigade telling us we are exceeding the planet's limited resources. They want us to go on a 'diet' from technology and consumerism to keep ourselves and the Earth healthy.

They have long warned of 'social costs' for this. Let's look at these alleged social costs.

People who were skeptical of "science-based" predictions of imminent mass starvation 40 years ago were branded "deniers" and uneducated. Do you think that experience had any impact on the fact that, today, similar doomsday prophesies have difficulty finding traction?

Is it easier, or more difficult, to persuade when activists for a cause are unwilling to acknowledge when they were completely wrong and revise their theories?

One area where activism has been successful in hijacking a field of science is in climate research. We have shown throughout this book and via the writings of analysts such as Dr. Tim Ball, that the greenhouse gas theory was a construct of propagandists more concerned about population control than genuinely wanting understand our climate system.

A good example of the mess created out of 'do gooder' intentions and the misguided zealotry of certain government scientists is shown in *The Tragic Tautology of the Greenhouse Gas Effect* where the the author reveals:

> *Independent American climate researcher Carl Brehmer reminds us of a crucial internal conflict within the "greenhouse effect" hypothesis. So vague and self-contradictory are the myriad explanations given by climatologists of this "theory" that anyone who critically examines it soon understands that it is best explained as a tautology.*[23]

---

[23] John O'Sullivan, https://principia-scientific.org/the-tragic-

In rhetoric, 'tautology' is defined as using different words to say the same thing, or a series of circular, self-reinforcing statements that cannot be disproved because they depend on the assumption that they are already correct. We never have and never will get a detailed scientific explanation of the mechanism of the "greenhouse gas" effect (GHE) because it would require advocates to dissect it, thus exposing the truth that it hangs on nothing of any substance.

While science is all about how things work, we will never get the "how" for the GHE. When Principia Scientific International (PSI), comprised of 200 experts in science and engineering, sought clarification from the supporters of the GHE they were either ridiculed or ignored. So, with no answers as to the "how", inquiring minds turned to the "why" behind the rise of this climate chimera.

Sad and deluded fools—who swallow the inane argument that the only experts we should listen to about climate are government climate scientists—miss the point.

To the sad and deluded, if you are a climate scientist, you can silence professional physicists who tell you that you're not doing your physics correctly, since climate scientists know physics better than physicists.

Fools swallow the argument that engineers and professional physicists do not understand fundamentals and make mistakes post-modern climate scientists can fix for them.

To help the rational and sane unpack that nonsense, we showed in a series of articles that the idea of a GHE driven by carbon dioxide was re-invented in the late 1970's after being widely rejected in science before 1950.[24]

The re-invented greenhouse gas theory gained acceptance during the 1980's as government-funded climatology grew. Despite massive public investment in climate research, no rigor

---

tautology-of-the-greenhouse-gas-effect/

[24] https://johnosullivan.wordpress.com/2013/01/16/national-academies-and-the-non-greenhouse-gas-effect-part-5/

was applied to provide a standard definition of the GHE.

Analogous, but Different

Incredibly, despite a multi-billion-dollar, taxpayer-funded carbon reduction industry avidly pursuing control of the alleged climate thermostat, there are no agreed equations or descriptions of how this thermostat actually works. The Intergovernmental Panel on Climate Change (IPCC) adds to the confusion by glibly declaring our atmosphere is analogous to a greenhouse, but different.

The hand-waving proponents of the hypothesis always start out by admitting the only meaningful source of heat to the surface of the Earth is the Sun, but then, they will declare that certain gases serve to drive down-welling radiation (or back radiation) from the atmosphere as a primary heat source.

A well-argued dissembling of the back radiation illogic came from Joseph Postma with his *No Radiative Caveat for 'Back-Conduction' And Alarmist Physics* where he wrote:

> *I'm not going to repeat the description of alarmist radiative physics in their simulacral version of the greenhouse effect, because readers should already know by now how that argument goes. What I will do instead is put that argument in terms of conduction.*[25]

> *Note: the colour codes below represent increasing temperature in terms of RYGBV.*

> *The Back-Conductive Warming Effect (BCWE, the physical version of the alarmist Radiative Greenhouse Effect—RGHE):*

---

[25] https://principia-scientific.org/no-radiative-caveat-for-back-conduction-and-alarmist-physics/

1) Start with a cold metal rod insulated around its circumference which is then heated at one end. The end of the rod opposite to that being heated is not insulated.

2) As the heat transfers down the rod, the molecules which now have increased thermal energy can vibrate in any direction.

3) When they randomly vibrate back toward the direction of the heat source, they bump into molecules closer to the heat source which are also warmer due to the temperature gradient established from heat conducting down the rod.

4) When the cooler molecules randomly vibrate towards the warmer end of the rod and bump into the warmer molecules in that direction, they therefore send their energy back towards the hot end of the rod.

5) Because the warmer end of the rod is now not losing as much heat because the cooler end of the rod is warming up and the cooler molecules are now randomly vibrating back towards the warm end of the rod and sending their energy in that direction, the warm end of the rod must then become hotter.

6) The far-end of the rod must have the original temperature of the heat source in order to conserve energy, but the heat source and the rod in contact with it there must now have a higher temperature.

So how does that strike you? Have you ever put a cold metal block against something only to find that the thing gets hotter? Of course, that doesn't happen. Imagine how useful that would be if it did happen?! Industrialization is all about the practical application of thermodynamics and in getting temperature gradients to do work for you. This would be useful if either conductive or radiative heat transfer worked this way. They don't. You cannot increase temperature without doing work (heat is equivalent to work)!

The climate alarmists however argue that while this does not occur with conductive heat transfer, it does occur with radiative heat transfer and hence there is a back-radiation greenhouse effect, but no back-conduction warming effect.

The thing is, there is no caveat to the Laws of Thermodynamics such that radiative heat transfer is singled out and explained to not follow the usual behaviour of physical heat transfer. You do not find any especial statements in thermodynamics about radiative heat transfer that it will behave qualitatively differently than conductive heat transfer. Do you want to know why that is? You should understand why that is.

The reason is because both "physical" and "radiative" heat transfer are mediated by the exact same underlying fundamental force of physics: electromagnetism. In both cases of physical heat transfer and radiative heat transfer, the mediating particle is the photon.

We all should know by now that there is no real such thing as "rubbing up" or "bouncing off" from hard little particles in physical contact as such; rather, there are electromagnetic fields which exchange photons and this exchange of information results in impulse reactions which we call force, and which result in friction, or reactionary motion, or heat flow, etc.

In terms of the fundamental forces of physics, there is no difference in the mechanism of physical heat transfer vs. radiative heat transfer, because it is electromagnetism and the exchange of photons which is exclusively at work. This is why there is no caveat in the Laws of Thermodynamics that radiative heat transfer may manifest different over-all behaviour as compared to physical heat transfer.

For what it's worth, the actual end-state of the heat source and metal rod is shown in the next diagram.

The above diagram represents the definition of

thermal equilibrium. The conductive and radiative heat flow equations take on forms like $Q = k(T_h - T_c)$, or $Q = \sigma(T_h^4 - T_c^4)$ respectively. One can see that they are qualitatively the same, as in heat flows from hot to cold only, and one must also understand that the only way we have to solve these equations to determine the end-state, i.e. thermal equilibrium, is by setting them (Q) equal to zero.

We have never ever encountered a climate alarmist claiming the existence of back-conductive warming. Why is that? Why not? After-all, it would have been totally consistent for them to do so: given that it is the same underlying force of physics, they would have been entirely consistent in claiming back-conduction warming along with back-radiation warming, and the argument for either is exactly the same. It is so telling that they've created this inconsistency here!

Imagine if we cut the rod in half and created a small vacuum gap for only radiative transfer to then mediate heat flow within. We can start with the rod from the condition as that from the back-conductive scenario figure below point 6, or from the equilibrium condition as just above.

The results for back-conduction being in effect or not being in effect is shown below:

If the alarmist physics was consistent then it would

argue for the existence of back-conduction as well, however we have never witnessed them doing so. But either way, if one splits the rod with it starting from either the back-conductive scenario or the non-back-conductive scenario, the result in either case is that by the simple expedient of cutting the rod in half, one can increase the temperature of half of the rod! The reason is because of the climate alarmist radiative greenhouse effect operating by radiation in the vacuum gap between the bar-halves.

We don't so much care here anymore as to whether back-conduction warming exists (it doesn't), rather the important result in either case is that if we simply cut the rod in half in order to create a vacuum gap for radiation to mediate heat there, then the climate alarmist greenhouse effect should increase the temperature of the bar closest to the original heat source.

Wouldn't that be an amazing and useful result? Simply cut a heat conductor in half, create a small vacuum gap between facing ends within the heat conductor, and half of the conductor will become hotter. Cut something in half, get higher temperature! And actually, the temperature of the rod closest to the heat source will increase directly as a function of the number of cuts in the rod!

There is simply no internal or external consistency to the "physics" of the alarmist greenhouse effect. This can be expected because something which doesn't exist, and which is false, and which is a simulacrum, can have no internal consistency to the logic of that which can exist by the very definition of reason.

And of course, the flat Earth climate alarmist

movement is nothing but an attack on reason itself. It's meant to be inconsistent, because that's how the negative dialectic is applied in order to render a mind unconscious and unable to think.

The inconsistency of climate alarm "physics" is its FEATURE, not its problem!

What is Heat?

We have a confusing issue to address.

What is heat?

Time and again, this simple, but tricky term has been mangled by alarmists in an effort to create and fuel confusion over the very concept of 'heat.' PSI contributor, Anthony Bright-Paul addressed the issue with his excellent article, *Magma is a Substance.*[26]

In his piece, Anthony explained:

> *Magma is a substance that is hot, but when it is erupted out of a volcano it cools and is called lava. Water is a substance and can be either hot or cold. Air is also a substance and can be warm or very chilly.*
>
> *However, 'heat' is not a substance. Heat is defined as the transference of kinetic energy between two systems. Heat is always either being generated or being dissipated. There is no static state.*
>
> *Unfortunately, it appears that this is a concept that is simply too difficult for some people to understand. If they once understood this concept there would never be any more talk of Greenhouse Effects. Nor would there be arguments among*

---

[26] https://principia-scientific.org/magma-is-a-substance/

scientists about wrong measurements. All such arguments are irrelevant once a person understands that heat is not a substance.

A hot water bottle may be filled with hot water. So, the water may be hot and temporarily have a high temperature. But the heat is not a substance and inevitably will escape. It is such a simple thing to understand.

It is possible to heat the air in a living room to a fairly high temperature, because air is a substance made of several gases. But heat is not a substance. The temperature of the room can only be maintained whilst heat is being generated. Otherwise the air will seek equilibrium and the heat will disperse. The air may remain, but the heat will disappear. The same goes for a glasshouse or a conservatory.

Heat can be generated in various ways, such as friction, compression and combustion. In Physics this is enshrined in the 1st law of Thermodynamics and is called 'by work done'. The Sun generates enormous amounts of heat. Running a motorcar will make the engine hot. Rubbing two sticks together can produce a fire—if you have some dry tinder and a lot of patience. So heat can be generated in a number of ways. But by itself heat will always flow from hot to cold—it never fails. That is the 2nd law of Thermodynamics. Any simpleton can observe this effect a hundred times a day—except alas the Warmist simpletons for whom this concept is too difficult to grasp.

A gas is a substance that can be warmed or cooled. If it is warmed it is warmed by 'work done'. If it cools, it cools by itself. There is no way that a gas can either generate heat or trap heat.

Therefore, it follows inevitably that it is utterly impossible for Mankind to warm the Globe. There is not and cannot possibly be any such entity as Anthropological Global Warming. All talk of Saving the Planet by means of limiting a certain trace gas called Carbon Dioxide are either the hysterical ravings of the deeply illiterate or the machinations of small clique driven by the Material Life Force, intent on self-enrichment at the expense of an uncomprehending multitude.

Please take no one's word on this.

Do your own research.

Definitions of the "greenhouse effect" either overtly assert or imply that downwelling IR radiation from the atmosphere adds additional heat to the ground and sea water.

But nowhere will you be told where the extra heat generated by the atmosphere goes, because all Outward Longwave Radiation (OLR) at the Top of the Atmosphere (TOA) is equal to, and in balance with, all the absorbed sunlight.

So, within the "greenhouse effect" hypothesis, all that "additional" thermal energy the atmosphere generates disappears as mysteriously as it appeared in the first place (see diagram).

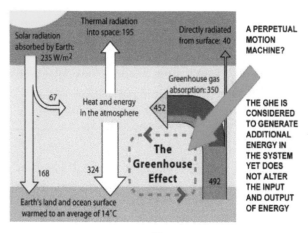

Astrophysicist Joseph E. Postma speaks for most critics of this shape-shifting GHE. Postma points out that the duty of modern empirical science is to seek to identify the physical principles that underlay observed phenomena.

He writes:

> By identifying and understanding the underlying principle, we thus understand reality. If we can mathematize the principle and justify it on a-priori mathematical absolutivity, then the phenomenon becomes a scientific Law, such as the Laws of Thermodynamics or Kepler's Law of Universal Gravitation, or the Laws of Least Action or Least Time. We can also engineer the physical principle and use it to our benefit, to produce products, services, and generally, to create wealth and increase the standard of living of people, etc.
>
> The obvious question: is the underlying principle of the atmospheric greenhouse effect actually defined, anywhere? All I have to tell you, is that "No, it is not."

A healthy skepticism demands that we look again at the above diagram, sold to us as the basic model of the greenhouse gas effect. Imagine what difference the addition or removal of that cyclical flow of phantom internal energy would make on the system as a whole. It makes no difference scientifically at all and we could easily discard it if we wished by applying the accepted principle of 'Occam's Razor' ("plurality should not be posited without necessity"). But, to a charlatan looking to pick your pockets for tax dollars, it is one of the cleverest and most powerful tautologies ever sold.

To appreciate the monumental global fakery in play, it is well worth readers taken a look at 271 thoughts on *Thirty Years*

On, How Well Do Global Warming Predictions Stand Up?[27]

NASA's James Hansen famously sounded the greenhouse gas alarm in 1988—over 30 years ago. Hansen is famed as one of the world's first computer climate modelers and his alarmist predictions worked to scare world governments into action.

We addressed two of Hansen's papers—the first from 1981 on CO_2 forcing was the bedrock of all his later work in computer modeling man-made global warming. We accurately describe Dr. Hansen as the father of computer climate modeling.

The Slayers have been the world leaders in debunking Hansen's CO_2 climate theory. When we published our earlier, groundbreaking book, reasonable souls admitted there was insufficient proof or any testable model for carbon dioxide's effect on a physical climate.

Now, scientists can draw a scientific conclusion. It is an opportune time to weigh 30 years of well-instrumented weather data and test the climate models.

Why? Because the well-trodden maxim in climate science is that weather is not climate, but 30 years of weather data is long enough to judge the longer-term impact on climate. What does the sum of the actual weather data from 1988 to 2018 show?

Hansen, as now retired director of NASA's Goddard Institute of Space Studies (GISS), sat at the pinnacle of the establishment's scientific endeavor to brainwash the world humans were dangerously warming the planet.

Let's set out how his predictions fared:

1) In 1988 he predicted that the Hudson River would overflow and New York would be underwater by 2008 because of rising sea level caused by CO_2. FAILED
2) In 1986 he predicted that the Earth would be 1.1°C higher within 20 years. FAILED

---

[27] https://Wattsupwiththat.com/2018/06/22/thirty-years-on-how-well-do-global-warming-predictions-stand-up/

3) He said that Arctic would be ice free by 2000. FAILED
4) In 2009 Hansen said that Obama had 4 years left to save the planet. FAILED

What has 30 years of trillion-dollar government climate research bought us? Falsification of models offered as evidence for the rigged system of climate propaganda.

Hansen is not alone in responsibility. The blame is shared by other incompetents and biased actors. That role of infamy should include:

- Dr. Syukuro Manabe, Princeton University, pioneer of AGW theory
- Dr. Robert Cess, Stony Brook University, mechanics researcher
- Dr. Michael E. Mann, Berkeley, Yale and Penn State Universities and hockey stick graph fabricator
- Dr. Michel Schlesinger, University of Illinois, rocket engineer

We could add others, but for brevity, we cite the above scientists as they have done much to destroy the credibility of government-sponsored climate research.

Despite having produced ZERO EVIDENCE that CO_2 causes warming in a convective atmosphere, the achievement of these vaunted experts was only self-serving promotion of the lie that carbon dioxide is our climate's control knob.

As independent Japanese climate researcher and PSI contributor Kyoji Kimoto observed:

> The models have more than 100 tunable parameters. You can do anything to fit model output with observed temperature time series. Therefore, the point is that the AGW theory is based on the theoretically erroneous papers of Manabe(1967), Cess(1976), Hansen(1981) and

Schlesinger(1986).[28]

Hansen, along with Schlesinger, were primarily responsible for the positive feedback scam which provided the theoretical basis in AR1 for a climate sensitivity large enough to justify the formation of the IPCC, thus enabling the UNFCCC and its repressive agenda of wealth redistribution under the guise of climate reparations.

Hansen, along with Lebedeff, were responsible for erroneously validating the homogenization of sparse data to approximate the behavior of the whole.

Hansen hired Gavin Schmidt as his chief propagandist to run the Real Climate web site and he did such a good job, Hansen picked him as his successor. What Hansen began at NASA, Schmidt continues to this day. Among other absurdities, they promoted the nonsensical claim that there is a noticeable greenhouse gas effect on other planets (there isn't). The Slayers identified the huge error in 2010—it was there for all to see, if people opened their eyes.

In his paper Hansen stated:

> *The greenhouse theory can be tested by examination of several planets, which provide an ensemble of experiments over a wide range of conditions. The atmospheric composition of Mars, Earth, and Venus lead to mean radiating levels of about 1, 6, and 70 km, and lapse rates of ~5°, 5.5°, and 7°C/km, respectively. Observed surface temperatures of these planets confirm the existence and order of magnitude of the predicted*

---

[28] see: http://notrickszone.com/2017/07/30/for-fame-and-fund-japanese-scientist-accuses-four-climate-researchers-ipcc-of-fake-science/comment-page-1/#comment-1224355

greenhouse effect.[29]

But there is no empirical scientific reason for cavalier Hansen to write that Mars, Earth, and Venus confirm the theoretical greenhouse effect when Mars has an atmospheric composition of 95% CO_2 (950,000PPM) compared to the Earth's 0.04% (400PPM), but yet Mars is about 75°C colder than Earth. It belies any rational critical reasoning.

However, as the Slayers (now PSI) showed, the more reasonable scientific statement is that the temperature of the planets can be explained predominantly by two parameters:

(1) atmospheric pressure/density and...
(2) distance from the Sun. Mars has an atmosphere that is about 100 times less dense than Earth's and it's further away from the Sun than Earth.

If readers take home one clear message from this book, we hope it is this: Venus' atmosphere is about 90 times denser than Earth's, and it is closer to the Sun than Earth. Like Mars, CO_2 makes up about 95% of its atmosphere. Therefore, the Venusian temperature can also be explained by (1) and (2) above.

The CO_2 concentration of Mars (950,000PPM), Venus (965,000PPM), and Earth (400PPM) have little to do with planetary temperatures relative to (1) and (2).

We commend the excellent paper of Nikolov and Zeller which reinforces our original analysis.

They write:

> *Our analysis revealed that GMATs [global mean annual temperatures] of rocky planets with tangible atmospheres and a negligible geothermal surface heating can accurately be predicted over a broad range of conditions using only two forcing*

---

[29] https://pubs.giss.nasa.gov/docs/1981/1981_Hansen_ha04600x.pdf

*variables: top-of-the-atmosphere solar irradiance
and total surface atmospheric pressure.*[30]

A key entailment from the model is that the atmospheric
'greenhouse effect' currently viewed as a radiative phenomenon is
in fact an adiabatic (pressure-induced) thermal enhancement
analogous to compression heating and is independent of
atmospheric composition. Consequently, the global, downwelling, long-wave flux assumed to drive Earth's surface warming
is a product of the air temperature determined by solar heating
and atmospheric pressure.

NASA's Gavin Schmidt wants us all to believe 110% of the
temperature changes since the mid-20th century were caused by
humans, predominantly via CO_2 emissions. Schmidt and the
IPCC promote the lie that CO_2 is the dominant factor in both
the greenhouse effect and planetary temperature changes.

One of the best scientists working on solar variance impacts
on climate is American Astrophysicist Dr. Willie Soon who has
long argued that the UN IPCC and other alarmists intentionally
ignore the role variations in solar output have on our climate.

In an interview with Dr. Jeffrey Foss, Dr. Soon lamented:

*The Intergovernmental Panel on Climate Change
keeps using the wrong numbers! It's making me
feel sick to keep seeing this error. I keep telling*

30

https://www.researchgate.net/profile/Karl_Zeller/publication
/317570648_New_Insights_on_the_Physical_Nature_of_the_A
tmospheric_Greenhouse_Effect_Deduced_from_an_Empirical_
Planetary_Temperature_Model/links/594052cba6fdcce572339
879/New-Insights-on-the-Physical-Nature-of-the-Atmospheric-
Greenhouse-Effect-Deduced-from-an-Empirical-Planetary-
Temperature-Model.pdf

them—but they keep ignoring their mistake.[31]

Dr. Soon is on the same page as the Slayers in asserting that the empirical evidence shows very clearly that the Sun controls our climate, not CO_2. After over three decades working in this field, Dr. Soon confirms that changes in the Sun's brightness, sunspots and energy output, changes in the orbital position of the Earth relative to the Sun, and other powerful natural forces drive climate change.

Ironically, the UN's IPCC initially showed agreement with him, citing his work approvingly in its second (1996) and third (2001) Assessment Reports.

But as skeptics succeeded in making their case that the Sun is the dominant climate forcer, the IPCC backtracked and stopped citing Dr. Soon's work in their reports.

The alarmists admit that the Sun causes the waxing and waning of the ice ages, as solar scientists say. But for anyone backing the greenhouse gas theory as the key to understanding climate change, it is necessary to their position to play down the Sun's role and exaggerate the effect of atmospheric carbon dioxide (CO_2).

Discomforting for alarmists is that solar scientists have a compelling argument that solar changes very well explain Earth's most recent warming period that began way back in the 1830s— long before we burned hydrocarbon fuels.

Also, a superb empirical factor was the observed shrinking of the Martian ice-caps in the 1990s. Their return in the last few years coincided perfectly with the waning and waxing of Arctic ice caps on Earth.

It is evident to any dissenter of the greenhouse gas theory that our Sun—not CO_2 from industrial emissions—causes Earth-

---

[31] https://climatechangedispatch.com/dr-soon-vs-climate-apocalypse/?utm_source=feedburner&utm_medium=email&utm_campaign=Feed%3A+ClimateChangeDispatch+%28Climate+Change+Dispatch+Latest+News%29

Mars synchronicity.

Moreover, it is no coincidence that a grand maximum in solar brightness (Total Solar Irradiance or TSI) occurred in the 1990s as the ice caps on Earth and Mars shrank, or that the Sun cooled (TSI decreased) as the ice caps on both planets grew once again.

As we have shown repeatedly, in the official climate models, solar variation, water vapor and cloud factors are largely ignored or treated as non-significant to the temperature change despite their rather large role in their supposed greenhouse effect.

The entire theory, as sold to the public and non-scientists, is that the GHE increases and decreases planetary temperature primarily due to the concentrations of atmospheric CO_2, despite the fact many will admit CO_2 is not the sole or only factor.

In short, so much is a play on words—not science, but political spin.

As an example, let's give deserved recognition to what climate author, Bob Webster, writes in his book, *Is Climate Change Really Human-Caused? / The Trial of Carbon Dioxide in the Court of Public Opinion.* Webster's book is for non-scientists and scientists and is ideal for newbies to this field. It avoids complex theoretical discussions and uses The Scientific Method as a guide—requiring every hypothesis or theory to be consistent with observation (in this case, historic and geologic).

Webster cleverly presents his case as testimony and evidence in a trial in the court of public opinion—where the prosecution (IPCC, et al) had decades to formulate an indictment of defendant carbon dioxide on the basis of its expedient assumptions. Among the trickery and assumptions relied on by the UN IPCC, he documents the following:

> *Atmospheric CO_2 concentrations had not changed appreciably over the preceding 850 years (IPCC; The Scientific Basis) so it may be safely assumed that they would not have changed appreciably in*

> *the 150 years from 1850 to 2000 in the absence of human intervention.*
>
> *Anthropogenic greenhouse gas emissions have ... led to atmospheric concentrations of carbon dioxide...that are unprecedented in at least the last 800,000 years...and are extremely likely to have been the dominant cause of the observed warming since the mid-20th century.*
>
> *Anthropogenic greenhouse gas (GHG) emissions since the pre-industrial era have driven large increases in the atmospheric concentrations of carbon dioxide (CO_2)...[40% of] cumulative Anthropogenic CO_2 emissions...have remained in the atmosphere...the rest was removed from the atmosphere and stored on land (in plants and soils) and in the ocean. The ocean has absorbed about 30% of the emitted Anthropogenic CO_2, causing ocean acidification.*[32]

Note, "may be safely assumed", "are extremely likely" and "causing ocean acidification" are conjecture...expedient conjecture for the alarmists.

But is any of it true?"

Readers are "jurors" in this trial and the objective is to present the jury with compelling evidence that is easily understood so the reader (juror) reaches the right verdict and exonerates carbon dioxide from any charges relating to a climate change crime.

To this end, Webster analyzed global average atmospheric CO_2 and global anthropogenic emissions records maintained by the U.S. Government since the mid-19th century. Also, the U.S. Government records for global average near surface temperature (GAST) anomalies (merged land+ocean, land, ocean) over the

---

[32] Webster, R., *Is Climate Change Really Human-Caused? / The Trial of Carbon Dioxide in the Court of Public Opinion*

same period. These are as good a record as are available. Other sources are also tapped (geologic, satellite, etc.).

As you might expect, the evidence exonerating CO_2 is compelling. All one needs to do is look at the data.

In real-world science, carbon dioxide heats nothing. It merely is a conduit for energy transfer—an innocent bystander who happened to have gotten in the way. Thankfully, many rational scientists, especially those in the applied sciences and engineering, have the empirical, practical expertise to verify such facts. One such scientist is Angelo Campanella, Ph.D., P.E., FASA—Penn State.

Dr. Campanella says:

> *CO_2 Change: Turning to the primary effect of more carbon dioxide (CO_2) in the air: More CO_2 in the air will increase the infrared emissivity of the exposed atmosphere, which may be a cooling effect on the average. This occurs by the fact that oxygen and nitrogen can neither absorb nor emit infrared radiation (Tyndall observed this first) since they are both symmetrical molecules. Only asymmetrical molecules with a dipole moment such as water vapor (H_2O) and CO_2 are capable of absorbing the infrared radiation energy in sunlight, and also capable of re-radiating that infrared energy back to cold space at night. Pure air is the best insulator against conduction of heat, but it is also a perfect window for infrared energy to escape. This leaves only convection (or winds) as a means the atmosphere to transfer energy to another location. Addition of H_2O and CO_2 vapors make air less of a window. Condensation of water vapor into clouds makes an overcast to be a warm blanket for the Earth, but continues to allow heat to be radiated from cloud tops that face outer*

space.[33]

The greenhouse gas theory focuses on CO_2, not the water cycle, but this is not how Earth's climate thermostat operates. In the past 30 years we have seen an increase in atmospheric carbon dioxide levels (now over 400PPM) and global temperatures, by any measure of statistical significance, are unaffected.

Instead, climate researchers should be honest and admit that it is the water cycle and adiabatic pressure which are far more dominant forces, coupled with the Ideal Gas laws.

Dr. Campanella continues:

> *Energy Storage and Transport: Local temperature anywhere on Earth is critically dependent on energy storage and energy transport of water bodies (oceans, bays, lakes, and rivers) how much solar energy has been stored and where it is transported. The most familiar of these is, in a word; "Gulfstream". Solar energy is readily stored in seawater surfaces. That stored in the Caribbean Sea is transported in a "river" current known as the Gulfstream that reaches across the Atlantic Ocean to linger off the west coasts of Europe to warm the adjacent lands, notably the British Isles. Thus, a temperature up-tick of a several degrees C has been enjoyed those peoples for millennia. In the Pacific, we have recently been enamored by such storage and transport there (vis "El Ninio" and the recent "Blob". These huge heated bodies can travel thousands of miles to affect peoples on other continents. This storage/transport mechanism, critical to climates it affects, has largely been ignored by the politicians, the media*

---

[33] http://campanellaacoustics.com/InfraredClimate.pdf

and the scientists that so prominently address "climate" in our time.[34]

It is mantra of the Slayers, so let's repeat it: Carbon dioxide can never generate heat, delay cooling or trap energy to control climate.

Pseudo-science claims of a CO_2-driven greenhouse effect are not premised on how heat generation works. We should all know that the act of pulling a blanket over a loaf of warm bread does not mean that the blanket produces or generates heat. The blanket prevents existing heat (from a heat source [the oven]) from escaping so easily so the warm bread stays warm longer.

Likewise, we see that caves are often the same temperature year-round, seeming much warmer in winter and much cooler in summer. But caves are not warmer in winter because caves are actively heating the air. The caves are but passive players in the temperature game, as is CO_2.

"CO_2 concentration heating" is a joke, as would be "cave concentration heating."

To be blunt, if Gavin Schmidt et al do not know how the gravity thermal gradient operates, then it is time for these government experts to learn respect for basic physics. But Schmidt, like his predecessor Hansen, is a fanatic, which by Winston Churchill's definition is: "Someone who can't change his mind, and won't change the subject."

We live in a dystopian world where government experts claim that black is white, up is down and warm is cool, etc. Contrary to the media spin, it is those government climate scientists who are the real deniers.

In the past decade, many of this book's authors have been dedicated to exposing this fraud and we learned something about the mindset of the established climate cabal: the longer you've been wrong and the more fame reaped from it, the harder it is to

---

[34] Ibid.

admit. Your cause, no matter how bogus, becomes part of your identity. That is a sad fact of human nature.

In the interests of human progress and sanity, we appeal to these discredited bad actors to stop DENYING the gravity-based thermal gradient exists. It is PROVEN by measurement on all atmospheric planets. Accept the obvious that gravity is a better fit as the key to climate, not carbon dioxide.

We urge all climate alarmists to come out of their faux science bubble and to read the ever-increasing body of peer-reviewed science that backs PSI/Slayer claims on this point.

For example, we commend the excellent paper of Heinz Thieme, where he writes:

> *The climatologists derived the theoretical foundation of the greenhouse hypothesis from the concept of radiative equilibrium over the entire gas area of the atmosphere, right down to the Earth's surface. But the fundamental premise of radiative equilibrium—a balance of incoming and outgoing radiation—is correct only as long as it is limited to the vacuum-like zone of the upper atmosphere. In the lower regions of the atmosphere, the heat balance is essentially determined by thermal, i.e. thermodynamic equilibrium, which includes the thermodynamic characteristics of the components of the atmosphere as well as their changes in status.*
>
> *From the upper atmosphere down to Earth's surface, air pressure rises continuously. The determinant of atmospheric pressure is the mass and the weight of that part of the atmosphere above the point in question. And as pressure increases, so does temperature. The rise in temperature is caused by the thermodynamic characteristics of the main components of the*

atmosphere, i.e. N_2 and O_2. Everyone knows that compression causes gases to warm: the effect is noticeable even when inflating bicycle tires. The atmosphere is no different.[35]

Then, there is the excellent paper by Jelbring, The "Greenhouse Effect" as a Function of Atmospheric Mass.[36]

Here, using a different approach, it is shown that GE [the Greenhouse Effect] can be explained as mainly being a consequence of known physical laws describing the behavior of ideal gases in a gravity field.

A simplified model of Earth, along with a formal proof concerning the model atmosphere and evidence from real planetary atmospheres will help drawing proper conclusions. The distinguishing premise is that the bulk part of a planetary GE depends on its atmospheric surface mass density. Thus it can be exactly calculated for an ideal planetary model atmosphere.

Building from the Slayers's work comes Connolly and Connolly, presenting, characterizing and writing about a previously-overlooked mechanism for energy transmission throughout the atmosphere.[37]

This mechanism, which we call *pervection*, involves the transmission of mechanical energy through a mass—in this case, the atmosphere. It is distinct from convection in that it does not require mass transport. It is also distinct from conduction in that conduction involves the transmission of thermal energy, not mechanical energy.

Atmospheric climate models assume energy transmission in

---

[35] *Greenhouse Gas Hypothesis Violates Fundamentals of Physics*, http://realplanet.eu/error.htm

[36] http://ruby.fgcu.edu/courses/twimberley/EnviroPhilo/FunctionOfMass.pdf

[37] http://oprj.net/oprj-archive/atmospheric-science/25/oprj-article-atmospheric-science-25.pdf

the atmosphere is dominated by radiation and convection and neglect pervection. Experiments were carried out to measure the rate of energy transmission by pervection in air. It was found that pervection is rapid enough (up to at least 39.4 $\pm$ 0.9 m/s^{-1}) to ensure the troposphere, tropopause and stratosphere remain in thermodynamic equilibrium. This contradicts a fundamental assumption of the current atmospheric models which assume the atmosphere is only in local thermodynamic equilibrium.

Obviously, the greenhouse effect hypothesis has many, many problems. Many researchers latched onto the big problem of Mars.

The alarmists never addressed Slayer analysis on this problem. When we mention Mars, the experts defending the GHE will focus on 96.5% CO_2 atmosphere Venus. They do this while simultaneously glossing over the pressure/density difference between Venus and Earth (92 times greater for Venus) and the fact that Mars also has a 95% CO_2 atmosphere that is 100 times less pressurized than Earth's—which is why Mars is so much colder despite having 950,000PPM CO_2. They can't explain this, of course, and in our experience since our first book's publication, they avoid answering questions about it.

It wouldn't matter how much CO_2 is added or removed from the air—the temperature isn't altered by such addition or removal of any particular gas.

What many people assume is the 'greenhouse effect' is not a radiative phenomenon driven by the atmospheric infrared optical depth as presently believed. Instead, it is a pressure-induced thermal enhancement analogous to adiabatic heating and independent of atmospheric composition.

As skeptics, we remain open to reading explanations that might better explain our climate. Indeed, we heartily promote and endorse serious scientists, like Nikolov and Zeller, who are adding to our body of work. However, we baulk at their claims they discovered the adiabatic gravitational component of the climate system. That's clearly shown described in *Slaying the Sky*

Dragon where we show how atmospheric pressure on many planets in our solar system is a key player in surface temperatures.

So far, the adiabatic theory reinterpreting the supposed greenhouse effect—that does not assign a critical role for trace gases—is far more satisfying than the more popular CO_2-radiation obsessed greenhouse effect that became popular in the late 1970s.

As fellow researchers, we are genuinely excited to read about newer explanations emerging that don't have as many holes as the CO_2-climate explanation. For instance, we see great merit in Svensmark's 'cloud' theory on cosmic rays being an overlooked climate player.

We see a rise in solar scientists saying Earth is heading into a new mini ice thanks to the new Grand Solar Minimum (fewer sunspots). Cooling, not warming is life's big threat. For, as the solar experts assure us, a weaker Sun means weaker solar wind which normally protects Earth from cosmic rays. Hence more cosmic rays hit Earth, which seed and form more clouds, driving even more cooling.

Among the Slayers, we observe that other planets affirm the connection between adiabatic pressure and cloud cover (and by implication, surface temperature). On Venus, scientists see lots of pressure and lots of cloud cover. On Mars, scientists see very little pressure and very little cloud. On Earth, where there is middling air pressure, half the planet is covered by cloud and experiences an albedo cooling effect.

The Slayers wrote much about albedo cooling. Alan Siddons is perhaps our best proponent at offering real-world examples to guide non-scientists.

For example, imagine wearing black clothes outside on a summer's day. Did you notice this often makes you feel terribly hot? Or, recall walking across a blacktop (tarmac) road a on a summer day. Did you feel relieved when you got to the cooler sidewalk? These scenarios involve the effect of albedo, which is a measure of how much radiation from the Sun is reflected by the Earth's surface. Our cities built of asphalt and concrete and depleted of organic ground cover (natural heat sinks) are monotonously warmer than surrounding natural environs. It is why the 'urban heat island effect' is well documented. Albedo is an important climate player, too.

This is why we have enormous support for Svenmark's ideas in guiding science towards a unified climate theory that works well on other planets, not just on our watery globe. Like us, Svensmark embraces empirical observations which will always trump the a-priori opinions of so-called climate experts.

Independent scientists recognise climatic changes are observed on decadal to centennial time scales due to Sun-induced variations in cloud cover. These can help explain global temperature fluctuations of $\pm 1.0°C$ around any long-term mean set by adiabatic pressure and solar irradiance.

Adherents to the greenhouse gas theory, being obsessed by radiation, hang their hats on the simplistic (Kiehl-Trenberth-style) IPCC models that 'look' like they have science and physics in them, but don't. They can't represent reality, because they don't show how sunshine creates the water cycle (ocean evaporation $\Rightarrow$ cloud formation $\Rightarrow$ albedo $\Rightarrow$ cooling).

When examined closely, not only Kiehl-Trenberth diagram, but variants promoted by greenhouse gas theory promoters, your attention really ought to focus on the most insane claim of the theory. The GHE 'theory' requires you to believe that 'back radiation' heating from the atmosphere has equal heating capacity of the solar radiation.

Do you comprehend what that means?

In short, to believe the 'theory' you must accept that the Sun has no more power to heat our planet's surface than the gases in the atmosphere!

We urge readers to go check out any of the Earth energy budget diagrams by such experts. They invariably show the atmosphere emitting 342 W/m^2 down to the Earth's surface.

Incredibly, that would represent an average temperature of 279K for a black body opaque object. That really is pure craziness.

Any fool knows that on a sunny day, if a cloud covers the sky you immediately feel cooler. Surely, that must tell you what enormous heating power the Sun possesses. So, for climate 'experts' to fudge their calculations to crassly show that CO_2 and other gases are as powerful as the Sun is absurd.

We are not making this up.

Readers can see for themselves with the following examples from mainstream academic sources.

At one website, academics extend the number of layers so a two-layer atmosphere has double the heating power from the atmosphere when compared to solar radiation.[38]

At another site, they remove the idiotic multi-layer claim, but elaborate on their "simple model" of the greenhouse effect by using the claimed measured radiation to space of 239.7 W/m^2 and because the "layer emits both up and down" the surface must emit 479.4 to balance this.[39]

With 239.7 solar radiation equivalent to 255K and the surface emitting 479.4 at 303K they explicitly claim atmospheric back radiation has equal heating power to incident solar radiation!

Of course, this whole construct is nonsense as the 239.7K solar input is not the incident power but the value emitted over a sphere to balance four times that value incident on a disk.

It's a fudge factor that crassly converts the Earth's spherical shape into a flat disk. It seems climate 'scientists' cannot handle complex three-dimensional equations, so they botch them into an erroneous flat-Earth simplification.

Any armchair detective can see this simplification fuels the

38

https://www.atmos.washington.edu/2001Q1/211/notes_for_01100 1_lecture.html

39

https://atmos.washington.edu/2002Q4/211/notes_greenhouse.html

misunderstanding that carbon dioxide and other gases playing a role in heating our planet's surface. When, in fact, the empirical evidence shows that gases promote cooling rather than warming.

Nevertheless, the claim is there in black and white—the entire field of climate research relies on the false assumption that atmospheric back radiation has equal heating power to incident solar radiation!

Whichever way they try to baffle you with BS there is no way that 239.7K + 239.7K can equal sigmaT^4.

Assuming Earth's average temperature is 15°C, that's 298K. Using Wien's Law the peak radiation at that wavelength is just under 10 micrometers. At that wavelength, and for a considerable amount either way (Mars to Venus temperatures), carbon dioxide is completely transparent to IR radiation. It has ZERO absorption. This is simple, first-year Physics!

This sky dragon and rainbow-unicorn pseudo-science somehow has been permitted to be peddled in universities for 30 years.

Academia should hang their heads in shame—no matter what your opinion of the greenhouse effect is, it is patently absurd to suggest that infra-red radiation emitted by an atmosphere at 255K has equivalent heating power to sunlight!

Furthermore, the so-called "back radiation" must be completely different than the solar radiation with much lower wavelength. They conveniently leave out the fact that solar radiation is short wave while their magical "back radiation" is long wave. And by the way, "back radiation" must be even longer wave than the radiation emitted from the surface. Every time radiation is absorbed and re-emitted, its wavelength gets longer. To think otherwise is farcical!

Of course, policymakers only listen to scientists who cite evidence affirming their manipulative policies. Inconvenient, real-world scientific data is ignored and the scientists and technologists who uncover it are insulted and called deniers. In matters of government science, it is consensus that rules, and the consensus is bought and paid for with generous government research grants. In this post-normal mockery of a scientific process, facts are trumped by opinion and perfidy distorts science with fallacious arguments from authority.

Our disgust at this cynical manipulation—the wilful construction of a mass of pseudo-science to fool a trusting, scientifically ignorant populace—served more than anything to motivate our team of contributors to produce books and papers to debunk the greenhouse gas theory.

We can think of no bigger or more socially and financially costly deception perpetrated on the many by a few. It is a monumental travesty that policymakers and non-scientists have, for three decades, been browbeaten by argument from authority (logical fallacy)—aided and abetted by a complicit mass media machine.

We urge readers to take no one's word on any issue. Trust only your own reasoning and diligent research—both for and against any proposition.

In that vein, we recommend three more peer-reviewed papers explaining the adiabatic greenhouse effect which fully explains planetary temperatures, including Venus' and Earth's, without referencing CO_2 as a meaningful contributor.

As follows, from Florides and Christodoulides:

> *Convection accounts for approximately 67% of the total amount of heat transfer from the Earth's surface to the troposphere, the condensation of water vapour for 25% and radiation accounts for only 8%. As the heat transfer in the troposphere occurs mostly by convection, accumulation of CO_2 in the troposphere intensifies the convective processes of heat and mass transfer, because of the intense absorption of infrared radiation, and leads to subsequent cooling and not warming as believed. ... The analysis indicates that the average*

surface temperature of the Earth is determined by the solar constant, the precession angle of the planet, the mass (pressure) of the atmosphere, and the specific heat of the atmospheric mixture of gases.

If the CO_2 concentration in the atmosphere increases from 0.035% to its double value of 0.070%, the atmospheric pressure will increase slightly (by 0.00015 atm). Consequently the temperature at sea level will increase by about 0.01 °C and the increase in temperature at an altitude of 10 km will be less than 0.03 °C. These amounts are negligible compared to the natural temporal fluctuations of the global temperature.[40]

From Sorokhtin et al:

According to the adiabatic theory of greenhouse effect (see below), besides the Sun's radiation, the main determining factors of the Earth's climate are the Earth's atmosphere pressure and its composition. The denser the atmosphere (i.e., the higher the atmospheric pressure), the warmer the climate. Thus, the high surface temperature at the ocean level during the Archaean time, at a low Sun's luminosity, may only be a result of higher atmospheric pressure. The gradual decrease in the oceanic water temperature with a smooth increase of Sun's luminosity may only be a result of a

---

[40]

https://www.researchgate.net/profile/Paul_Christodoulides/publication/23226792_Global_warming_and_carbon_Dioxide_through_sciences/links/0fcfd50fd4db9a04f6000000/Global-warming-and-carbon-Dioxide-through-sciences.pdf *gradual decrease in the atmospheric pressure.*[41]

From Chilingar et al:

> *The quoted comparisons indicate that average temperature distribution in the planet's troposphere is completely defined by the solar constant, atmospheric pressure (mass), heat capacity of its gas composition and the precession angle. The theoretical temperature on Venus surface turned out to be Ts = 735K, and on Earth's surface, 288K. The empiric values are 735.3 and 288.2K, respectively. This close fit cannot be accidental and presents the convincing evidence in favor of the adiabatic theory of heat transfer in a dense atmosphere.*[42]

We have read Svensmark's work and been encouraged by his approach in looking beyond "the usual suspects" for climate change. Indeed, why should the massive forces in the Universe be exerting some transient impacts on Earth, if as Big Bang theory would have it, all celestial bodies are monotonously and rapidly being spun apart.

There is growing awakening in the scientific community. A cross-disciplinary approach is essential if we are meaningfully tackle these new and emerging issues. To us it is difficult to reconcile the imagined massive effects CO_2 is alleged to have on this planet's climate when significant changes (in dust and clouds) can be precipitated by quasi-cyclic events (~100kyr) that are outside this planet.

For example:

---

[41] http://www.ask-force.org/web/Global-Warming/Sorokhtin-Evolution-Earths-Global-Climate-2009.pdf

[42] https://file.scirp.org/pdf/ACS_2014111714391836.pdf

Spectral analysis of climate data shows a strong narrow peak with period ≈100 kyr, attributed by the Milankovitch theory to changes in the eccentricity of the Earth's orbit. The narrowness of the peak does suggest an astronomical origin; however the shape of the peak is incompatible with both linear and nonlinear models that attribute the cycle to eccentricity or (equivalently) to the envelope of the precession. In contrast, the orbital inclination parameter gives a good match to both the spectrum and bispectrum of the climate data. Extraterrestrial accretion from meteoroids or interplanetary dust is proposed as a mechanism that could link inclination to climate, and experimental tests are described that could prove or disprove this hypothesis.[43]

In the shorter term, there is study about weather/climate events being influenced by meteors.

Examination of rainfall figures for a large number of stations shows that there is a tendency for more rain to fall on certain calendar dates than on others. There is a close correspondence between the dates of the rainfall maxima in both the northern and southern hemispheres, and this is difficult to explain on a climatological basis. The effect might, however, be due to an extraterrestrial influence.

The rainfall peaks occur approximately 30 days after prominent meteor showers, and it is suggested that they are due to the nucleating effect of meteoritic dust falling into cloud systems in the

---

[43] http://www.pnas.org/content/94/16/8329.full

lower atmosphere, the time difference being accounted for by the rate of fall of the material through the atmosphere.[44]

And what about the yellow, fiery ball in the sky? We believe the Sun does not get proper credit as a driver of our global climate.

The Sun gets short shrift in the computer climate models used to buttress the mainstream view of anthropogenic (human-caused) global warming. That's because the climate change narrative, which links warming almost entirely to our emissions of greenhouse gases, trivializes the contributions to global warming from all other sources. According to its 5th Assessment Report, the IPCC attributes no more than a few percent of total global warming to the Sun's influence.

That may be the narrative but it's not one universally endorsed by solar scientists. Although some, such as solar physicist Mike Lockwood, adhere to the conventional wisdom on CO_2, others, such as mathematical physicist Nicola Scafetta, think instead that the Sun has an appreciable impact on the Earth's climate. In disputing the conventional wisdom, Scafetta points to our poor understanding of indirect solar effects as opposed to the direct effect of the Sun's radiation, and to analytical models of the Sun that oversimplify its behavior. Furthermore, a lack of detailed historical data prior to the recent observational satellite era casts doubt on the accuracy and reliability of the IPCC estimates.

---

[44] The Relation between Rainfall and Meteor Showers, http://www.pnas.org/content/94/16/8329.full

I've long felt sorry for solar scientists, whose once highly respectable field of research before climate became an issue has been marginalized by the majority of climate scientists. And solar scientists who are climate change skeptics have had to endure not only loss of prestige, but also difficulty in obtaining research funding because their work doesn't support the consensus on global warming. But it appears that the tide may be turning at last.

Judging from recent scientific publications, the number of papers affirming a strong Sun-climate link is on the rise. From 93 papers in 2014 examining such a link, almost as many were published in the first half of 2017 alone. The 2017 number represents about 7% of all research papers in solar science over the same period and about 16% of all papers on computer climate models during that time.

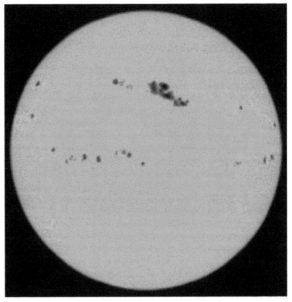

This rising tide of papers linking the Sun to climate change may be why UK climate scientists in 2015 attempted to silence the researcher who led a team predicting a slowdown in solar activity after 2020.

Northumbria University's Valentina Zharkova had dared to propose that the average monthly number of sunspots will soon drop to nearly zero, based on a model in which a drastic falloff is expected in the Sun's magnetic field. Other solar researchers have made the same prediction using different approaches.

Sunspots are small dark blotches on the Sun caused by intense magnetic turbulence on the Sun's surface. Together with the Sun's heat and light, the number of sunspots goes up and down during the approximately 11-year solar cycle. But the maximum number of sunspots seen in a cycle has recently been declining. The last time they disappeared altogether was during the so-called Maunder Minimum, a 70-year cool period in the 17th and 18th centuries forming part of the Little Ice Age.

While Zharkova's research paper actually said nothing about climate, climate scientists quickly latched onto the implication that a period of global cooling might be ahead and demanded that the Royal Astronomical Society—at whose meeting she had originally presented her findings— withdraw her press release. Fortunately, the Society refused to accede to this attack on science at the time, although the press release has since been removed from the Web. Just last month, Zharkova's group refuted criticisms of its methodology by another prominent solar scientist.

Apart from such direct effects, indirect solar

effects due to the Sun's ultraviolet (UV) radiation or cosmic rays from deep space could also contribute to global warming. In both cases, some sort of feedback mechanism would be needed to amplify what would otherwise be tiny perturbations to global temperatures. However, what's not generally well known is that the warming predicted by computer climate models comes from assumed water vapor amplification of the modest temperature increase caused by CO_2 acting alone. Speculative candidates for amplification of solar warming involve changes in cloud cover as well as the Earth's ozone layer.[45]

In the early days of the global warming hysteria (late 1980s-early 1990's), international policy makers put the policy cart before the scientific cart with a focus on CO_2 and dangerous climate change. This focus led climate scientists to make a serious framing error by focusing only on CO_2-driven climate change. In a drive to remain relevant to the policy process, scientists focused on building consensus and reducing uncertainties. They also began providing probabilities—though these were unjustified by the scientific knowledge base. Policy makers wanted this. This led to fat tails and cost/benefit analyses that are all but meaningless (no matter who they give Nobel prizes to).

An insane level of groupthink came about in pursuit of the appearance of unity across both the science and policy arenas— all to hoodwink the scientifically ill-informed majority into believing it was 'a good thing' to tackle climate change (even if climate as always changed with or without human input).

It has taken those three decades for a critical mass of skepticism to seep into the minds of the confused majority—the

---

[45] *Solar Science Shortchanged in Climate Models,* https://www.scienceunderattack.com/blog/2018/10/1/solar-science-shortchanged-in-climate-models-1s

once ill-informed have now become better informed.

Ever-more, ordinary folk are awakening to the reality that the policy was cooked up first and the phony scientific justification for the policies to strangle CO_2 emission came after.

The Trojan horse to seal the deal was the widespread implicit belief among laypeople and scientists alike that modern computing was sufficiently advanced to simulate the chaotic, non-linear climate system. And if you are among the majority of folk who don't understand the nuances of the first and second laws of thermodynamics, you can be persuaded of the value of a ready-made computer model of the climate system (sans inconvenient solar and cosmic hydrological impacts).

Modellers simulated a faux atmosphere with a huge (unphysical) sensitivity to a trace gas comprising a miniscule 0.04 percent of the air around us. By telling their computers (via rigged coding) to assume very high sensitivity while simultaneously putting in front of our eyes a toy model greenhouse gas theory, it was a cinch for the climate cabal to bury the truth that CO_2 was innocent.

The crisis in science may have four significant causes; at its root is a general dumbing down of western education standards. This coincided with an unavoidable need for greater science specialization, compelled from a need to manage an explosion of information. In turn, this precipitated an over-reliance on so-called experts rather than a broad critical analysis of empirical data. Coupled with the faster pace of modern life, the solution is too often a cognitive shortcut (groupthink) which seduced us into a convenient over-reliance on computer models. We are now at the point where we can no longer reliably trust the expertise of specialized sciences to collaborate and solve real world problems.

No wonder that seasoned analysts argue modern scientists lack the skills and training to even attempt to perform the Herculean feat of safely landing a man on the moon with little more than slide rules and paper and pen calculus.

John Horgan of the Wall Street Journal wrote:

> *In 2005 statistician John Ioannidis presented evidence that "most published research findings are wrong." That is, the findings cannot be replicated by follow-up research. Many other scholars have now confirmed the work of Mr. Ioannidis. The so-called replication crisis is especially severe in fields with high financial stakes, such as oncology and psychopharmacology.*
>
> *But physics, which should serve as the bedrock of science, is in some respects the most troubled field of all.*
>
> *Over the last few decades, physics in the grand mode practiced by Hawking and Mr. Rees has become increasingly disconnected from empirical evidence.*
>
> *Proponents of string and multiverse models tout their mathematical elegance, but strings are too small and multiverses too distant to be detected by any conceivable experiment. In her new book "Lost in Math," German physicist Sabine Hossenfelder offers a far more candid and compelling assessment of modern physics than her English elders. She fears that physicists working on strings and multiverses are not really practicing physics. "I'm not sure anymore that what we do here, in the foundations of physics, is science," she confesses."[46]*

This is scientific fraud.

As with strings and multiverses, so with climate models and doomsday prophecies. Climate science meandered down the

---

[46] https://www.wsj.com/articles/brief-answers-to-the-big-questions-and-on-the-future-review-serious-doubt-on-serious-earth-1539909146

same dark and lonely blind alley as cosmology because of the erroneous belief that mathematical modeling can reliably replicate reality. It cannot. The band of brothers (and sisters) known euphemistically as the Slayers have been in the trenches for a decade fighting against the arrogant delusions of academic fools who placed theorization above empirical, applied science and confirmation bias over critical reasoning.

It is mistake that befell wider society, too. For too long we bought into the myth that it is within the hallowed halls of academia that the smartest minds reside and drive scientific advances. They are not. Rather, it is grassroots innovators in the applied sciences and engineering grappling daily in labs and on test benches where the cruelest tests applied by Mother Nature expose the fallibility of their pet theories.

Unlike academia, where the slickest mathematical presentation can win the greatest accolades and where empirical verification of a hypothesis is not the prime arbiter of success, but often the last.

We intend this book to provide our readers with healthy caution against the neo-tribalism exacerbated by mainstream propaganda's appeals to authority and Internet echo chambers. We warn of more insidious cancers in the system: the broad, systemic failure of the education industry. For at least two generations, higher education has been using Orwell's *1984* as an instruction manual rather than a warning.

In researching and preparing material for this book, we were fortunate to have the inside insights of a former NASA climatologist who worked under Dr. James Hansen, Dr. Duane Thresher, a retired Canadian climatologist who taught the subject at college level, Dr. Tim Ball; as well as a John O'Sullivan, a UK schoolteacher with recent classroom experience of delivering science subjects.

Between 2013 and 2019, O'Sullivan taught in south Wales, in classrooms and science labs as a substitute teacher of children aged 11 to 16. He saw first-hand how a state-funded education system indoctrinates young minds with the climate lie. No critical thought is permitted in the classroom, only adherence to a message that the planet is facing a climate crisis.

What also irked O'Sullivan were school reports about his academically gifted teenage son (now a professional physicist) who spoke of students being systematically awarded lower grades for daring to cite empirical evidence exposing the man-made global warming fraud. The message from the teachers being that if you want to get along, you'd better stick to the officially approved version of reality.

Our brightest young minds are forbidden to dissent or speak facts and hard evidence if they discredit the prevailing government narrative.

Such concerns for the unrelenting indoctrination of our youth were often aired among the Slayers group and PSI members. Canadian climatologist, Dr. Tim Ball, who also taught for many years in academia, reports:

I recall, because of graduate seminars on the topic and participation in a Canadian inter-disciplinary group organized by the National Museum of Canada, about the growing mistrust in the science. This group, formed by the late paleontologist Dr. C. R. Harington, of which I was proud to be a participant, met annually under the auspices of the National Museum of Natural Sciences on a Project on Climatic Change in Canada During the Past 20,000 Years. We met every year and presented papers on a different topic at a symposium. An example of the concerns was a personal conversation I had with glaciologist the late Dr. Fritz Koerner. He was one of the few people to drill ice cores in Antarctica and on Baffin and Ellesmere Islands in the Arctic. He told me in the late 1980s that his preliminary Arctic results *showed temperature changing before CO_2.*

Yet the Big Lie that CO_2 rises were the precursor of temperature rises has, and is, the bedrock of establishment claims for three decades of man-made global warming indoctrination in our education system.

The recent (2018) Intergovernmental Panel on Climate Change (IPCC) Report said there are only 12 years left to save the planet. We are all doomed!

If a pupil questions the narrative and comes to a different conclusion based on their own examination of the evidence, they will be punished with lower grades. Teachers are not allowed to teach content that questions or undermines the approved narrative or they risk censure or even dismissal.

Inquisitive young minds, predisposed to self-directed learning, will find many inconvenient truths undermining the Big Lie. For example, digging deep into the original scientific literature, you will find that from 1940 to almost 1980 the global temperature went down. Concerns back then were about global cooling and no one spoke of any greenhouse gas climate threat.

In the case of Dr. Tim Ball, while teaching college students in Canada in the 1980s and 1990s, he found that:

> *The problem then was, and is still now, that people are educated in the false philosophy of uniformitarianism: the misguided belief that natural change is gradual over long periods of time. Consequently, most people did not understand that the cooling was part of the natural cycle of climate variability, changes that are often huge and sudden. Just 18,000 years ago we were at the peak of an Ice Age. Then, most of the ice melted and sea levels rose 150 meters because it was warmer for almost all of the last 10,000 years than it is today.*

In the case of Dr. Thresher, a NASA climate scientist who turned whistleblower, we see that even in America's prestigious space agency, pseudo-science promoting a fake global warming crisis takes precedence over determining the truth about the Earth's climate.

In 2017, Dr. Thresher wrote two articles on the follow-the-money theme. He advises:

> *Follow the money. Always good advice in journalism and government oversight. Particularly for climate research. At the end of the Cold War, there was a demilitarization. There were a lot of now-pointless bomb physicists and mathematicians around waiting to be axed. There was also a lot of government money supposedly freed up.*[47]

Exploiting the basic need of many scientists simply to make a regular income, western governments put them to work on schemes to prop up contentious or unpopular tax-raising policies.

While working for NASA in climate research and modelling Dr. Thresher noticed:

> *Taxpayer money was shovelled at them. Since they were supposedly saving the planet what they did with the money wasn't questioned.*

NASA's Goddard Institute of Space Science (GISS) where Thresher worked alongside the public faces of American climate science (Dr. James Hansen and Dr. Gavin Schmidt), Thresher saw that computer modelling was more farce than science. He recalls when a new supercomputer was delivered:

> *NASA had no proper place to put it, no tech*

---

[47] https://principia-scientific.org/dr-duane-thresher-follow-the-money-ii/

support, no qualified climate modelling programmers.[48]

But Dr. Thresher was later to find that U.S. government climate science wasn't alone in being utterly incompetent:

> *After my Ph.D. from Columbia and NASA GISS, I went to Germany to work in German climate science as a modeller. Germany has a much smaller population than the United States but is per capita relatively wealthier, so the problem was even worse. One place I worked in Germany hired a bank teller with no education in computer science or climate science to be its climate modeller. He was a nice guy and it was just plain cruel to put him in that tortured position. German claims about global warming are thus just as questionable as American claims since their climate models are also almost certainly full of bugs.*

So, we are faced with the ultimate farce of the blind leading the blind.

Through one-sided pedagogy, CO_2 is painted in classrooms as a poison while stupid humans send Mother Earth hurtling towards doomsday.

Rarely, if at all, are students shown that carbon dioxide is a crucial atmospheric gas necessary for the growth of all life. It is not toxic—a plant food ingested via photosynthesis. The more of it there is the air, the more our planet grows greener. But it is not just in the air that this benign gas boosts life.

The ocean region with the highest dissolved CO_2 levels, the

---

[48]

http://realclimatologists.org/Articles/2019/01/03/Climate_of_Incompetence/index.html

Humboldt Current off Peru, produces 20% of global fish catch because CO_2 is a fertilizer in the sea, too.[49]

Meanwhile, in fake news, world decarbonization is the essential stoichemetric element in the oligarchy's depopulation and despotic global warming scam.

And yet what do we do when we search our universe for signs of life? We look for Carbon based life! Organic Chemistry is Carbon Chemistry. Carbon is the primary building block of life. Carbon Dioxide Gas is the primary nutrient for life.

Thankfully, the rise in levels of CO_2 in the atmosphere will keep on rising well beyond the current 400PPM level. Indeed, we see no good reason why we would not want to go to over 2,000PPM—around the level that is found in many horticultural greenhouses—where plant yield is optimized.

Human industrial emissions are simply helping to restore the natural balance, which is closer to 2,000PPM. When examining levels in geological timescales, the biosphere has been hovering at dangerously low levels. CO_2 came down from +/- 2,000PPM around 100 million years ago to 180PPM during the last ice age.

During the next ice age CO_2 levels will go down again.

We should all be aware that 150PPM is the levels where plants die (see graph).

---

[49] http://science.sciencemag.org/content/320/5874/336

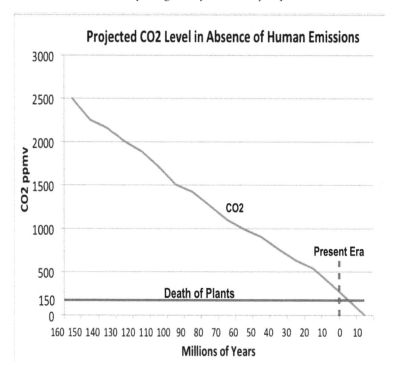

Even NASA is forced to concede more CO_2 in the air makes our planet greener:

> From a quarter to half of Earth's vegetated lands has shown significant greening over the last 35 years largely due to rising levels of atmospheric carbon dioxide, according to a new study published in the journal Nature Climate Change on April 25.[50]

And if upwards of half the planet is getting greener how does this impact the global climate? At minimum, this implies an imbalance

---

[50] https://www.nasa.gov/feature/goddard/2016/carbon-dioxide-fertilization-greening-earth

created for the 'energy in = energy out' characterisation of the climate models.

PSI's Dr. Pierre Latour provided useful calculations explaining this greening:

> *Organic molecules are made by living flora by photosynthesis chemical reaction of xCO_2 + $0.5yH_2O$ + sunlight = $CxHy$ + $(x+0.25y)O_2$, catalyzed by chlorophyll, according to biology. CxHy are hydrocarbon molecules: sugars, starches & cellulose, and which decay slowly to oil, gas, peat, tar and coal along with decaying fauna residue. CxHy can be natural gas, CH_4, methane.*
>
> *Surface does not obey Kirchhoff's law either, a0 = e0, because of this non-radiation chemical energy transfer mechanism. CO_2 is green plant food driving the cycle of flora—fauna life. Flora make O_2 for us fauna. Fauna make CO_2 for flora.*
>
> *Reaction rate, consumption of CO_2 and incident solar energy, P is*
>
> $P = k*p*Ss [CO_2][H_2O]^{(-E/RT1)}$
>
> *p = pressure at leaf, atm*
>
> *Ss = sunlight impinging on green surfaces, w/m^2 <160. = a(1 – alb)S/4, a = absorptivity*
>
> *$[CO_2]$ = atmospheric composition, vol % = 0.0390*
>
> *$[H_2O]$ = atmospheric composition, vol %*
>
> *T1 = temperature of surface leaf, K*
>
> *k = kinetic rate constant*
>
> *So increasing $[CO_2]$ will increase P and reduce T, cooling. Increasing S or T1 will have the same effect.*[51]

---

[51] https://principia-scientific.org/the-four-known-scientific-ways-carbon-dioxide-cools-earth-s-climate/

So the sensitivity of T to CO_2 depends on which temperature you are talking about: T, T1, T0. And what the net effect of all relevant mechanisms is. It is easy to see why there is so much confusion and controversy.

Or, to put it simply, not all solar energy entering Earth's atmosphere has left the planet. Instead, a larger proportion is being locked-up in that increased plant growth (locked in these natural chemical bonds). To argue against this simple analysis is to argue against the very premise of the 'fossil fuel' theory.

Our watery-green planet (due to nature) converts solar energy to form organic chemical bonds and grows organic structures (plant life on land and sea). Later this energy will be released during natural decomposition. If this was not how life works on Earth then there would be no fossils, no coal, and maybe no oil.

Over climate epochs, during warm periods, the total solar energy used by all life expands (the amount of solar energy returning to space diminishes), life sequesters more solar energy. The paleoclimatic record indicated when life reduces so less solar energy is stored. During the transition between warm and cold epochs, such stored energy gets released via decomposition or held for longer in peat and coal reservoirs.

Keep in mind natural decay is exothermic—a functioning compost heap is very warm. Also, peat bogs can be very warm while they are release more CO_2, methane, etc. to the oceans and atmosphere.

The gravest omission in modern climate computer modelling is how all natural living flora and fauna are not allocated ANY role in the ebb and flow of CO_2-driven of climate change. If you examine any of the 'expert' diagrams (all are mostly variations of the Kiehl-Trenberth cartoon below), you would think Earth was a lifeless planet.

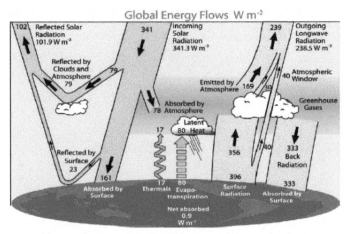

Fiᴏ. I. **The global annual mean Earth's energy budget for the Mar 2000 to May 2004 period (W m⁻²). The broad arrows indicate the schematic flow of energy in proportion to their importance.**

6/22/2013 5:44:28 PM
Trenberth, Fasullo, Kiehl, 2009, "Earth's global energy budget"

Do you see anywhere in the diagram above where the biosphere's impact on climate has been accounted?

We don't either. It is very grave omission from a vibrant, life-filled pulsating planet. If you have read or heard of the James Lovelock's Gaia hypothesis you will be convinced of the huge importance.

We see Lovelock's basic claim as reasonable. This is that living organisms interact with their inorganic surroundings on Earth to form a synergistic and self-regulating, complex system that helps to maintain and perpetuate the conditions for life on the planet.

The synergy includes the key role of the water cycle as a thermostat—keeping our wet planet from not getting as hot or as cold (during night and day) as with our nearest planetary body, the moon.

No attempt is made by government climate experts to factor in how the biosphere would impact global temperatures.

The greenhouse gas believers have nothing green in their house—no plants or fauna grow there. Yet these are the very people who want us to believe they are champions of the green movement!

Any reasonable non-scientist can fathom that the enormous abundance of forests and other life forms must have *some* influence, controlling both weather and climate! To ignore these natural effects is to regard anything but the sterile mechanistic view as unworthy of research. Natural life has been on this planet for so long it is surely foolish to disregard it as a non-player in the grand scheme of things.

Life takes solar energy and sequesters it away with chemical activity building new chemical structures. A tree is not just the sum of its chemical constituents but also of the solar energy it has gathered over its lifetime. An indeterminate quantity of solar energy entering the biosphere is stored. To deny this is to also deny that 'fossil fuels' are often the manifestation of the stored energy of dead plants.

Thus, solar 'energy in' can hardly ever equal 'energy out'. Our blue-green planet, through life, acquires, stores, redistributes and releases energy with the timing life commands, it does not follow the notion of 'energy in = energy out' until life itself expires—when entropy has the final say.

The greenhouse gas theory believers will tell you that "as solar forcing increases, then surface temperature needs to change to maintain the global energy balance. It has to change. It must!"

They are wrong. Look at their K-T energy budget diagrams to the exclusion of what we *know* happens all around us in the biosphere, because we can *see* it.

But the above quote could only be true if the only thing that could change was the forcing, which would mean that the air molecules of the atmosphere could not move, i.e. they were held rigidly in place as if they were atoms of a solid. And that is simply untrue. The consensus science on climate is wrongly premised on a black body calculation which assumes a solid body. But nature is not solid and fixed, it is highly responsive to energy input; it moves and flows in a continuum.

To help non-scientists better grasp the overall mechanism of climate, think in terms of simple analogy, not as a replacement for scientific understanding, but as a means to formulate a mental picture of the processes involved.

In our first book, *Slaying the Sky Dragon*, contributing author Alan Siddons made reference to thinking of energy flow from the Sun to Earth and beyond into space as akin to the flow of water in a river.

This use of a 'water flow analogy' is also favored by American climate researcher, Gary Novak who provides excellent resources at his blog.[52]

Novak tells us:

> *If you put a pan of water outside during the summer, it will evaporate. Put a lid over half of the pan, and it will evaporate at almost the same rate, because the rate of heat entering will determine the evaporation rate, not the manner in which the vapor escapes.*

This tells us that if so-called greenhouse gases blocked the escape of radiation from Earth like a window, there would be a continuous build-up of heat which would never stop. Heat coming in must equal heat going out over the long run.

Novak writes:

> *Radiation is absorbed and re-emitted in the atmosphere over and over. It is absorbed by greenhouse gases at their fingerprint wavelengths and then re-emitted as black-body radiation. The difference is that greenhouse gases only absorb*

---

[52] https://nov79.com

part of the black-body wavelengths allowing the rest to go through the atmosphere to cool the planet.

This is a mesh. A black, polypropylene mesh of this sort is used to cover greenhouses and restrict light. Global warming alarmists are assuming greenhouse gases do this. They don't. If you pour a gallon of water over the mesh, how much goes through? Half a gallon? It all goes through. Radiant cooling of the atmosphere goes around the blocked areas just as water does, because heat equilibrates.

Believers in the 'greenhouse gas' theory will reduce their arguments to a simple logic based on the nature of a window. If you paint half of a window black, half as much light goes through. The result is supposed to cause a build-up of heat.

This is key to the GHE argument because their analogy revolves around such 'window logic.' When you speak with anyone who defends the GHE, they tailor their explanations to justify the window concept.

But the Slayers have always preferred the better alternative concept of a river. If you build a concrete barrier halfway across a river, the same amount of water flows down the river. The only effect is a slight back-up (height increase) behind the barrier.

Atmospheric radiation functions like a river, not a window. If it didn't, there would be no end to the continuous build-up of heat. You can't have less energy leaving the Earth than entering. Both quantities must be equal over the long run. Only the river concept equalizes incoming and outgoing energy. The window concept does not.

Through satellite measurements, Lindzen and Choi showed that the river model is correct.[53] They showed that increases in surface temperature result in increases in outgoing radiation. Yet, Lindzen has yet to renounce the GHE so heavily predicated on the window analogy.

What then is the mechanism for the river concept? First off, the atmosphere emits radiation from a three-dimensional source, not a two-dimensional surface. When scientists apply the Stefan-Boltzmann equation[54] to the atmosphere, they are analyzing it as a two-dimensional surface.

As Joseph Postma eloquently shows, gases in the atmosphere do not model well in any two-dimensional frame.

Postma writes:

> ...gases don't follow the Stefan-Boltzmann Law in terms of radiative output. If you have an ensemble of gases the most you can assign is an effective radiative equivalent of the entire ensemble, to that of a solid blackbody surface.[55]

Therefore, modelling Earth as a 2D system enables weak or corrupt scientist to promote a greenhouse gas effect causing an additional bogus 33°C degrees of warming—which is statistical, not physical.

The standard greenhouse model breaks down when it is applied other planetary bodies, and subsequently by inspection of its mathematical limits and boundary conditions. First, Venus is roughly the square-root-of-two times closer to the Sun than the Earth, and so it experiences about twice the Solar flux. Venus'

[53] Geophysical Research Letters, July 14, 2009,
https://nov79.com/gbwm/forcing.html
[54] https://nov79.com/gbwm/sbc.html
[55] page 8, https://principia-scientific.org/publications/The_Model_Atmosphere.pdf

albedo is 0.7 and its ground temperature is approximately 730K. Then by equation...

$$f = 2\left[1 - \frac{(2*1370)*(1-0.7)}{4\sigma 730^4}\right]$$

$$f = 1.97 \text{ or } 197\%$$

...which ostensibly implies that Venus' atmosphere absorbs more energy than the surface flux even produces. This is a violation of the conservation of energy law.

Second, if the presumed effect of a thicker and thicker atmosphere with more and more GHG's is to increase the strength of the GHE, and thus increase the surface temperature, then the limit of the GHG absorption factor 'f' is an asymptote of 2. The ground temperature is actually seemingly independent of the Solar insolation, and, the linearly closer the 'f' factor gets to 200%, the exponentially higher the surface temperature is; this is nonsensical.

Once this paradigmatic illogic is exposed it becomes all the easier to question various qualitative and quantitative aspects of the standard model GH. One of the first is the implicit and systemically tautologous conjecture that "back-radiation" from GHG's increase the surface temperature of the Earth or slow its rate of cooling.

If this behavior (a source raising its own temperature by having its own radiation fall back upon it) is the result of a fundamental physics property of GHG's and atmospheres which contain them, then a higher concentration of GHG and a higher flux of radiation which interacts with it should result in higher temperatures.

Such a physically real scenario is found in the comparison of day-time desert and tropical conditions at similar latitude: the desert which is nearly devoid of the strongest GHG, water vapor, easily reaches 50-60°C, whereas the tropical region saturated with water vapor only reaches into the 30-40°C. This is in direct contradiction to an expected universal physics of a GHG back-radiation phenomenon.

Additional insight may be found in comparison of a desert with an atmosphere to a desert without one at all, such as is found on the Moon. Clearly, the role of an atmosphere, independent of GHG's, is that it modulates and smooths the variation of Solar insolation induced surface temperature. When a GHG is present, it does this even more efficiently due to the additional heat-transporting abilities within the gas.

The back-radiation GHE postulate is contradicted by real-world atmospheric behavior. This is shown via experiment as described elsewhere in this book.

As a three-dimensional source of radiation, the atmosphere emits radiation much more effectively than a two-dimensional surface. This is where the 'extra' 33 degrees of heating gets conjured up—in the botched GHE calculations first derived by British mathematician Lewis Fry Richardson.

Richardson's own equations from the 1920s were relied on by Myhre et al who used radiative transfer equations:

> 'Myhre' would have us accept that the amount of heat added to the atmosphere (Watts per square meter) equals 5.35 times the natural log of the amount of CO_2 after an increase divided by the amount before.
>
> Heat increase $(W/m^2) = 5.35 \ln C/C_0$
>
> This equation states that doubling the amount of CO_2 in the atmosphere (natural log of 2 times 5.35) will result in a heat increase of 3.708 Watts per square meter. It's total nonsense, as there are no square meters in the atmosphere. But the result points to a change in energy going into and out of the atmosphere when looking at the cross-sectional

*area of the Earth from a distance, where the Sun's
energy is 1367 W/m².*

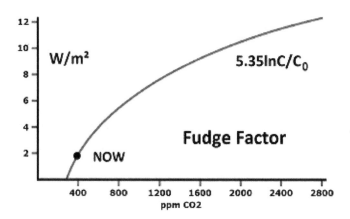

*The Watts per square meter are then converted
into a temperature increase by applying the Stefan-
Boltzmann constant.*[56]

Novak, as per the Slayers, noted that the greenhouse gas theory
depends on a bunch of Radiative Transfer Equations (RTEs). But
there is no way to produce an equation or number for
atmospheric effects.

According to promoters of the GHE, radiative transfer
equations show 3.7 Watts per square meter radiation less leaving
the Earth than entering from the Sun upon doubling CO_2. There
is no such thing as less. The amounts must always be equal. How
could some get trapped, when all the rest (1367 W/m²) moves
in and out constantly? Such idiotic logic stems from the total
incompetence of most so-called climatologists.

Gary Novak writes:

> *The official climatology position is not an
> explanation; it's fake mathematics that shows a*

> *number to represent heat trapped in the atmosphere, when there is no such thing as trapping heat in the atmosphere. The math is called Radiative Transfer Equations (RTEs). The result is not a measurement; it is a series of calculations.*
>
> *Fake radiative transfer equations were used to show the primary effect of global warming. The supposed result of the radiative transfer equations was converted into a rudimentary fudge factor for simple calculation of the result. It says that doubling the amount of carbon dioxide in the air, even from one molecule to two molecules, would add 3.7 Watts per square meter of energy to the Earth.[57]*

The problem is not that the fudge factor is a simplified representation; the problem is that there is no science in the calculation.

C over C sub zero is the increase in CO_2. The question is what would happen upon doubling the amount of carbon dioxide in the air. For this the ratio of C over C sub zero is 2. So the fudge factor is 5.35 times the natural log of 2, which is 3.7 Watts per square meter. Climatologists call this effect "forcing."

This subject is discussed in the 2001 publication of the IPCC, chapter 6.[58]

Stefan Rahmstorf cited the IPCC saying:

> *Without any feedbacks, a doubling of CO_2 (which amounts to a forcing of 3.7 W/m^2) would result in 1 °C global warming, which is easy to calculate and is undisputed.[59]*

---

[57] https://nov79.com/gbwm/rte.html

[58] http://www.ipcc.ch/ipccreports/tar/wg1/219.htm

[59] The Future of Globalization: Explorations in Light of Recent

The fudge factor is totally invalid because it removes saturation. Nothing can remove saturation. Nowhere is there an explanation of how or why saturation was removed in the calculation of the fudge factor. The fudge factor is derived out of muddle with no other purpose than removing saturation from the effects.

There is no theoretical method of calculating the fudge factor because radiation absorption by CO_2 must be measured, it cannot be calculated. So why do a calculation after measuring the result? The measured results show saturation in 10 meters, while the calculation shows almost no saturation throughout the atmosphere. Muddling the subject and contriving the endpoint is the only reason for doing a calculation.

The fudge factor is absurd—it shows the same result no matter how little CO_2 is in the air. If there is one molecule of CO_2 in the air, doubling it to two molecules will supposedly add the same 3.7 W/m^2 to the entire surface of the Earth.

The muddling, fudging and fixing was done consciously, intentionally in a coordinated plan to ensure a once-forgotten, discarded hypothesis (the CO_2-driven radiative greenhouse gas effect) could justifiably be resurrected as a viable explanation of climate change (it isn't).

Independent climate researcher Ron Clutz neatly summarises for us some of the essential take-home points on the myth of CO_2 as a significant driver of global warming climate change and our weather. He notes:

> To believe humans are dangerously warming Earth's climate, you have to swallow a bunch of unbelievable notions;
>
> You have to think the atmosphere drives temperature, instead of the ocean with 1000 times the heat capacity;
>
> You have to disregard the Sun despite its obvious

effects from summer to winter and longer term;

You have to think CO_2 drives radiative heat transfers, instead of H_2O which does 95% of the radiative work;

You have to think rises in CO_2 cause temperatures to rise, rather than the other way around;

You have to forget it was warmer than now in the Middle Ages, warmer still in the Roman era, and warmest of all during Minoan times. And on and on.[60]

The global warmist narrative is full of ideas upside down and backwards, including many reversals of cause and effect.

The human-caused global warming theory is like a massive hot air balloon, so why doesn't it deflate? Answer: because many interests are served in keeping it alive and pumping up public fears.

Now even the lukewarmers—those docile skeptics who somehow want to allow a free pass to the GHE—are slowly recognising that the idea of CO_2 as our climate's control knob is fast disappearing if we accept what we are told about 'CO_2 climate sensitivity.'

All greenhouse gas theory believers, from the most rabid alarmist to the most self-centred lukewarmist, will preach to you about the key measure: EQUILIBRIUM CLIMATE SENSITIVITY (ECS). This term is how scientists define the potency of the 'CO_2 effect' in the climate system.

Since the 1980s, advocates of the GHE tried to determine what precisely this number is. They search for the Equilibrium Climate Sensitivity or ECS—the hypothesised amount of temperature increase per doubling of CO_2, keeps shrinking even

---

[60] https://rclutz.wordpress.com/2018/10/27/self-serving-global-warmism/

as carbon dioxide rises.

The number keeps changing—despite the fact this is supposed to be 'settled science.' Greenhouse gas theory promoters must constantly re-evaluate the potency of their trace gas villain.

The graph below shows how the mainstream peer-reviewed literature on the subject is headed downward on this CO_2 'climate sensitivity' question.

Quite simply, the more time and analysis is spent on the question, the more the answer contradicts the idea that CO_2 drives the climate.

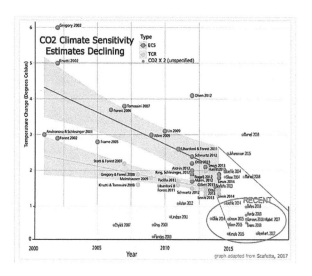

What the scientists find (but do not yet publicly admit) is that the case for believing in the CO_2-driven greenhouse gas theory is in full retreat. If we look at the downward trend from the graph, it appears that on or around the year 2030 'climate sensitivity' to CO_2 will officially be ranked at zero. In other words, in around a decade's time, even the slowest witted, most biased GHE believer will be compelled to confess their theory is dead.

It is no exaggeration to say that the world's most vaunted scientific organizations have put their reputations on the line in backing this junk science. We told them they got it badly wrong in our book in 2011. Even their own peer-reviewed literature backs the Slayers on this.

Apparently, none of the "scientists" who promoted the greenhouse gas theory were aware that the solubility of gases, e.g., carbon dioxide, is inversely proportional to temperature.

As we discussed in our first book, ocean temperatures likely increased during the last half of the 20th century, most likely due to a very active Sun and deep ocean volcanism. It cannot be stressed enough: oceans cover 70% of the Earth's surface and out-gassed more carbon dioxide than they did before the ocean warming began. Nothing in the greenhouse gas theory addresses the fact that 70% of the Earth's surface covered by water. Nothing in their discredited theory accounts for deep ocean volcanism, which itself also releases large quantities of carbon dioxide into the oceans and puts upward pressure on the out-gassing of carbon dioxide into the atmosphere.

Most scientists would agree that only the upper ~10m of seawater is heated by the Sun. So, what then of the internal heating effect of our very hot planetary core? We know Earth's core has a temperature of 5,000°C. Surely, that energy must rise outward to the surface and exhibit *some* impact on global surface temperatures? Below is a typical graph of the range of temperatures associated with depth beneath the surface.

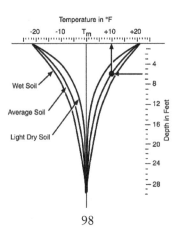

Scientists agree whether the soil is dry, wet or average, there is a temperature effect. The same holds true for our oceans. Heat content below ~500m is completely supplied from inside the Earth.

On the moon, the Sun only warms the upper 50cm or so of the surface layer. During the day, temperatures rise according the incoming radiation with a little lag. During the night, the surface cools down to far below 100K. Some craters near the poles have a constant temperature of ~25K. This is most probably the energy from the internal heat being radiated away to space. None of this is noted in, let alone factored into, any Earth energy budget you will ever see published.

We hope that by now, readers will understand the utter stagnation of cause and effect built into climate sensitivity science where billions in funds, time and computer power were wasted. The sky dragon of greenhouse gas theory is a myth that additional billions in research funds, time and computer power will never make real.

To make their sky dragon real, all the peculiarities and perturbations of the Earth's orbital path around the Sun are kept static and are not taken into account. As we indicated, the Earth's varying orbit is the biggest climate-driver by externally varying the climate forces.

Anyone who looks back at the reception our book received from the scientific community when published in January 2011 will note the virulent blowback our science generated. We were scathing when exposing the errors in the GHE and our analysis pointed strongly towards intentional fakery and fraud in the fudging of the numbers relied on the standard greenhouse gas theory.

For those readers who have read the UN IPPC climate reports, you may have spotted that these charlatans decided in 2006 to collude to remove all hints pointing to the climatic effects of our planet's orbit, keeping climate internal (atmospherical, tropospherical) and solar.

No real progress in mainstream climate science will ever occur until it becomes widely recognized in government-funded academia that Earth's orbital anomalies are still poorly understood and efforts must be made to develop this area of research to better inform climate analysis.[61]

Because any research based on reality reduces the equilibrium climate sensitivity factor—revealing the CO_2 charade to be a complete non-problem. Rather than raise the white flag and admit they had it wrong all along, they scorned what the Slayers show without good reasons. They refuse to acknowledge the existence of the problems we identified. We give them credit for relentlessly sticking with their talking points even when they are dead wrong.

Over geologic time—and even just during the lifetime of our species—the Earth's average temperature fluctuated widely and wildly. Our planet has been covered in an ocean of molten rock and of solid water ice and has experienced every climate state in between. Its average temperature has ranged from an estimated -50°C to 25°C. Yet, paleoclimatologists cannot link these temperature changes with carbon dioxide.

Temperature change often happens rapidly, as when coming out of long glacial intervals into interglacials, and between stadials and interstadials within glacial phases.

Despite the swing dampening effect of our water world's oceans, its thermostat can still get rapidly turned up and down. Never, never, never has a sudden change been preceded by a change in atmospheric carbon dioxide concentration.

The Sun's power increases about one percent per 110 million years. Despite this, the Paleozoic and our present Cenozoic Eras had ice ages but in the intervening Mesozoic, not so much. And our current ice age is probably not over, despite the alleged effect of humans on global climate.

Let's enjoy the Holocene interglacial while we can. Too bad

---

[61] http://www.knowledgeminer.eu/climate papers.html

we can't get CO_2 back up to an optimum of 1200PPM from today's low level of 400PPM, which so suppresses C3 [62] plant growth.

Authors Dr. Tim Ball, Dr. Claus Johnson, Dr. Martin Hertzberg, Joseph A. Olson, Alan Siddons, Dr. Charles Anderson and John O'Sullivan were roundly vilified and mocked as much by so-called fellow skeptics (the lukewarmers) as by the government-sponsored alarmists.

Dr. Ball was sued in the Canadian libel courts by UN IPCC climatist, Dr. Michael Mann; Dr. Johnson was severely censured by his employing university; O'Sullivan had his reputation trashed by Huffington Post in a fake child sex scandal and more recently, our good friend and inspiration, Martin Hertzberg passed away. So, while we may fairly title this book our Victory Lap, it came at great personal cost to us.

Tragically, students are indoctrinated with Mann's fraudulent hockey stick graph. They were never told about Mann's corrupt Nature trick to "hide the decline" or about Climategates 1, 2 and 3.

Ex-NASA climate modeller-turned-whistleblower, Dr. Duane Thresher, gives us some insight into how Michael Mann deceived so many for so long:

> *I was not only a climate modeller but I also took courses and did hands-on work with climate proxies, so I could expertly model them. One of the reasons I went to the University of Arizona was it was world famous for tree ring research, having started the field themselves.*
>
> *Tree ring research is heavily dependent on*

---

[62] Plants which use only the Calvin cycle for fixing the carbon dioxide from the air are known as C3 plants. In the first step of the cycle CO2 reacts with RuBP to produce two 3-carbon molecules of 3-phosphoglyceric acid (3-PGA). Taken from: http://hyperphysics.phy-astr.gsu.edu/hbase/Biology/phoc.html

statistics. These statistics are very complicated so are done with computer programs. And there are only a few programs, each written by a single IT incompetent scientist and never peer reviewed. They are almost certainly full of bugs and their results are thus questionable.[63]

It was Dr. Ball's unswerving dedication to exposing the junk science of Michael Mann that precipitated Mann's unsuccessful multi-million-dollar libel suit versus Ball in the British Columbia Supreme Court.

And how have our other opponents fared? Within a year of our book publication, the United Nations Framework Convention on Climate Change (UNFCCC) issued a formal request for immunity from prosecution to "protect" researchers who have provided "evidence" supportive of the man-made global warming scare story.[64]

Coincidence?

As our first book revealed, the phony scientific consensus that anthropogenic carbon dioxide is the primary driver of global warming and climate change is just that—perception only, not reality.

True science is not based on perception; it is based on empirical data. The fact that the leadership of science organizations rubber-stamped and parroted a phony consensus is not itself scientific evidence.

63

http://realclimatologists.org/Articles/2019/01/03/Climate_of_Incompetence/index.html

[64] https://www.foxnews.com/world/u-n-climate-organization-wants-immunities-against-charges-of-conflict-of-interest-exceeding-mandate-among-others#ixzz1xaeHBzTK

Why We Must All Be Wary of the Technocrats

Technocracy can be defined as the science of social engineering, which is no science at all. The use of science as a tool for social manipulation thoroughly confuses most people until they understand the motive behind the deception.

Canadian climatologist, Dr. Tim Ball, spent much of the last three decades as a sentinel to the dangers of technocrats. It is no coincidence that Tim is a key figure representing the Slayers and Principia Scientific International.

Tim writes:

> It's difficult to convince people that the science behind the claim of human-caused global warming is wrong. The technocrats developed their own language and technical terms to protect their control over the information; to make people pay a higher price for their services; to ensure they remain unaccountable for their actions. The three lawsuits filed to silence me from explaining their science in ways the public could understand, and all came from technocratic members of the Intergovernmental Panel on Climate Change (IPCC). After you successfully convince the people about the deceptive use of science, you confront a more difficult problem. You must explain the motive to people who can't believe that scientists would corrupt science, use it for a political agenda, or that a few people can fool the world.

The bureaucratic technocrats, including those funded by them, who created and promote the deception, rarely respond to scientific challenges. Why bother when the public doesn't understand? However, they respond when you discuss the motive behind their actions.

There are signs that skeptics are influencing public opinion, but overall little has changed. The public is in a holding pattern. They know something is wrong as reflected in a growing distrust of science generally, and climate science specifically. A quote from a Pew Center report explains…

> *Overall, many people hold skeptical views of climate scientists and GM food scientists; a larger share express trust in medical scientists, but there, too, many express what survey analysts call a "soft" positive rather than a strongly positive view.*[65]

This partially confirms the holding pattern. They don't know whom to trust, so they set it aside. They are afraid of talking about a subject they don't understand. This aligns with Mark Twain's sage advice:

> *It's better to keep your mouth shut and appear stupid than open it and remove all doubt.*

Respecting Twain's words, the cautious approach defers to most basic of widely agreed facts on the matter. In this case, no one would dispute that in 1972, universally respected scientists Carl Sagan and George Mullen, stated that the "greenhouse effect" kept the average global temperature between 286 Kelvin and 288 Kelvin (287 Kelvin is Celsius 12.85°C which is Fahrenheit 56.93°F).[66]

---

[65] http://www.pewinternet.org/2017/12/08/mixed-messages-about-public-trust-in-science/
[66]

https://www.google.ie/url?q=https://courses.seas.harvard.edu/climate/eli/Courses/EPS281r/Sources/Faint-young-sun-paradox/Segan-Mullen-

We are told a minimum 30-year period of temperature data is what is needed to discern a climatic effect. Over the last five decades, global greenhouse gas emissions increased 75% according to government sources.[67]

Many retrospective "adjustments" to temperature data later, and the Earth's surface temperature is still 288 K, which is within the accepted normal or "average." According to NASA, as at 2017, the average global temperature was 288K.[68]

So, despite a truly massive 75% increase in the amount of CO_2 in the atmosphere, thermometers barely budged, if at all. Doesn't that prove to any reasonable person that in the laboratory of our atmosphere, CO_2 is not a climate driver and the greenhouse gas theory is thereby invalidated?

And what does the peer-reviewed literature tell us about the measurable, empirically-known consequences of current levels of atmospheric CO_2?

The known (measured and empirical) result of increased CO_2 levels is increased plant growth which precipitated increased cloud cover which results in cooler temps more precipitation turning to snow increased artic ice, etc.[69]

Increasing atmospheric carbon dioxide levels have caused increasing photosynthetic rates, biomass growth, and seed yield for all of the important C3 food and feed crops.[70]

Meanwhile, climate alarmists deny empirically-proven scientific evidence in favor of make-believe, fake-data computer models rigged to only show doom and gloom.

1972.pdf&sa=U&ved=2ahUKEwinhsef0Z3eAhWHCsAKHXUGBWk
QFjACegQICBAB&usg=AOvVaw2vaKm-vbZYqQqBYCVjkU0T
[67]

http://www.pbl.nl/en/dossiers/Climatechange/TrendGHGemissions
1990-2004
[68] https://nssdc.gsfc.nasa.gov/planetary/factsheet/earthfact.html
[69] https://www.nap.edu/read/1911/chapter/8#106
[70] Acock and Allen, 1985, Enoch and Kimball, 1986, Warrick et al, 1986, Allen 1990.

The fakery in demonizing carbon dioxide and promoting the so-called radiative greenhouse gas effect is very much a product of the success of political activists in seizing control of the senior positions in government funding in this area of research.

As we show, the hype in the GHE alarmist narrative took hold in the 1980s. By contrast, in the 1970s the U.S. Central Intelligence Agency advised of impending climate cooling—22 of 27 forecasting methods predicted a cooling trend for the next 25 years, and "meteorological experts" thought a return 1800s climate was around the corner, with the concomitant monsoon failures, shorter growing seasons and "violent weather." [71]

Those of us old enough to remember those times recall no mention of any greenhouse gas effect, only of climate cooling due to industrial pollution whereby particulates from smoke stacks, especially from burning wood and coal, would send us into a new ice age before the end of the 20th century.

According to Stewart and Glantz in the early 1970s, the prevailing view among scientists was that the Earth was headed into another ice age. [72]

According to Dr. Hubert Lamb, the original founder of the now infamous Climatic Research Unit (CRU) at the University of East Anglia (think 'Climategate'), the cooling trend noted since the 1960s was set to cause...

> ...shorter growing seasons for Canada, northern Russia and north China. Europe could expect to be cooler and wetter ... [I]n periods when climate change [cooling] is underway.

Stewart and Glantz affirm the work of the well-respected Dr. Lamb and wrote:

71

http://documents.theblackvault.com/documents/environment/poten tialtrends.pdf

[72] http://link.springer.com/article/10.1007%2FBF00140504

By the late 1970s that prevailing view had seemingly shifted 180 degrees to the belief that the Earth's atmosphere was being warmed as a result of an increasing CO$_2$ loading of the atmosphere. ... The causes of global climate change remain in dispute. Existing theories of climate, atmospheric models, and actuarial experience are inadequate to meet the needs of policymakers for information about future climate.[73]

We count at least 285 scientific publications that run counter to any alleged CO$_2$-warming consensus opinion before the 1980s. The list is divided into several sub-sections.

- Cooling Since 1940, Forecasts for Continued Cooling/Ice Age (156 papers)

- Dubious Human Influence on Climate, Low CO$_2$ Climate Sensitivity (44 papers)

- Rising CO$_2$ Leads to Cooling (7)

- Uncertainties, Lack of Climate Understanding, Climate modelling Problems (30)
- Miscellaneous Questionable Human, CO$_2$ Influence on Climate (12)

- Non-CO$_2$ Climate Change Mechanisms (26)

- Warmer past despite lower CO$_2$ (10)

The complete list of 285 Global Cooling/Weak CO$_2$ Influence papers from the 1960s to 1980s can be found using the below

---

[73] http://www.albany.edu/cpr/stewart/Papers/J1290-StewartGlantzNDU1985cap.pdf

links:

> **Part 1** http://notrickszone.com/285-papers-70s-cooling-1/#sthash.PJoHxopP.dpbs
> **Part 2** http://notrickszone.com/285-papers-70s-cooling-2/#sthash.lRcCIvlK.dpbs
> **Part 3** http://notrickszone.com/285-papers-70s-cooling-3/#sthash.Tw3Ix8qy.dpbs

Despite the considerable rise in the level of carbon dioxide in the atmosphere it appears solar scientists are anticipating the onset of global cooling due to changes in the Sun.

Would it surprise you to learn the greatest global two-year cooling event of the last century recently occurred? From February 2016 to February 2018, global average temperatures dropped 0.56°C. You have to go back to 1982-84 for the next biggest two-year drop, 0.47°C—also during a so-called global warming era.

The data for this comes from *GISTEMP Team, 2018: GISS Surface Temperature Analysis* (GISTEMP), NASA Goddard Institute for Space Studies.[74] This is the standard source used in most journalistic reporting of global average temperatures.

The reason we draw your attention to this is because we know you haven't seen it on the news or read it in the print media. Why? Because it isn't newsworthy to those who push the man-made global warming narrative.

Any such statistical cooling outliers will never garner media attention. If, anywhere in the world, a temperature record is exceeded, it will make headlines. If they can find a big increase over a previous month, or the same month in the previous year, that's newsworthy. If a sequence of warming months or years can be found, that's a big story. But when the data shows cooling of any sort—and there have been *more* cooling months than

---

[74] https://data.giss.nasa.gov/gistemp/

warming months since supposed anthropogenic warming began—there's no story.

Annual atmospheric CO_2 levels have risen in almost a straight line since 1960. If temperatures did the same thing, the link to CO_2 would be direct and obvious. But instead, we see cooling despite such a monotonic rise in atmospheric carbon dioxide. It isn't difficult to expose the flaw in what is supposed to be happening—according to the greenhouse gas theory.

In other words, the case for global warming is non-empirical. It relies on computer models with garbage in-garbage out biases. It relies on historical studies where the history is rewritten by interested parties, researchers who rely upon their university/government grants. And it relies on 'secret science' which no amount of FOIA requests brought out into the light. The general public is simply not permitted to test for themselves the veracity of the evidence relied upon by those experts behind the academic curtain.

Nevertheless, these same scientists ignore global cooling because it reflects negatively on their models, income and prestigious positions in academe.

Of course, the UN IPCC is also not at all interested in historic records indicating a link between sunspots and climate change.

From ice core records, we know that climatic changes with glacial periods linked with solar activity. Scientists who study the ice core records and follow the Sun very closely report that we have a Bond Event[75] happening now. In other words, solar cycles appear to be converging. They include the following:

- 22 year Hale

- 179 year barycentric

---

[75] Bond Events are rapid climate changes recorded in ice core data described in the next section.

- 1450 year Bond

- 23,000 year precession

- 25,800 year plane

- 100,000 year ice age (when all solar-planetary cycles converge as they are now)

What are Bond Events?

Bond events are North Atlantic climate fluctuations occurring every 1,470 ±500 years throughout the Holocene.

Eight such events have been identified, primarily from fluctuations in ice-rafted debris.

These events are believed by some scientists to be interglacial relatives of the glacial Dansgaard-Oeschger events[76] and are said to be evidenced by a 15-20% glacial-interglacial temperature change.

Based on Greenland ice core data, the Younger Dryas began and ended very abruptly. Its start dates to 10,900 BC, and its ending (the final warming) began circa 9700 BC and may have occurred within an incredible three-year period.

---

[76] Bond, G.; et al., 2001, *Persistent Solar Influence on North Atlantic Climate During the Holocene*, Science. 294 (5549): 2130–2136. Bibcode:2001Sci...294.2130B. doi:10.1126/science.1065680. PMID 11739949.]

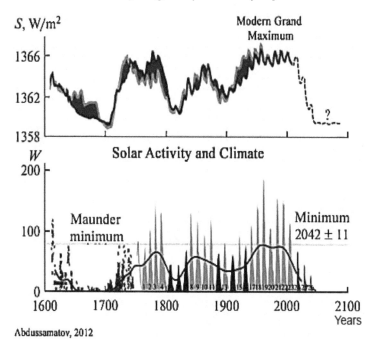

Abdussamatov, 2012

Above we show a graph by eminent Russian solar physicist, Habibullo Abdussamatov who predicts another Little Ice Age within the next 30 years.

In 2017 alone, there were no fewer than 120 papers linking historical and modern climate change to variations in solar activity and its modulators (clouds, cosmic rays) published in scientific journals.[77]

At Principia Scientific International, readers can find an excellent article by Kenneth Richards called *Seven New Papers Forecast Global Cooling & Mini Ice Age* which identifies the most recent seven new studies affirming the likelihood of a coming ice age.[78]

---

[77] http://notrickszone.com/skeptic-papers-2017-1

[78] https://principia-scientific.org/seven-new-papers-forecast-global-cooling-mini-ice-age/

Quantum Mechanics and Raman Spectroscopy Refute Greenhouse Theory

2018 was also the year we saw the first peer-reviewed scientific paper showing that quantum mechanics and Raman Spectroscopy could be used to refute the greenhouse gas theory.

Blair Macdonald, researcher and author of the paper *Quantum Mechanics and Raman Spectroscopy Refute Greenhouse Theory* caused a stir when his findings at Academia.edu and Researchgate site.[79]

What were Macdonald's findings?

A core claim in greenhouse gas theory is that nitrogen and oxygen are not 'greenhouse gases' because they do not register with infrared (IR) spectroscopy.

But, by performing actual lab experiments to test this assertion, Macdonald proved they do!

To show the gases absorb at IR spectra frequencies the operation of the N_2-CO_2 laser was studied using first principle physics.

According to Planck's law of radiation, all matter above absolute zero Kelvin absorbs and emits infrared radiation, and this should apply N_2 and O_2.

Readers should be aware that Raman is a detection method. When 1 in 10,000,000 has a Raman scattering signature at a given wavelength, that means it absorbed 1.

So, just like opinion polls only sample a few people, we multiply the Raman results by population/sample size. Wavelengths that have 0 Raman signature have no absorption.

---

[79]

https://www.researchgate.net/publication/328927828_Quantum_Mechanics_and_Raman_Spectroscopy_Refute_Greenhouse_Theory

Portable Raman Spectrometer with High Sensitivity

To show these gases absorb at IR spectra frequencies, the operation of the N_2-CO_2 laser was studied including practical applications and experiments of Raman IR spectroscopy. It was found that O_2 and N_2 emit a small amount of IR, so then, clearly they are the heat trapping gases—unlike CO_2 which emits IR within microseconds of absorption—making it an effective coolant.

We remind our non-science readers that there is 1,600 times more N_2 and 400 times more O_2 in our atmosphere than CO_2. The IR signature of the total of CO_2 in the atmosphere is something like $1/80^{th}$ of that of H_2O. One CO_2 molecule is surrounded by 2,500 other atoms and molecules. CO_2 is rarefied in our atmosphere. All in all, CO_2's effect can only be negligible.

With such incontrovertible evidence, either quantum mechanics is wrong, or the GHE theory is wrong.

As has been the case so often with the establishment, the reaction to Macdonald's work was to circle the wagons and nullify wider exposure of his results. Upon joining Principia Scientific International where his work found a warm welcome,

Blair lamented:

> *Academia won't let me update my paper and submit others. Seems I have kicked the bee hive there. I saw John O'Sullivan posted my paper on the PSI site, I really appreciated that, and the words he added were among the most decent I have received.*[80]

2018 was also the year we saw a valuable contribution backing Slayer science from a former senior establishment scientist. Dr. Peter L. Ward, who worked 27 years as a geophysicist and program leader for the United States Geological Survey, added his authority to our growing bandwagon.

After retiring, Dr. Ward applied a full-time, ten-year effort into understanding what really causes global warming. He created a 20-page paper called *A Most Inconvenient Reality— Greenhouse Gases Cannot Physically Explain Observed Global Warming*[81] which was submitted to the Journal of Geophysical Research on May 28, 2018 and describes these issues in more detail. Naturally, his submission was rejected for being contrary to GHE groupthink. His correspondence file includes the editor's email rejecting the paper without review.

In his 'Conclusions,' Dr. Ward wrote:

> *Greenhouse-warming theory cannot physically cause observed global warning. It is physically impossible for a body of matter to be warmed by its own radiation because its own radiation does not include the higher amplitudes of oscillation at*

---

[80] Ibid,
https://www.researchgate.net/publication/328927828_Quantum_Mechanics_and_Raman_Spectroscopy_Refute_Greenhouse_Theory
[81] https://whyclimatechanges.com/wp-content/uploads/JGRAtmospheres.pdf

every frequency of oscillation required to cause a higher temperature as shown by Planck's law.

Greenhouse gases cannot act as a blanket warming Earth because a blanket has no way to increase the amplitudes of oscillation at every frequency of oscillation required to cause a higher temperature unless it is an electric blanket providing thermal energy from elsewhere.

Greenhouse-warming theory assumes that radiation from Sun is the same physical thing as radiation from Earth except that there is a much larger amount of it. Planck's law shows clearly that the physical properties of solar radiation are distinctly different from the physical properties of terrestrial radiation. Radiation from Sun is observed to burn your skin. No amount of radiation from Earth can cause sunburn.

Greenhouse-warming theory assumes that fluxes of heat are additive. Heat flux, however, is clearly observed in warming and cooling curves to be a function of the average of the existing and ultimate temperature at any moment in time. Such averaging is done in Nature by resonance between discrete molecular-bond-scale oscillators oscillating at the same frequency on the surface of the emitting and absorbing bodies. Radiation is the result of the simultaneous resonance of a very large number of oscillators at all the frequencies contained within the frequency spectrum for a body at a given temperature shown by Planck's law.

Greenhouse-warming theory is clearly mistaken. Reducing greenhouse-gas emissions will not decrease observed global warming. There is no physical basis to support climate models that predict major global warming in the next few decades. We can burn fossil fuels safely provided we minimize pollution.

Skepticism Encourages Personal Research

We hope readers adduce a fundamental difference between climate change skeptics and realists, and climate change alarmists.

An implicit message we offer is that skeptics must evaluate alarmist 'science' and corresponding media propaganda to glean a broader understanding of both sides of the debate.

As Slayers and supporters of the traditional scientific method, we encourage objectivity and performing your own oversight. We trust that reading this book sharpens your mistrust of mainstream media and supposed scientific authorities—those national academies and institutions so readily prepared to hide errors, exaggerations and outright lies within so much mainstream climate change information disseminated about the horrors of carbon dioxide.

If, like us, you see carbon dioxide as more a saint than sinner in the grand scheme of nature, then you would likely accept that for most of the 500 million years or so terrestrial animals have lived on Earth, CO_2 levels were several times higher than they are today, and life flourished abundantly.

The relatively few periods when temperatures and CO_2 levels were comparable to today were associated with glaciation and mass extinction events.

So, go ahead, open that can of carbonated soda. It might not be good for you, but it's good for the environment.

The Slayers (now formally and collectively known as members of Principia Scientific International) are adamant that our science (and all science) must abide by the traditional scientific method. In short, any hypothesis shall be testable and subject to open trial by empirical evidence. In that regard, the greenhouse gas hypothesis is refuted.

To any *real* scientist, it's simple. Propose a hypothesis. It should make predictions about the world. If the predictions are wrong, the hypothesis is wrong. Climate modellers say CO_2 will reduce outward longwave radiation (OLR). It doesn't. Since 1985, OLR increased. The models are wrong.

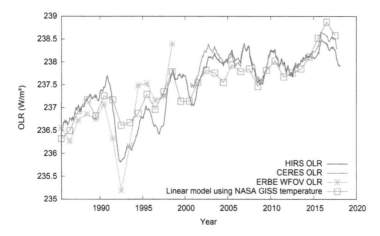

Figure 4. Purple curve: HIRS OLR. Green curve: CERES OLR.
Blue curve: ERBE WFOV OLR.
Orange curve: linear regression model based on NASA GISS T anomaly.

Source: Dewitte & Clerbaux; Remote Sensing 2018, 10, 1539; doi:10.3390/rs10101539

A reasonable scientist would thus abandon such a discredited hypothesis.

But, as we have seen for the last three decades, the insanity of climate alarm prevails. All because many sad and deluded fools choose to believe the inane argument that the only experts to be believed on the subject are approved government climate scientists.

Fortunately, a great awakening is occurring—following so many of the GHE theory's failed predictions. Many more citizens see the obvious flaw in the old argument that a self-serving government climate scientist knows basic physics and chemistry better than independent professional physicists, engineers and chemists.

It's been a long time since we wrote and published *Slaying the Sky Dragon: Death of the Greenhouse Gas Theory*. Steadily but surely, we notice an inexorable shift towards our position from scientists who probably haven't read our book, or even know much if anything about our work.

We are greatly encouraged to see eminent scientists we hold in high regard coming out and making statements on the issue.

Among the very many, we cite Professor Will Happer who expressed his concerns in a 2014 interview. Asked by the interviewer whether he saw evidence of a correlation between CO_2 and temperature, this was his reply:

> **Happer:** Yes. (However), temperature always changes first, and CO_2 follows.
> **Host:** Has there been any global increase in temperature since 1998?
> **Happer:** No. A thousand parts per million (PPM) of CO_2 would actually help the planet.
> **Host:** How?
> **Happer:** Because agricultural productivity would go up.

Professor Happer acknowledges for all to see that CO_2 is systematically and necessarily pumped into commercial greenhouses for a good reason: it is benign plant food and several thousand part per million (PPM) in greenhouses is an optimum amount to ensure plentiful plant yield.

> **Happer:** If you look around the world, many greenhouse operators put several thousand parts per million into their greenhouses.
> **Host:** Would there be any negative effects on humans from breathing a thousand parts per

million?

Happer: *No, absolutely not. Our primate ancestors were here roughly 70 to 80 million years ago when CO_2 levels were 3,000 parts per million. That's when we evolved. So, it was ten times what it is now.*

We also let our sailors in submarines live in atmospheres that are several thousand parts per million.

Glacier Bay glaciers disappeared long before any increase in CO_2. The glaciers in Alaska's Glacier Bay are all gone. They disappeared in the 1800s.

In fact, that was one of the most famous trips of John Muir. Muir, the founder of the Sierra Club, was visiting Glacier Bay in 1879, and he pointed out all the glaciers were gone. That was long before there was any increase of CO_2.[82]

Professor Happer and former astronaut Harrison H. Schmitt co-authored an article entitled *In Defense of Carbon Dioxide*, published in The Wall Street Journal.[83]

Professor Happer's point on John Muir's visit to Glacier Bay bears further elucidation.

Between 1934 and 2008, we experienced six of the highest output solar cycles since 1780. Warm sea water causes tidal terminus glaciers to retreat. Increases in CO_2 lag the rise in temperature of sea water by 10-15 years.

It is entirely consistent that CO_2 will continue rise for a few more years before pausing and then falling, lagging behind the

---

[82]

https://www.wsj.com/articles/SB10001424127887323528404578452483656067190

[83]

https://www.wsj.com/articles/SB10001424127887323528404578452483656067190

decline in world temperatures mid-way though the new solar cycle (SC25).

As we often say, "It's the Sun, stupid!"

Our Concluding Remarks for Chapter 1

We hope readers now feel better equipped to objectively assess the vast body of climate science that contradicts the human-caused global warming dogma. At least, we envisage reading this book will help you realize that much government-funded science is about selecting and promoting research which best fits the alarmist's catastrophic narrative—where dissent is automatically disqualified among such so-called experts.

We hope you will check out our website and evaluate for yourself the merits of Principia Scientific International's mission. Above all else, we hope you see the need to defend the traditional scientific method and expose subjective bias and pseudo-science nonsense where you see it. This is a much-needed course of action in an age of groupthink where objectivity is heresy, skepticism is denial and questions are forbidden.

We have sought to reveal in some detail in this volume that for many decades, scientific discovery and advancement has been deliberately stifled and debate is intentionally shut down.

Of course, those who stifle debate are the very same people who advocate a shift away from the traditional scientific method of open debate, critical analysis, focus on the raw data and that thorny old word 'falsifiability.'

In post-modern science, there is no need to actually prove a hypothesis right or wrong with facts and data. In the modern paradigm of government-controlled pseudo-science the key determinant of truth is a simple showing of hands among a select elite—a clique of hand-picked experts approved by government institutions who act in the service of government.

The Slayers are old-school scholars committed to verifiable

testing and repeated experimentation in the real world. We prefer seeing physical evidence from independent labs and observations made openly in the light of day. We eschew slick, manipulated computer presentations followed by a consensus of groupthinkers persuading policymakers and raiding the checkbooks of the scientifically illiterate.

The greenhouse gas hypothesis is slain by real world scientists despite defense from the fantasy realm of biased university computer models.

In a powerful comment posted on the PSI website, Carl Brehmer summed it all up nicely:

> *The fact is, the "greenhouse effect" hypothesis has been tested in the open atmosphere and has been falsified by the empirical evidence that contradicts it.*

Cold, hard empiricism trumps wishful thinking every time.

As an empiricist who holds steadfastly to the traditional scientific method, Brehmer's reasoning is faultless.

He continues:

> *This experiment has been and is still being run on the "most potent greenhouse gas" water vapor by weather balloon soundings. You see, if water vapor were a "greenhouse gas" that causes an increase in surface level air temperature it would cause the temperature lapse rate seen within Tropospheric air to increase, but virtually all of the 100's of thousands of weather balloon soundings that have been taken over the past century show that water vapor decreases the lapse rate.*

The GHE hypothesis claims that water vapor—our most potent greenhouse gas—traps thermal energy in the lower Troposphere, where most of the water vapor resides.

For example, weather balloon soundings show that by ~5 km in altitude, most of the water vapor content of the air is gone because air at -18°C (where the average temperature at ~5km according to the ISA, the International Standard Atmosphere) is not able to hold very much water vapor and, indeed, what one sees in weather balloon soundings is a precipitous drop in absolute humidity with altitude.

Brehmer continues:

> When looking at the temperature lapse rate what is seen in weather balloon soundings is this: In the upper Troposphere between ~5km in altitude and the Tropopause (~11km in altitude) the temperature lapse rate is ~8°C/km. In very arid climates, like the one above Las Vegas, Nevada, that ~8°C/km lapse rate continues all the way to the ground. Above very humid climates, on the other hand, like those in the deep South, i.e., Mississippi, Louisiana, etc., because of the high water vapor content in the lower Troposphere the lapse rate below ~5 km can be as low as 5°C/km.

We Slayers say: just do the maths.

What one observes in these weather balloon soundings is that the air temperature at ~5 km above Las Vegas is nearly the same as the air temperature at ~5 km above Mississippi. Ergo, if one were to skydive from ~5km in altitude above Las Vegas one would experience a ~40°C increase in air temperature by the time one reaches the ground. Whereas, if one were to skydive from ~5km in altitude above Mississippi one would experience only a ~25°C the increase in air temperature by the time one reaches the ground.

This is why the average yearly air temperature in very humid climates is predictably lower than the average yearly air temperature in very arid climates that lie along the same latitude once compensation is made for altitude. The fact that water vapor decreases the temperature lapse rate of the lower Troposphere drives down the average surface-level air temperature in very humid climates.

Can water vapor be rightly called a greenhouse gas causing a greenhouse warming effect if it does not actually cause an increase in surface-level air temperatures, but actual decreases them?

The fact is, if the GHE hypothesis was real and water vapor was truly a greenhouse gas, the presence of water vapor in the lower Troposphere would have the opposite effect—it would increase the lapse rate of the lower Troposphere instead of decreasing it.

Since it doesn't, the GHE hypothesis is falsified by the hundreds of thousands of weather balloon soundings gathered over the past century that show that water vapor decreases the lapse rate of the lower Troposphere. Anyone interested can access these weather balloon soundings at the University of Wyoming web site.[84]

So, with empirical evidence telling us the GHE is a myth, the threat of which is now extinguished, let us enjoy a more convincing physical manifestation of a 'sky dragon' as seen below on February 18, 2019 courtesy of NASA.[85]

---

[84] http://weather.uwyo.edu/upperair/sounding.html.
[85] https://apod.nasa.gov/apod/ap190218.html

Chapter 2—From the Science Labs to the Law Courts

Doubt is not a pleasant condition, but certainty is absurd.
—Voltaire

PERHAPS WHAT WILL go down in history as one of the most heroic achievements of any of the authors was marked on August 22, 2019. On that day, the Supreme Court of British Columbia dismissed Dr. Michael Mann's defamation lawsuit versus Canadian skeptic climatologist, Dr. Tim Ball. Full legal costs were awarded to Dr. Ball, the defendant in the case.

Dr. Tim Ball was the lead author of our first volume, *Slaying the Sky Dragon: Death of the Greenhouse Gas Theory* published in 2011. A few short months after the book's publication the *'world leading climate scientist'* Dr. Michael E. Mann began a multi-million-dollar libel case against Tim for an off-the-cuff remark about Mann being from Penn State when he should be in the State Pen.[86]

---

[86] https://www.independent.co.uk/news/world/americas/donald-trump-climate-change-rebellion-michael-mann-global-warming-scientists-a7556696.html

Dr. Ball's quip was made because Mann stubbornly refused to show in public his 'secret science' to substantiate the core claim made with the graph, that Earth's modern temperatures were unprecedented.

That 'secret science' was the hidden 'R2 Regression Numbers', which are the methods and mathematics Mann used to create the Hockey Stick graph. If you have evidence that will prove you are right, you don't withhold that evidence in court. But this is precisely what Mann did. He refused repeatedly all of Dr. Ball's legal requests, as part of the lawful discovery process, to show those crucial calculations.

The Penn State professor had persistently refused to honor the binding concessions agreement[87] he made to Ball which ultimately gave his legal team the *coup de grace* to win the case for the defendant due to Mann's 'Bad Faith.' [88]

Dr. Ball always argued that those numbers, if examined in open court, would have conclusively prove Mann was motivated to commit a criminal fraud. It was at this point legal minds could discern Ball was closing in on victory—a triumph for 'David over

---

[87] https://principia-scientific.org/breaking-key-un-climate-fraudster-makes-concessions-tim-ball-lawsuit/

[88] https://legal-dictionary.thefreedictionary.com/bad+faith

Goliath.'

And Mann certainly is a science 'Goliath'. Ever since featuring so famously in the UN IPCC 2001 Third Assessment Report (TAR) Mann's graph has been an iconic image cited relentlessly by environmentalists clamoring for urgent action on man-made global warming.[89]

As scientists and non-scientists alike know all too well, the only reason anyone withholds evidence is if it would prove them wrong. If this had been a criminal case, Mann could be jailed for refusing to disclose such key information.

INDEPENDENT   News   Voices   Culture   Lifestyle   Tech   Sport   Daily Edition   Charity Appeal

World-leading climate change scientist calls for 'rebellion' against Donald Trump

Professor Michael Mann says the US is 'firmly back in the madhouse' as new president launches 'dizzying, ongoing assault on science'

Will U.S. President initiate an investigation into the now disgraced "world-leading climate change scientist"?

Indeed, not just a fawning MSM, but many hundreds of subsequent climate studies rely on Mann's findings. Mann's

---

89

https://web.archive.org/web/20060913043522/http:/www.grida.no/climate/ipcc_tar/

reputation was such that most climate researchers merely accepted his graph in a stereotypical example of groupthink.

Therefore, upon Ball's applications, the judge decided to dismiss the case on the back of Mann's bad faith contempt—his failure to release his hidden numbers. Dr. Mann had, in fact, also breached the binding agreement he had previously signed with Ball to hand over these very numbers as part of a series of concessions agreed between the litigants.

This dismissal of the Mann-v-Ball libel case is a victory for common sense and free speech and brings huge relief to the whole Ball family after eight long years of expensive legal battling. Tim's son, David, spoke to one of this book's co-authors on social media, and commented, "...this has huge implications..." for climate science. The judge also awarded court costs to Dr Ball believed to be over $700,000, though we suspect getting the deadbeat Mann to part with any money will be somewhat difficult.

Michael Mann said he was taking a stand for science in the court case, and it's interesting to note that the Canadian author and journalist Mark Steyn said not a single scientist or scientific institution filed an Amicus Brief in support of him, therefore, science was not prepared to take a stand for Michael Mann.

What possibly dissuaded Mann's scientific colleagues and abandon him was his increasingly unhinged abuse of the scientific method.

Apart from playing with statistics Mann made his proxy fit the thermometer data by appending thermometer values to the proxy values known as "Mike's Nature trick" in the climategate email scandal.[90]

From the emails released during the Climategate scandal, [91]

90

https://www.telegraph.co.uk/comment/columnists/christopherbook er/6679082/Climate-change-this-is-the-worst-scientific-scandal-of-our-generation.html

[91] https://www.conservapedia.com/index.php?title=Climategate

Professor Phil Jones, Britain's top climate scientist at the University of East Anglia, was shown to have written the following to his alarmist colleagues.[92] An email[93] sent by Prof Phil Jones of the CRU in 1999, states:

Dear Ray, Mike and Malcolm,

Once Tim's got a diagram here we'll send that either later today or first thing tomorrow.

I've just completed Mike's Nature trick of adding in the real temps to each series for the last 20 years (ie from 1981 onwards) amd from 1961 for Keith's to hide the decline. Mike's series got the annual land and marine values while the other two got April-Sept for NH land N of 20N. The latter two are real for 1999, while the estimate for 1999 for NH combined is +0.44C wrt 61-90. The Global estimate for 1999 with data through Oct is +0.35C cf. 0.57 for 1998.

Thanks for the comments, Ray.

Cheers
Phil

The authors, researchers, editors and other contributors to this book believe there is now the increased possibility of prosecuting Mann and his co-conspirators under the U.S. RICO anti-racketeering laws. These being the very same laws that Senator Sheldon Whitehouse wanted to use to silence climate skeptics a couple years ago, as he had convinced himself climate skeptics were effectively criminals and should be jailed for their crimes.

Readers interested in gaining a deeper understanding of what is widely accepted as a criminal conspiracy between Mann

---

92

https://jhammerton.wordpress.com/2009/11/29/climategate-on-the-mikes-nature-trick-email/

93

http://www.eastangliaemails.com/emails.php?eid=154&filename=942777075.txt

and other 'elite' researchers should see the exhaustively researched and entertainingly written *The Hockey Stick Illusion* by Andrew Montford.[94]

The Hockey Stick Graph

For the purpose of this book, let's examine some of the facts in this case that go to the heart of why we believe government-funded climate science is riddled with fraud and bias.

In their original First Assessment Report in 1990, the IPCC included the illustration below by Hubert Lamb, the founder of the Climatic Research Unit at the University of East Anglia in the UK. It clearly shows the Medieval Warm Period and the Little Ice Age (LIA). Along with other evidence, their existence had been proven from ice core data from both Greenland and Antarctica, and no-one in academia disputed they had happened as they had been in the scientific literature for decades.

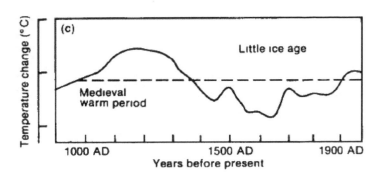

The Medieval Warm Period (MWP) is regarded by most historians as an era of significantly warmer temperatures than today—perhaps by several degrees. The MWP lasted from around 950AD to around 1250AD during what is known in Europe as the High Middle Ages.

---

[94] https://www.amazon.com/Hockey-Stick-Illusion-Andrew-Montford-ebook/dp/B0182I73BA

A preponderance of historical records indicates this was hugely beneficial, and saw the flowering of Medieval society, agriculture, science and art. During this time, it was warm enough for the Viking Erik the Red to establish a colony in 985AD at Hvalsey in the south of Greenland and raise crops. Vineyards were sown in England as far north as Northumberland, and citrus was grown near Hadrian's Wall, neither of which is possible now as it's too cold. This period was followed by the Little Ice Age, which began around 1300AD and lasted to the middle of the 19th Century.

During the LIA, northern hemisphere temperatures dropped significantly and the Vikings were forced to abandon Greenland. Harsh winters plagued northern Europe and parts of North America. There were multiple crop failures during the short, cold summers and many European rivers froze each winter. There were mass deaths from starvation and record low temperatures—diseases became rampant.

The Little Ice Age was recorded in paintings depicting what were described as 'frost fayres' on the river Thames in London. Historical records show farms and villages in the Swiss Alps were destroyed by encroaching glaciers during the mid-17th century.

Canals and rivers in Britain and the Netherlands were frequently frozen deeply enough to support ice skating and winter festivals. The first River Thames 'frost fayre' was held in 1608 and the last in 1814. Freezing of the Golden Horn and the southern section of the Bosphorus took place in 1622.

In 1658, a Swedish army marched across the Great Belt to Denmark to attack Copenhagen.

In the winter of 1780, New York Harbour froze, allowing people to walk from Manhattan Island to Staten Island. The winter of 1794-1795 was particularly harsh: the French invasion army under Pichegru was able to march on the frozen rivers of the Netherlands and the Dutch fleet was fixed in the ice in Den Helder harbour.

This image is one of many on the internet depicting such a

frost fayre on the Thames and is believed to have been painted around 1683.

In 1998, former University of Massachusetts researcher Michael Mann, unveiled his infamous and contemptible 'Hockey Stick' graph shown below, which completely removed both the Medieval Warm Period and the Little Ice Age.

In 2001, the IPCC published its Fourth Assessment Report, in which the previous Medieval Warm Period illustration had been removed—replaced by Mann's Hockey Stick graph as seen below.

The Hockey Stick was favourable to the IPCC as it accentuated the 20th Century warming, and thus helped promote their human-caused warming agenda.

Also, look at the scale on the left. By putting large gaps between each half-degree increase, you artificially inflate any given warming.

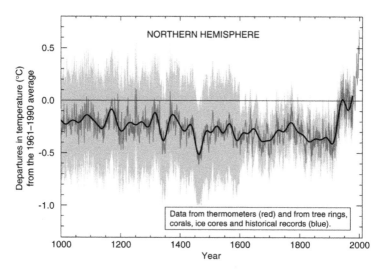

To show a one degree increase accurately, the graph should look closer to this:

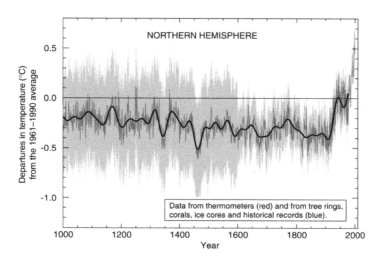

It later came to light that Mann had used smashed-together ensembles of tree-ring and other proxy data for the shaft of the stick and tacked on thermometer data for the blade. Tim Ball said grafting two datasets together is something that should not be done unless it's accompanied by a detailed explanation of why it was necessary, and subsequently made an off-the-cuff remark that Mann was from Penn State when he should be in the State Pen. This resulted in Mann serving him the previously mentioned libel writ for defamation.

In 2001, the Canadian author Mark Steyn had become interested in the climate issue, and on viewing the Hockey Stick, described Mann as "...a disgrace to the profession" and even wrote a book with that as its title. It will be interesting to see if the dismissal of Mann's libel case against Tim Ball will set a precedent in his similar case against Mark Steyn after he called the Hockey Stick fraudulent in *National Review*, and Mann sued for defamation. Steyn rather comically commented on it during his speech at the Heartland Institute's 10th International Conference on Climate Change in 2015:

> *The Hockey Stick is what's known as a proxy reconstruction, and there are only two problems with it; the proxies and the reconstruction.*[95]

On June 12th 2006, Dr. David Deming of the University of Oklahoma presented testimony to the U.S. Senate on Environment & Public Works, and the relevant part of his statement is shown below.

In the statement, note the highlighted sentence with '*We have to get rid of the Medieval Warm Period*.' This incident occurred as shown in 1995, and by 1998 Michael Mann had indeed made the MWP and LIA vanish with his Hockey Stick graph.

Incidentally, the Climate Research Unit at East Anglia University would later become embroiled in the Climategate affair, when they too were proven, through a series of emails leaked from their servers, to have been involved in deliberately

---

[95] https://www.youtube.com/watch?v=6bARjABDqok

tampering with data to reduce past recorded temperature records and increase recent ones to make the observed warming appear steeper than it actually is. This altered data was then used to deceive the public and policymakers.

**U.S. Senate Committee on Environment & Public Works
Hearing Statements**

Date: 12/06/2006

Statement of Dr. David Deming
University of Oklahoma
College of Earth and Energy
Climate Change and the Media

Mr. Chairman, members of the Committee, and distinguished guests, thank you for inviting me to testify today. I am a geologist and geophysicist. I have a bachelor's degree in geology from Indiana University, and a Ph.D in geophysics from the University of Utah. My field of specialization in geophysics is temperature and heat flow. In recent years, I have turned my studies to the history and philosophy of science. In 1995, I published a short paper in the academic journal Science. In that study, I reviewed how borehole temperature data recorded a warming of about one degree Celsius in North America over the last 100 to 150 years. The week the article appeared, I was contacted by a reporter for National Public Radio. He offered to interview me, but only if I would state that the warming was due to human activity. When I refused to do so, he hung up on me.

I had another interesting experience around the time my paper in Science was published. I received an astonishing email from a major researcher in the area of climate change. He said, "We have to get rid of the Medieval Warm Period."

The Medieval Warm Period (MWP) was a time of unusually warm weather that began around 1000 AD and persisted until a cold period known as the "Little Ice Age" took hold in the 14th century. Warmer climate brought a remarkable flowering of prosperity, knowledge, and art to Europe during the High Middle Ages.

The existence of the MWP had been recognized in the scientific literature for decades. But now it was a major embarrassment to those maintaining that the 20th century warming was truly anomalous. It had to be "gotten rid of."

The Hockey Stick, or *Hokey Schtick* as it has become known, has been comprehensively shown to be a fraudulent representation of historic temperature, yet this proven fallacy is one of the most effective propaganda tools in the world, and is even being used as a teaching aid in schools, where climate change is being taught as if it is an unassailable fact.

A free teaching aid of our own to counter such propaganda peddled in schools and which is downloadable, printer-friendly and aimed at non-scientists, may be found online.[96]

Our Final Words

As we have shown, since our first book, *Slaying the Sky Dragon: Death of the Greenhouse Gas Theory*, science pursued by climate realists has grown in popularity through openness and embracing empirical, objective new evidence.

Conversely, what passes as science among government researchers today has been exposed as capricious, agenda-driven, anti-empirical and backward-looking; an exercise in damage limitation to cover the cracks of a half-baked hypothesis.

Frankly, the greenhouse gas theory, the very cornerstone of science blaming human emissions of carbon dioxide for unprecedented global warming, is slain as a credible scientific explanation of how our Earth's climate operates.

Government-funded climate research is pseudo-science concocted elaborately by biased activists who were more interested in pursuing a one world global government than in understanding how climate actually works.

While the scientific arguments we have presented in our two books may be lost on many who are turned off by science, few can argue that when scientists will not and cannot show their evidence, something is gravely amiss.

Not only, as a community, have government climate modelers never revealed anything other the simple one-dimensional model of the greenhouse gas theory (which we Slayers conclusively refuted), the 'world's leading climate scientist' never revealed the secret of how he concocted his iconic 'hockey stick' graph.

As with the macrocosm, so goes the microcosm.

Dr. Michael E. Mann's resounding courtroom defeat by Dr.

---

[96] https://greatclimatedebate.com/tutorial-anthropogenic-global-warming-agw/

Tim Ball should be taken as a stark warning to those basing key international public policies on secret science. Never again should citizens permit politicians to coerce, browbeat and deceive them into surrendering to unproven, incomprehensible and unverifiable 'science' bought and paid for by a self-serving political elite.

Among those paying attention, Mann's Hockey Stick is well and truly consigned to the trash can of junk science—as is the nonsensical and false hypothesis that atmospheric carbon dioxide *'traps'* heat and makes our planet *'warmer than it would otherwise be.'*

Publisher's Note

Perhaps Dr. Mann can apply a back radiation principle to his wallet. He could take out some cash, wave it in the air, then put the money back in his wallet—along with added "downwelling" cash. It might help him pay the legitimate, court-ordered fees he intends to dodge.

It's too bad the State Pen isn't a debtor's prison.

Chapter 3—The Greenhouse Effect

It doesn't matter how beautiful your theory is, it doesn't matter how smart you are. If it doesn't agree with experiment, it's wrong.
—Richard Feynman

WHAT IS THE greenhouse effect? Does it affect me? The Intergovernmental Panel on Climate Change (IPCC) is rather coy about explaining the supposed natural effect or the "theory".

However, the United Nations IPCC is more forthcoming on the matter. They state that humans, by their activities, emit carbon dioxide. This accumulates in the atmosphere, intensifying the natural greenhouse effect, and thus the world warms due to human activities. The UN describes the supposed affect of humans by their activities are having upon the effect, not the "theory" of how it is supposed to work.

The IPCC explanation of the supposed greenhouse effect theory can be summarised as follows.

- The Earth's surface is warmed by both the Sun and energy coming back from the atmosphere.

- The Earth's surface then radiates all that energy, which is

138

wholly absorbed by the atmosphere.

- The atmosphere then radiates half of that energy into space and the other half back to the Earth's surface.

- The result of this continual process is that the Earth's surface becomes warmer than it would be if it were only warmed by the Sun.

This is the so-called greenhouse effect (GHE) as approved and promoted by the UN's official body the Intergovernmental Panel on Climate Change (IPCC). Since the late 1980's, governments have been telling us to "lower our carbon footprint!" What that means is they want us to use less energy powered by hydrocarbon fuels (coal, gas, petroleum oil). The UN IPCC tells us that it is those "richer" western nations that are the biggest "carbon polluters" (which isn't true as we shall see later). We have been told that 97 percent of the world's climate scientists agree.

So, you are repeatedly told, you have no choice in the matter, you must cut your carbon dioxide (CO_2) emissions, and pay more in taxes for your selfish addiction to "dirty energy" which will cause "tipping points" of "runaway" human-caused environmental disasters.

This is all because of a supposed 19th century hypothesis about an invisible "heat trapping" blanket of CO_2 that was going to fry us with higher global temperatures. But so far in the 21st century, Nature hasn't cooperated with the climate "experts." If anything, quite the reverse has been happening. Despite continued increases in human emissions of CO_2, an increasing number of scientists predict global cooling as the next real threat.

We are told our industrial emissions of burnt hydrocarbons are adding "man-made" CO_2 to the atmosphere, creating a potent chemical cocktail that dangerously "traps" more heat energy—making our planet warmer. In a nutshell, that's the Greenhouse Effect (GHE) in play.

After 30 years of these 'Chicken Little' alarmist scare stories, independent scientists—specialists in a myriad-related disciplines—are speaking out about what they see is a pseudo-science. The experts—those generalists that dominate the undeniably infant field of climate science research—are finally being called to account.

Climate realists increasingly tell the alarmists to stop computer modelling Earth as if it were a greenhouse! It isn't! It is obvious to experts from the hard sciences that the Earth's atmosphere does not act in any way like a greenhouse.

A greenhouse works by reducing convection and heat losses due to the evaporation of water within the greenhouse compared to outside the greenhouse (for the same solar input). That is why it is warmer inside the greenhouse than outside the greenhouse. Opening the doors and windows of the greenhouse confirms this. Radiation is not trapped within the greenhouse, sensible and heat losses due to the evaporation of water are physically trapped within the greenhouse. In point of fact, the greenhouse being warmer than its surroundings is radiating MORE than its surroundings! That is not trapped radiation. The greenhouse analogy is simply wrong. It is a misnomer.

In the last 30 years we know that CO_2 emissions have grown from 19,000 million metric tonnes in 1981 to 33,000 million metric tonnes (2010 figure).That is a huge 74 percent increase in CO_2 emissions. If it is correct that more CO_2 equates to more warming, why is it that, when the correct figures are used, global temperatures are shown to have not risen since the start of the new century?

Despite the huge increase in human CO_2 emissions over recent decades our planet stubbornly refuses to get any warmer. In short, the real world shows no proof of any CO_2-driven GHE whatsoever.

Take the four point summary mentioned earlier, describing greenhouse effect theory.

Below are the reasons it is incorrect:

- The Earth's surface is warmed by both the Sun and energy coming back from the atmosphere.

The atmosphere is colder (-18°C), on average, than the Earth's surface (15°C)—therefore energy being radiated back from the atmosphere, which is emitted at its average temperature, will not warm the Earth's surface (because, colder cannot heat hotter).

- The Earth's surface then radiates all of that energy, which is wholly absorbed by the atmosphere.

Not all of that energy is radiated, some of it is stored within the Earth, i.e. mostly within the oceans and a very small part within the land and released over varying timescales. A lot of this energy is used to evaporate water. The energy which is actually radiated is not wholly absorbed by the atmosphere because some of it escapes straight into space.

- The atmosphere then radiates half of that energy into space and the other half back to the Earth's surface.

The portion of energy that is radiated back to the Earth's surface is, though, colder than the surface to which it is headed.

- The result of this continual process is that the Earth's surface becomes warmer than it would be if it were only warmed by the Sun.

However, because the energy radiated back from the atmosphere is colder than the Earth's surface, it cannot possibly warm it.

It needs to be pointed out that the "official" four points are from a radiation-only viewpoint. This is too simplified a viewpoint when addressing what happens inside our planet's atmosphere. But beyond the atmosphere, Earth is simply warmed by radiation from the Sun and cools by radiating excess energy into the void of space.

More importantly, the GHE theory as explained in more detail later in this chapter, and as calculated in all computer climate models, is based upon the notion that radiation does not follow the known Laws of Thermodynamics!

And how well are the models performing? In 2018, exactly 30 years since Dr. James Hansen's infamous presentation to the U.S. Congress which brought man-made global warming to wide public attention, very poorly!

According to six peer-reviewed studies (Luo et al., 2018; Hanna et al., 2018); (Scanlon et al., 2018); (Ollila, 2018); (Scanlon et al., 2018); Collins et al., 2018), consensus climate models, using physics from the greenhouse gas theory that does not follow the known laws of Thermodynamics lack scientific merit. These studies find the models are filled with errors and key deficiencies. We now learn that the models have a:

> CS [Climate Sensitivity] Parameter, including the positive water feedback doubling the GH Gas Effects, [that] does not exist.

In summary…

> We do not have theories that can adequately explain the reasons for an extreme cold or warm, or wet or dry, winter at continental scales. More importantly, we do not have the ability to credibly predict such states.[97]

All because climate scientists insist on relying on the greenhouse gas theory. A theory the scientific world is beginning to recognise was thoroughly destroyed in our first book, *Slaying the Sky Dragon: Death of the Greenhouse Gas Theory.*

---

[97] Collins et al., 2018

Specifically, every version of GHE theory describes, depicts or calculates that the (colder) atmosphere warms, or adds energy to Earth's (warmer) surface. Such is simply not possible. There are no known exceptions to the 2nd Law of Thermodynamics, which in a very simple form states that colder cannot heat hotter.

This alone completely invalidates any version of GHE "theory" that describes or depicts atmospheric back-radiation further warming or adding energy to Earth's surface. A theory cannot pick or choose which of the Laws of Thermodynamics it wants to abide by. A theory has to abide by all the known Laws of Thermodynamics. If a theory does not abide by all the known Laws of Thermodynamics, then it is a failed hypothesis and not a theory at all.

As far as science itself is concerned, it is possible that a Law of Thermodynamics may be wrong, but that has to be shown! It has to be proven that the Law is wrong. A Law shown to be wrong is simply no longer a Law. All current Laws of Thermodynamics have never been shown to be wrong. There are no known exceptions to any Law of Thermodynamics. Thus if a theory violates a Law of Thermodynamics, it is up to the proposer, supporter or advocate of the theory to first disprove the relevant Law of Thermodynamics. Then and only then can the hypothesis be further tested by experiment, to see if it is correct. After which, if it has not been shown to be wrong, the hypothesis may become a theory. A theory that has never been shown to be wrong may eventually be accepted as a Law.

Until it is proved wrong, of course.

It sounds rather too obvious to say that a Law of Thermodynamics should not be confused with a legal law, because they are two completely different things. However, the distinction between the two should be kept in mind. A Law of Thermodynamics always applies to all matter, and it is not open to interpretation. Matter has no choice in the matter. Matter obeys all the Laws of Thermodynamics, all of the time. This is proven via the scientific method, because if a proven theory has never been shown to be wrong, then it eventually becomes a law.

A legal law is something completely different; it is a rule, usually made by politicians, which the courts then enforce. Legal laws frequently change over time as the needs and wants of society change. Legal laws, because they are written, are often open to interpretation simply because of bad wording in the first place, or because the situation they may be being applied to does or does not apply to what the law was originally intended to address. Legal laws can, do, and should change over time and are open to interpretation at a moment in time, all of which is decided by the politicians and the courts.

Plainly, what a legal law is does not, and should not apply to, or describe, any of the Laws of Thermodynamics. The Laws of Thermodynamics cannot be broken, they are what they are, and they are the basis of physics, until one or more are disproved. In discussions of physics and of science it should always be remembered that a physical law is not a legal law. In physics and science, the law must always be obeyed, by all matter, all of the time and there are no exceptions. We repeat—no exceptions!

As described earlier, the scientific method starts with observation. It seems reasonable then to ask "Has the natural Greenhouse (gas) Effect (GHE) of Earth been observed?"

The answer to this question for many is a somewhat surprising "No."

Yes, Global Mean (near surface air) Temperature (GMT) is attempted to be measured. It should be noted that there are a lot of issues regarding the accuracy of published GMT figures. However most agree Earth's GMT is slightly lower than 15 degrees Celsius, but, where is the observation of Earth without an atmosphere?

Such is simply not possible.

Therefore the rise in Earth's surface temperature due to the presence of an atmosphere has never been observed. That might sound like a small or insignificant point, but it is not. Yes, we can observe that Earth with an atmosphere has a GMT (near surface air) temperature of about 15 degrees Celsius. However, no Earth's surface temperature without an atmosphere has never been, or can ever be, observed. Thus we cannot observe a surface temperature difference, or observe how large or small the difference would be, due to the presence of an atmosphere.

Global Mean (near surface air) Temperature is not Earth's actual surface temperature; GMT is the *average* temperature taken from many thousands of thermometers that are situated approximately 1.2 meters above the ground and none over the approximately 70% of the oceans, seas, lakes and rivers. This should be remembered because the natural GHE and GHE theory are attempts to explain Earth's *actual* surface temperature.

The two are quite different things.

Earth's surface being on average quite a bit warmer than the near surface air at a height of 1.2 meters. Most people who have studied this tend to generally agree that Earth's *surface* temperature is on average roughly 30 degrees Celsius. Some suggest the figure might be somewhat lower, nearer 27 to 28 degrees Celsius, which is not a great difference in this context.

The reason this is mentioned is that GHE theory attempts to explain a *surface* temperature of 30 degrees Celsius and not the calculated *average* GMT of roughly 15 degrees Celsius.

There is another massive difference between Earth with an atmosphere that we can observe and Earth without an atmosphere that we cannot observe, that to many is not immediately apparent. The reason for the difference is that it is a physical fact, a physical property of water, that liquid water cannot exist in a vacuum. Liquid water put into a vacuum appears to boil, regardless of its temperature. Strictly speaking, the water is not boiling, it is vaporising. Regardless of a vacuum or an atmosphere, water in effect always wants to be the gas, water vapor.

Whenever it has enough energy, liquid water evaporates to water vapor, the gas. When liquid water is put into a vacuum this effect is very pronounced. The liquid water appears to boil vigorously, then it turns to ice. The ice will sublime to gaseous water vapor as and when it receives enough energy. It is reasonable then to suggest Earth without an atmosphere would have no oceans.

Without an atmosphere, any liquid water at Earth's surface would become ice, and each day the Sun would burn the ice off, until none was left. Put simply, without an atmosphere, Earth's surface would be dry and there would be no oceans. Yes, we can observe the surface of the beautiful blue-green marble in space that is Earth with 70% of its surface covered in, on average, 2.5 mile deep oceans. But we cannot observe the dry brown-silvery lifeless ball it would most probably be without an atmosphere. One has to wonder—is any comparison possible at all? Plainly we cannot observe Earth without an atmosphere, but can we even guess at what it would be like?

Advocates of the GHE theory are very sure of what Earth without an atmosphere would be. It would be more accurate to say they are very sure of what the average surface temperature of Earth without an atmosphere would be.

How can they, when such cannot be observed?

According to GHE theory and its proponents, the answer is very simple and it is a straight forward deduction from basic physics. They state that the Sun baths the Earth in constant infrared radiation at an average power of $1368W/m^2$ at the top of the atmosphere. Then, because Earth is a rotating globe, which has four times the surface area of the same diameter disc, this power of received sunlight is divided by four (P/4). Thus, each square meter of Earth *on average* receives $342W/m^2$. However, the surface is not a perfect blackbody (BB) and so it reflects $102W/m^2$ straight back out to space. The surface, on average, therefore absorbs the remaining $240W/m^2$.

According to BB and the Stefan-Boltzmann equation, this means the surface is only warmed to, on average, MINUS 18 degrees Celsius.

The above description is based upon *average* powers, over a period divisible by one day, or rather 24 hours. This does not make sense from a thermodynamic viewpoint. A simple question may help to illustrate the problem of averages and when to use them and when not to use them when considering a heat flow or the thermodynamics of a situation. Is cooking a 4-pound chicken in an oven at 200 degrees Celsius for 1 hour the same as cooking a similar chicken over 4 hours in an oven at 50 degrees Celsius?

No.

The all-important highs and lows and times are omitted, leading to false conclusions. Would you eat a chicken cooked at 50 degrees Celsius for 4 hours? It is to be hoped you would not as no cooking takes place at that temperature.

It is also a fact, obvious to anyone, but forgotten by the climate modelers, that the Sun does not shine at a quarter of its power 24 hours a day, all over Earth. This average figure (the P/4 figure), that the rest of the reasoning is based upon is unphysical. It simply does not happen, and therefore should not be used. However for GHE theory, if P/4 is not used, then they have no line of reasoning. Without the use of the P/4 figure there is no theory. This is because, how then, without the use of the P/4 figure, would they attempt to explain the surface temperature figure used for Earth with no atmosphere?

The line of reasoning, as described above, which produces the -18 degrees Celsius answer is not that simple. In fact, it is complex and involved. It introduces and uses several other theorems, the blackbody theorem being the most important to the line of reasoning. This theorem is for an imaginary object. Objects in the real world may approximate to a BB, but they are never a true BB, because by definition such does not, and cannot, exist.

For example, a BB surface is stated by the theorem as a surface that has no mass! The Stefan-Boltzmann equation is an equation used to calculate the temperature a BB surface would reach for a given energy, thermal radiation, input. It is also used to calculate what a BB surface would emit in energy terms as a thermal radiation output at a given BB surface temperature.

The BB theorem and the Stefan-Boltzmann equation are both very useful (in physics) as rough guides. However, they merely predict a result for an *imaginary* surface, they do not describe the why, or the how, of a similar result occurring in physical reality.

The very simple "answer" described above also introduces the power unit W/m^2, which is Watts per area of one square meter.

Watts are a measure of the rate of conversion of, or the rate of transfer of, energy with respect to time.

This is how GHE theory and its advocates claim to have observed the natural greenhouse effect (GHE) upon Earth.

They claim it is an observation, yet the MINUS 18 degrees Celsius average surface temperature figure for Earth without an atmosphere cannot be observed.

When this is pointed out, the reply is that it is basic accepted physics, whilst omitting to mention the basic accepted physics referred to is for an imaginary surface!

It is also somewhat confusing about what is being referred to when GHE theory advocates state the GHE is a 33 degrees Celsius effect.[98]

Presumably they are asserting that without an atmosphere Earth's surface would on average be minus 18 degrees Celsius, but with an atmosphere the GMT (near surface air temperature) is 15 degrees Celsius.

Yet, GHE theory explains a surface temperature with an atmosphere of 30 degrees Celsius, which is a 48 degree Celsius

---

[98] Of many, here's a random example of this claim.
Scientists had already calculated that the Earth was about 59 degrees Fahrenheit (33 degrees Celsius) warmer than it should be, given the amount of sunlight reaching its surface. The best explanation for that discrepancy was that the atmosphere retained heat to warm the planet.
https://www.weforum.org/agenda/2019/09/why-carbon-dioxide-has-such-outsized-influence-on-earths-climate/

GHE!

With climate alarmists, like tossing a coin, it's heads they win, tails you lose (and thus they always win).

Principled Science gets its First Voice in Politics

Moving from the United States to Australia, we saw how the government there is being reshaped by the popular vote to accept that people are no longer prepared to tolerate leaders who base their policies on junk climate models.

Newly elected Senator, Malcolm Roberts, a great student of the work of the Slayers, gave an impassioned maiden speech to his nation's Senate:

> *Mr President, here are more undeniable facts proven by data; firstly, changes in the carbon dioxide level are a result of changes in temperature, not a cause. That's the reverse of what we're told. Second, we do not and cannot affect the level of carbon dioxide in air. Reverse of what we're told. We cannot and do not affect global climate. Third, warming is beneficial—after all science classifies past warmer periods as climate optimums. Again, the reverse of what we're told.*
>
> *It's basic. The Sun warms Earth's surface. The surface by contact warms the moving circulating atmosphere. That means the atmosphere cools the surface. How can anything that cools the surface warm it? It can't. That's why their computer models are wrong. The UN's claim is absurd.*
>
> *Instead of science, activists invoke morality, imply natural weather events are unusual, appeal to authority, use name calling-ridicule-and emotion, avoid discussing facts, and rely on*

pictures of cute smiling dolphins. These are not evidence of human effect on climate.

If it is clear that [human-caused] climate change is a scam, and also our prosperity relies on the human endeavours of industry and production, then why is it that in this great parliament there are extremist advocates of an agenda to de-industrialise our nation? Let me make it clear, I will stand firm against any political organisation whose primary aim is to destroy our prosperity and future.[99]

For reasons of dual-nationality, Senator Malcolm Roberts had to stand down.

The Trump Era and Dismantling of Government Climate Fraud

In 2016, Donald Trump wins the U.S. presidential election. One of the most popular, if controversial, of his aims is to defund the Big Green government scam that he and others believe to be killing American industry.

Famously, he tweeted:

The concept of global warming was created by and for the Chinese in order to make U.S. manufacturing non-competitive.

In December that same year, Dr. Tim Ball is summoned to Washington, DC to assist Trump's transition team in tackling the dismantling of the huge climate science fraud. As a key contributor to this book, Dr. Ball's aim is to make policymakers

---

[99] Herald Sun, September 13, 2016, Malcolm Roberts Drives Twitter Nuts

aware of the main scientific errors perpetrated by American government-funded researchers such as James Hansen at NASA.

Dr. Ball is one of the few climatologists who openly questions the greenhouse gas theory.

As such he plays a crucial role in seeking to get the new U.S. administration to recognise the very important historical evolution in the use of the term greenhouse effect, which is fake science used as the cornerstone of the man-made global warming narrative.

Chapter 4—Timeline 1871 to 1911

Balfour Stewart to the Bergen School of Meteorology

Those who have knowledge don't predict.
Those who do predict don't have knowledge.
—Lao Tzu

TODAY IT SEEMS a natural progression that we try to predict the weather over as long a time scale as possible by using the most powerful tools available to us—computers. How did we go from adages to computer climate model projection? That should be the story of how the new and young science of meteorology has recently developed.

We have always wanted to know what the weather will be in the future; hence there are so many old sayings about it. The weather we experience in our day-to-day lives is the result of Earth's massive, complex, naturally robust, dynamic and stable climate system. The Sun shines, clouds form, it rains, day turns to night, night turns to day. Summer follows spring, autumn follows summer, and that leads inevitably to winter. Sometimes we get sunburnt, other times we are left freezing cold in rain, sleet or snow. Sometimes it is frosty in the morning. Sometimes it is very windy, others it is not. Weather is the one variable we can rely on to be constantly changing. The never-ending wonder of the seasonal cycles that keep repeating, yet from year to year are never quite the same. Sometimes our crops fail, in other years they succeed as they should, and in yet other years they are bumper crops! The day to day weather is a constantly changing, yet constantly repeating natural wonder. It's complex, yet fascinating to try to understand. The weather shapes our everyday lives, from the clothes we wear to the food we eat. Understanding the weather and how it might possibly change is therefore very useful to our everyday lives. Is it going to be a good day? Is it going to be a good summer? Is it going to be a cold winter? From these questions, the science of meteorology was inevitably born.

There is also the sum of all the weather experienced each day on this planet. That is the climate. Sometimes the climate is warmer, sometimes it is cooler. Usually, from year to year, the overall climate varies very little, maybe a couple of tenths of a degree Celsius, at most. How this climate warming and cooling on a year to year basis is experienced at the local level varies greatly. Some places will warm more, some places will warm less. Some places when the climate is warming, even just a little, will experience cooling! That is the beauty of, and the frustration in trying to understand the complexity of Earth's climate system. Inevitably, nowhere on Earth is completely unaffected by changes elsewhere, but how much of an effect and how long will that effect take to happen, and how, is almost impossible to answer.

It should also be noted that Earth's climate system is thought to vary greatly, by up to tens of degrees Celsius, over far longer time scales. Over thousands of years, the climate has been colder, much colder than today, and it has been warmer, much warmer than today. The colder periods are often referred to as ice ages, and the warmer (than ice ages) periods are often referred to as interglacial periods. Some suggest that if there is ice on the planet at all, then we are in an ice age. Practically speaking, this definition is probably too strict, but it does lead to the question how much ice on the planet surface is an ice age? Most agree today we are in an interglacial. But, some would say that today we are in a relatively warm ice age!

The study of what is thought was Earth's previous climate is called paleoclimatology. It is a branch of the new and developing science of meteorology. Given the relative ease of observing the weather, it is of little surprise that meteorology developed by first trying to study the weather in a relatively small geographical area. If lots of areas could be studied then an overall picture of the climate could be built up.

Once the current climate is better understood, then studying the paleoclimate history of the planet can be done better. At present there are a lot of suggestions as to why for large tracts of time the climate of Earth was warmer and cooler in the past, but until the climate system is better understood, then such suggestions are merely suggestions. It is true that some suggestions, such as the Milankovitch cycles, make a lot of sense,[100] whilst other suggestions, such as Snowball Earth,[101] do not make as much sense. In fact, some climate theories are fanciful at best. Thus, understanding the climate system and how it works is the most important factor. All else follows from that basis—from the paradigm, the science is founded.

In the early to mid-19th Century meteorology did not have a basis, a paradigm, other than accepted physics, to be based upon.

However, in 1871, Balfour Stewart, in his book *An Elementary Treatise on Heat*, page 228, Figure 55 put forward a hypothesis...

---

[100] https://en.wikipedia.org/wiki/Milankovitch_cycles
[101] https://en.wikipedia.org/wiki/Snowball_Earth

228   *ABSORPTION OF*

There are yet other peculiarities exhibited by bodies in their action upon different rays, but these must be reserved until next chapter.

CERTAIN PRACTICAL CONSEQUENCES.

249. Suppose we have a large heated globe, as in Fig. 55 : and in the first place, let us suppose there is no en-

velope round it, but that it is free to radiate its heat into space without receiving back any in return. Let its velocity of radiation be denoted by R. Suppose now that this sphere is closely surrounded by a very thin envelope, opaque as regards the heat from the sphere; and let us imagine that there is no heat conveyed from the sphere to the envelope either by con-

Fig. 55.

vection or conduction, or in any other way than by radiation. Now let R' denote the radiation of this envelope outwards into space, then R' will also approximately denote the radiation of the envelope inwards towards the sphere, since as the envelope is very thin, both its surfaces may be imagined to be of the same temperature.

Hence the radiant heat which leaves the envelope will be $2R'$, while that which reaches it from the globe will be R.

But if the globe be very large and cool very slowly, the envelope will, it is clear, settle down into a state of equilibrium of temperature, and therefore its absorption will be equal to its radiation; that is to say,

$$R = 2R', \quad \text{or} \quad R' = \frac{R}{2}.$$

We see, therefore, that by an arrangement of this nature

Stewart suggested that the atmosphere (represented as an outer shell) absorbed and was warmed by the radiant energy emitted by the warmed body's (Earth's) surface. The outer shell then radiated half of the absorbed energy to space, and half back to the body's (Earth's) surface. Therefore, the Earth's surface would be warmer than, and cool slower than if the atmosphere was not there, because it was also receiving half the radiant energy the atmosphere had absorbed.

Stewart's suggestion did not really make much of an impact at the time, because it plainly violated the 2nd Law of Thermodynamics in that the colder atmosphere, according to the suggestion, warmed the already warmer Earth surface. The 2nd Law of Thermodynamics clearly states colder cannot heat hotter. Stewart's suggestion should have been abandoned, and indeed by most it was. However, the suggestion had its supporters, who could not let go of it. The suggestion will reappear over and over, with great affect as radiation theory, even though it was initially and correctly ignored as no effect.

It is important to note that Stewart did not suggest the atmosphere radiated twice what it received, but it would seem many scientists, over many years, later misinterpreted Stewart's suggestion in that manner. It is also important to note that Stewart's suggestion was one of the first attempts to explain the overall climate system, or rather a hypothesized basic operating principle of the system.

Given the complexity of the problem in trying to understand Earth's climate system from the overall view point, practically, the better approach would seem to be to study the weather in an area. Then, whilst taking into account physical laws, and how similar conditions had changed in the past, attempt to make predictions of how the weather would change in the observed area. Local weather forecasting being a far easier first step than trying to understand and predict the global climate.

The first person to meaningfully undertake the task in the above described manner was Vilhelm Bjerknes. He described what he observed, how he calculated using maths, plots and graphs, and to whom his weather predictions would be useful to, in several academic papers that culminated in a series of newspaper articles which were published in 1904. In order to understand why Vilhelm Bjerknes undertook the task, it is useful to briefly describe his career path, in relation to the times and the events that made him follow the path that he did.

The late 19th and early 20th centuries were a chaotic time for science in general. There were many new discoveries being made, in so many fields. It seemed that each new discovery would inevitably lead to yet another new discovery.

These were very exciting times.

Some of these new discoveries lead to new understandings and yet more new theories. Many scientists were rushing to be the first to publish new findings and to be the first to publish a new theory. All were clamoring to be the first to be credited and applauded for a new discovery or a new theory. With that came funding for further research; funding being the life blood without which a professional scientist cannot continue his academic work.

Indeed, how climate modelling chased funding in more recent times can be said to have become ever more important to the science over the years and has actually determined what modern climate science is.

The below book provides an excellent account of the beginnings of a new science, namely the science of meteorology—*Appropriating the Weather: Vilhelm Bjerknes and the Construction of a Modern Meteorology.*[102]

In 1891, Vilhelm Bjerknes (the son of Norwegian physics professor Carl Anton Bjerknes) went to Germany to defend his father's applied mathematics and aether-based works with Hertz. He was beaten to publishing an experimental and mathematical defence of his father's work by two weeks because a Swedish "informer" had told French physicist Poincare, who promptly put together his own mathematics only paper and published it before Vilhelm Bjerknes published his.

Vilhelm Bjerknes, because he was not the first to publish,

---

[102] http://www.amazon.co.uk/Robert-Marc-Friedman/e/B001H6PVXM/ref=dp_byline_cont_book_1
by https://www.hf.uio.no/iakh/english/people/aca/robertfr/

had little choice but to return to Norway as a physics professor. Albeit, a physics professor with a failing career in 1893.

Vilhelm decided upon a new direction—that of applied mathematics of accepted physics to an area no one had done before—weather prediction. The calculations were far too complex, although they were "merely" seven partial differential equations. From these equations Bjerknes devised a 'graph and pencil' system, drawn on maps. He thought the weather was simply too difficult to ever be calculated, even if or when mechanical computing machines (computers) were to be invented.

After publishing his 1904 academic paper, Vilhelm obtained government funding and Vilhelm's son (Jacob) started to work with him. A series of newspaper articles (an extended and simplified version of the academic paper, deliberately written and aimed at public understanding of the approach) was also published in 1904 to gain approval for his weather forecasting approach from fishermen, farmers, and aviators.

Their work became the Bergen school, which made great advances in meteorology, because of the public support, and public funding initially generated by the academic papers and the series of newspaper articles.

During this period, all seemed well with the maths and physics used. The approach was undoubtedly advancing the science of meteorology by improving our understanding of weather. Particularly by improving what it is thought is happening at the larger scale, which causes the weather we experience.

That is not to say Bjerknes or the Bergen school offered any overall explanations of how the climate system worked. The great work he and the school did was to try to start identifying and explaining some of the climate systems major features, such as cyclones, Rossby waves, and the general, overall 3-cell per hemisphere atmospheric circulation patterns, to name just some.

Wikipedia describes the Bergen school and its contributions

thus:

> The *"Bergen School of Meteorology" is a school of thought which is the basis for much of modern weather forecasting. Founded by the meteorologist Prof. Vilhelm Bjerknes and his younger colleagues in 1917, the Bergen School attempts to define the motion of the atmosphere by means of the mathematics of interactions between hydro- and thermodynamics, some of which had originally been discovered or explained by Bjerknes himself, thus making mathematical predictions regarding the weather possible by systematic data analysis. Much of the work was done at the Geophysical Institute, University of Bergen, in Bergen, Norway.*[103]

See also:

https://en.wikipedia.org/wiki/Norwegian_cyclone_model

and...

https://en.wikipedia.org/wiki/Polar_front

---

[103] https://en.wikipedia.org/wiki/Bergen_School_of_Meteorology

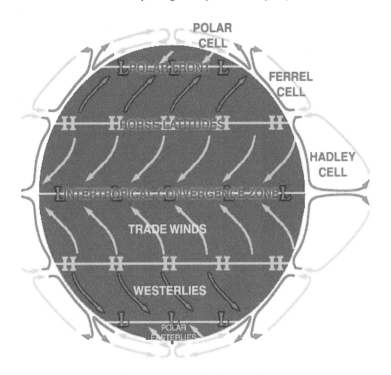

Carl-Gustaf Rossby was a student at, and of, the Bergen School.[104]

> *Atmospheric Rossby waves emerge due to shear in rotating fluids, so that the Coriolis force changes along the sheared coordinate. In planetary atmospheres, they are due to the variation in the Coriolis Effect with latitude. The waves were first identified in the Earth's atmosphere in 1939 by Carl-Gustaf Arvid Rossby who went on to explain their motion.*[105]

It would seem that the Bjerknes 1904 paper, and the Bergen school it helped create, laid down the basis of modern

---

[104] https://en.wikipedia.org/wiki/Carl-Gustaf_Rossby
[105] https://en.wikipedia.org/wiki/Rossby_wave

meteorology, but not in a strictly, or only mathematical modelling manner. Bjerknes stated publicly, on many occasions, he did not think such was possible, then, or in the foreseeable future.

The Bergen school method of weather prediction was a significant advance in meteorology, in that, it was the first attempt to move forward from the hindcasting approach most used at the time. Prior to the Bergen school, hindcasting was the generally accepted and used method for short term weather prediction.

Hindcasting as a method of weather prediction can literally be interpreted as "the last time the weather did that, according to our records, this followed." The weather forecaster would look at the current observations and then check the records for a similar weather pattern previously. From that, the forecaster would then predict what was most likely to happen, according to the records, and more often than not, also taking into account their own personal experience and knowledge of the locality. At best, the hindcasting method was hit and miss. It was also very dependent upon the personnel, and records for a given locality that the (local) weather prediction was being made for. But, it was also the best method available at the time.

Bjerknes built from the hindcasting method a much more mathematical approach. He employed seven partial differential equations that attempted to calculate how the weather would change over time. He realised there were parts of the equations he did not know how to calculate. For these parts he used graphs and plots built up over time from observations of the "missing" variables needed to complete the equations. The graphs and plots were open to some interpretation in helping to complete the equations, and did not always provide exact figures. Bjerknes described the method as still being a bit of a black art, but, a black art that the weather forecaster, with practice, could use with his or her knowledge and skill to provide useful, if not exact, nor certain, weather predictions.

Bjerknes and the Bergen school looked into completing the seven partial differential equations, but they could not. The approach used for the equations included the 2nd Law of Thermodynamics, as it should, but that meant certain parts of the equations simply could not be calculated. For these parts, observations were plotted and used to avoid, or rather, work around the issue(s). The issue being that the then-current understanding of what was thought to be happening simply did not add up in the calculations when the laws of thermodynamics were included.

However, as the "missing" parts to complete the equations could be observed, graphs and plots could be used to provide the figures that could not be calculated. He realised that nature had in effect done the calculations he could not do whilst including all the laws of thermodynamics. All he had to do was to graph and plot the observations to get the "missing" figures. He measured what he openly admitted not understanding how it happened, and used those figures for calculation. It was a scientifically correct approach and method to complete the equations.

As has already been made apparent in the Wiki description above, the Bergen school continued for many, many years. The school made many and great advances in, and for, meteorology. In point of fact, the Bergen method of weather prediction became internationally accepted as the way to make (local and regional) weather predictions. The Bergen school method was used, almost universally, until the mid 1980s.

By 1911, another way to complete the seven equations was being developed. Very few people knew of, or about this. However, it would eventually become the basis of the computer modelling for weather and climate prediction that replaced the Bergen method in the mid 1980s. To many at the time, and since, the change to computer weather and climate modelling prediction was a natural progression, in that it appeared to be the Bergen method put onto a computer.

Solving very complex problems, which we know how to

calculate on a computer, today is an obvious thing to do. At that time, Bjerknes openly admitted he did not know how to complete the partial equations of the method for it to be able to be put onto a computer, after (or if) computers were to be invented.

This raises the questions of who, when, and most importantly how, were the seven partial differential equations compiled into a mathematics-only method for weather prediction? It also raises the question of why the mathematics only (computer calculated) approach to weather prediction did not become more obvious until the mid 1980s?

The answers to these questions will be briefly described over the next few chapters of this book, as what may well appear to some to be, the secret timeline of greenhouse effect theory based computer weather and climate modelling is recounted.

Chapter 5—Timeline 1905 to 1911, then 1911 to 1922

L. F. Richardson, then L. F. Richardson and W. H. Dines

I do not pretend to have gone very deeply into the matter, and publish this note merely to draw attention to the fact that trapped radiation appears to play but a very small part in the actual cases with which we are familiar.
—Professor Robert R. Wood, 1911

LEWIS FRY RICHARDSON (LFR) was a pacifist, and a brilliant zoologist, psychologist, mathematician, and physicist, who preferred to work alone. He, with no meteorological training at all, decided to try and make a 'mathematical calculations only' approach to weather prediction based on, and being developed from the Bjerknes modelling approach. He incorporated a more complex grid system for modelling the weather. He completed, and made much more complex, the equations Bjerknes had used, but they were basically the same equations. The equations LFR used became much more complex, because he added many more factors than Bjerknes had taken into account. However, that is not the full story.

Although Richardson had little or no previous experience or academic training in meteorology, he is widely regarded as the 'father' of modern-day computer climate modelling, which still uses the same physics and calculations to this day. The 'radiation theory' basis within LFR's climate model was never questioned. This was because almost all simply did not know it was there. Again, this is not the full story.

LFR's modelling approach appeared to be the same (7 partial differential equations) direction of the undoubtedly successful Bergen school modelling approach that Vilhelm Bjerknes started in 1904. However, LFR disposed of the graphs and plots Bjerknes had used. LFR used 7 "complete" differential equations with no, and no need for, graphs or plots. Bjerknes had used graphs and plots, mostly from observations, to generate figures that he considered too difficult to otherwise calculate. In short, things we did not understand sufficiently to calculate, but that could be observed.

Completing the differential equations, and how LFR completed them, is therefore THE significant difference between Bjerknes's and LFR's climate models. How LFR completed the equations is partly a product of the man he was, partly a product of his sheer mathematical brilliance, and partly a product of the controversies that raged at the time he completed them.

Lewis Fry Richardson, born in 1881, was the youngest of five boys and two girls born to David and Catherine Richardson. The Richardson's being a family of tanners for over 300 years. The family story is told in a book by A. O. Boyce 1889, *Records of a Quaker family; the Richardsons of Cleveland.*

In 1894, LFR went to Bootham School, York, where he was taught by J. Edmund Clark, who for many years prepared the annual Phenological Report of the Royal Meteorological Society. LFR wrote, "Clark gave us many glimpses of the marvels of science."

He also wrote of his time at Bootham that:

Another master, J Neave Brayshaw (who later wrote a history of Quakerism) left me with the conviction that science ought to be subordinate to morals.

LFR's statement (made many years later for his memoirs) that he was left with the lifelong "conviction that science ought to be subordinate to morals" is, from a scientific point of view, a rather peculiar and concerning statement. Science, if it is to be science, is subordinate to nothing. Morals and beliefs do not determine facts. Nor should morals and beliefs dictate how observations should be viewed or interpreted. If morals or beliefs are allowed to determine how one views the science of a matter, then that, at best, is pseudo-science, and at worst, is religion.

In 1898, LFR went to Durham College of Science "acquiring information and techniques in mathematics, physics, chemistry, botany and zoology." In 1900 he entered King's College, Cambridge, as a Minor Scholar. There he "continued to acquire information and skill, from more brilliant teachers, notably in physics, from Professor J. J. Thomson, and Dr. G. F. C. Searle." His formal education was finished in 1903, although, he returned to formal education for a couple of years to study psychology in the late 1920s.

Brilliant student.

In 1903 to 1904, LFR was a student assistant at the National Physical Laboratory metallurgy department. In 1905 to 1906 he was a junior demonstrator in physics at University College, Aberystwyth. In 1906 to 1907 he was Chemist to National Peat Industries where he developed an interest in how water flows through peat.

From 1907 to 1909 he was Assistant at the National Physical Laboratory (Metrology department). He continued studies of flows and eddies, and wrote a paper.[106] Aware of Shaw-Dines research, he also worked on completing Bjerknes's equations.

Between 1909 to 1912 he was in charge of the chemical and physical laboratory at Sunderland Lamp Company, Gateshead.

It is both interesting and relevant to note that Professor Robert W. Wood published his *Note on the Theory of the Greenhouse* in The London, Edinburgh and Dublin Philosophical Magazine and Journal of Science in 1911, in which he stated:

> *...the fact that trapped radiation appears to play but a very small part in the actual cases with which we are familiar.*

It seems peculiar now that a world renowned and leading scientist of his expertise and status in the subject area of radiation did not perform, write up and publish his experiment at the time. He simply showed atmospheric back radiation has no observable warming effect at Earth's surface.

In other words, the ½ R radiated downwards does not add energy to, reduce the cooling rate of, or warm Earth's surface (as postulated by Stewart), therefore there cannot be a greenhouse effect.

Maybe Professor Wood did not think it important enough to bother with. Maybe he did not want to be responsible for potentially curtailing another scientist's hard earned funding stream, which was, in all good faith, attempting to improve the young science of meteorology.

Maybe he thought the science would improve and correct

---

[106] Big whorls have little whorls
      which feed on their velocity,
      And little whorls have lesser whorls
      And so on to viscosity.
      —LFR, 1920

any mistakes; hence he published the note in the hope it would be noticed at the appropriate time.

Professor R. W. Wood's Note on the Theory of the Greenhouse

By Professor R. W. Wood (Communicated by the Author)

THERE appears to be a widespread belief that the comparatively high temperature produced within a closed space covered with glass, and exposed to solar radiation, results from a transformation of wave-length, that is, that the heat waves from the Sun, which are able to penetrate the glass, fall upon the walls of the enclosure and raise its temperature: the heat energy is re-emitted by the walls in the form of much longer waves, which are unable to penetrate the glass, the greenhouse acting as a radiation trap.

I have always felt some doubt as to whether this action played any very large part in the elevation of temperature. It appeared much more probable that the part played by the glass was the prevention of the escape of the warm air heated by the ground within the enclosure. If we open the doors of a greenhouse on a cold and windy day, the trapping of radiation appears to lose much of its efficacy. As a matter of fact I am of the opinion that a greenhouse made of a glass transparent to waves of every possible length would show a temperature nearly, if not quite, as high as that observed in a glass house. The transparent screen allows the solar radiation to warm the ground, and the ground in turn warms the air, but only the limited amount within the enclosure. In the "open," the ground is continually brought into contact with cold air by convection currents.

To test the matter I constructed two enclosures of dead black cardboard, one covered with a glass plate, the other with a plate of rock-salt of equal thickness. The bulb of a thermometer was inserted in each enclosure and the whole packed in cotton, with the exception of the transparent plates which were exposed. When exposed to sunlight the temperature rose gradually to 65°C, the enclosure covered with the salt plate keeping a little ahead of the other, owing to the fact that it transmitted the longer waves from the Sun, which were stopped by the glass. In order to eliminate this action the sunlight was first passed through a glass plate.

There was now scarcely a difference of one degree between the temperatures of the two enclosures. The maximum temperature reached was about 55°C. From what we know about the distribution of energy in the spectrum of the radiation emitted by a body at 55°, it is clear that the rock-salt plate is capable of transmitting practically all of it, while the glass plate stops it entirely. This shows us that the loss of temperature of the ground by radiation is very small in comparison to the loss by convection, in other words that we gain very little from the circumstance that the radiation is trapped.

Is it therefore necessary to pay attention to trapped radiation in deducing the temperature of a planet as affected by its atmosphere? The solar rays penetrate the atmosphere, warm the ground which in turn warms the atmosphere by contact and by convection currents. The heat received is thus *stored up in the atmosphere, remaining there on account of the very low radiating power of a gas. It seems to me very doubtful if the atmosphere is warmed to any great extent by absorbing the radiation from the ground, even under the most favorable conditions.*

I do not pretend to have gone very deeply into the matter, and publish this note merely to draw attention to the fact that trapped radiation appears to play but a very small part in the actual cases with which we are familiar.

It would seem today that Professor Wood's note—and the concerns it raised—went unnoticed. However, at the time the note was published, the subject of radiation, and in particular, light, was quite controversial. As a physicist, LFR must have been very aware of, and understood the controversy. To understand the controversy it is necessary to better understand the history of our understanding of what light is.

The following short quote from a paper by Matthias Kleespies in 2011 titled *A Short History Of Radiation Theories—What Do They Reveal About Anthropogenic Global Warming?*, explains the basis of the controversy. The full paper is reproduced at the end of this chapter.

The different historical views of the nature of radiation or light can be summarized as follows:

—Pictet was uncertain and thought both a wave or particle model might explain his observed "reflection of cold." However, he preferred the particulate approach.

—Rumford was a strict "undulationist"—a proponent of the claim that only waves could explain what was observed.

—Prevost again was just as strictly adhering to his

particle model.
—Due to Newton's influence, particle models dominated until 1850.
—By 1850, wave models were generally accepted and after Hertz's experimental confirmation of Maxwell, his wave model again dominated.
—After 1900, photons, the wave-particle duality and quantum physics are dominating physics and radiation theories.

If this summary can show us one thing then it is that the wave-particle duality played a wicked game throughout the history of modern science. Like a huge pendulum, the attempts to explain the nature of radiation and light were deflected from one side to the other until the concept of wave-particle duality seemingly stopped the pendulum at a resting point and finally harmonized two fundamentally different concepts in a third and hitherto unknown theoretical approach.

But did this harmonization bring peace of mind?

Albert Einstein, whom some call the greatest physicist and genius of all time, as some of his quotes show, was never truly satisfied with Planck's findings—respective emphasis, if any, are by the author of this text:

> *In the year nineteen hundred, in the course of purely theoretical (mathematical) investigation, Max Planck made a very remarkable discovery: the law of radiation of bodies as a function of temperature could not be derived solely from the Laws of Maxwellian electrodynamics.*

Please note what is most important in the above quote: "...in the course of purely THEORETICAL investigation". It is ONLY a theory with NO experimental evidence.

This discovery became the basis of all twentieth-century research in physics and has almost entirely conditioned its development ever since. Without this discovery it would not have been possible to establish a workable theory of molecules and atoms and the energy processes that govern their transformations. Moreover, it has shattered the whole framework of classical mechanics and electrodynamics and set science a fresh task: that of finding a new conceptual basis for all physics. Despite remarkable partial gains, the problem is still far from a satisfactory solution.[107]

And finally:

All these fifty years of conscious brooding have brought me no nearer to the answer to the question, 'What are light quanta?' Nowadays every Tom, Dick and Harry thinks he knows it, but he is mistaken.[108]

It is relevant to recall that Bjerknes had defended his father's support of Hertz's works some time earlier. Bjerknes was firmly in the light-is-a-wave school of thought. This is why he used graphs and plots in his method. There were some figures that could be measured, plotted or graphed that he simply did not know how to calculate. LFR replaced some of those graphs and plots in his 1922 book with radiation theory as calculated by a method first described by W. H. Dines.

Radiation theory—as put in to the model by LFR—is based upon light as a particle. This difference between Bjerknes's and LFR's climate models is in what and how they calculate. LFR had

---

[107] Albert Einstein, 1950
[108] Albert Einstein, 1954

to accept the calculation method he put into his model violated the 2nd Law of Thermodynamics, but, it seemed to give the correct answers!

LFR does not mention that the radiation theory that he and Dines put into his model violates at least one Law of Thermodynamics, but it is clearly described within the text of his 1922 book, on page 174.

LFR states in the preface of *Weather Prediction by Numerical Process* that he originally began work on his model in 1911, and that developed into a more complete modelling approach by 1913, whilst he was employed as the Superintendent at Eskdalemuir Observatory, in Southern Scotland.

He was employed at the Observatory to develop his model to help bring a more theoretical approach to the understanding of meteorology, and be a more critical eye on measurement methods used. The first draft of the book was titled *Weather Prediction by Arithmetical Finite Differences*. He resigned from the post in 1916 to join the Friends' Ambulance Unit in France transporting the wounded from the front, which was financially supported by the Society of Friends (Quakers).

From 1916 to 1918 he conducted, when time allowed, an example calculation which was added to the text of the book. After World War 1 ended, LFR rejoined the Meteorological Office at Benson in Oxfordshire, but he was compelled to resign on grounds of conscience when it was amalgamated into the Air Ministry in 1920.

He was then employed as the Head of the Physics Department at Westminster Training College. The text of the book was extensively rewritten with the help of W. H. Dines in 1920, and 1921, before it was eventually published in 1922, titled *Weather Prediction by Numerical Process*.

LFR received funding from the Royal Meteorological Society in 1916 (£100) to help with the publishing costs of his book (Weather Prediction by Arithmetical Finite Differences). The first version of the book does not appear to have been published and is apparently lost.

The first draft of the book however was mostly rewritten with Dines in 1920, 1921, and LFR received further funding (£50) to help with publishing costs. The second version of the book was published in 1922 under the title *Weather Prediction by Numerical Process.*

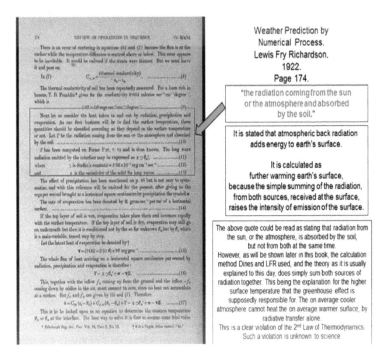

Weather Prediction by Numerical Process. Lewis Fry Richardson. 1922. Page 174.

"the radiation coming from the sun or the atmosphere and absorbed by the soil."

It is stated that atmospheric back radiation adds energy to earth's surface.

It is calculated as further warming earth's surface, because the simple summing of the radiation, from both sources, received at the surface, raises the intensity of emission of the surface.

The above quote could be read as stating that radiation from the sun, or the atmosphere, is absorbed by the soil, but not from both at the same time. However, as will be shown later in this book, the calculation method Dines and LFR used, and the theory as it is usually explained to this day, does simply sum both sources of radiation together. This being the explanation for the higher surface temperature that the greenhouse effect is supposedly responsible for. The on average cooler atmosphere cannot heat the on average warmer surface, by radiative transfer alone. This is a clear violation of the 2nd Law of Thermodynamics. Such a violation is unknown to science

It seems rather odd that in LFR's 1922 book, the radiation theory he and Dines put into the model they developed is given scant mention. Dines had papers on the subject published in 1917 and 1920. The latter whilst helping LFR to completely rewrite the book. Within the book itself there are but a few references to Dines papers, for example on page 56 LFR writes "Mr. W. H. Dines* has used this simplified process extensively to compute the radiation at all heights according to various trial values of absorptance." At the bottom of the page "* Q. J. R. Met. Soc.

April 1920." To find which paper LFR is actually referring to one has to go to the end of the chapter, and at the bottom of a section titled *Some Papers on Long Wave Radiation*, one finds, W. H. Dines, *Atmospheric and Terrestrial Radiation*, Q. J. R. Met. Soc. April 1920. Given the importance to the calculations that Dines is explaining and describing in that paper, the mention and reference by LFR seems at least a little strange.

Dines 1917 paper gets even less mention within LFR's book. On page 64 in a section titled *Publications on Solar Radiation*, one of the papers listed is W. H. Dines, *Heat Balance of the Atmosphere*. Q. J. R. Met Soc. Apr, 1917. These are the total mention of Dines theory and calculation method within LFR's 1922 book. It is interesting to note that Dines at the start of his 1920 paper writes:

> *For the method of calculation I am indebted to Mr. L. F. Richardson; this method is being published, but by his kind permission I am enabled to set it out here.*

Dines states in his 1920 paper:

> *In a paper read before the Society in February 1917, "The Heat Balance of the Atmosphere," the amounts of the various kinds of radiant energy crossing the upper and lower limits are considered; in the present paper an estimate is made of the atmospheric and terrestrial radiation crossing any level surface in the atmosphere itself, certain assumptions being made and certain conditions assumed.*

Dines is clearly stating that the theory is described in his 1917 paper and the calculation method is described in his 1920 paper. It is difficult to see why something so absolutely central to LFR's model, and that was completely different from Bjerknes's model that LFR was developing is mentioned so little, if at all, by LFR in his book.

Certainly, from reading LFR's book alone, one has no explanation of the radiation theory he is using, or the actual calculation method the theory uses. It is almost as if it was deliberately hidden.

Is it possible the controversy that raged at the time about whether light is a wave or a particle, and Einstein's proposed solution, played a part in this? As a physicist, LFR was certainly aware of the controversy and he must have realised that it had repercussions in regards of radiation theory that he and Dines had put into his climate model.

On page 70 of his book, LFR writes in regard to eddies and turbulence that:

> *If molecules did that sort of thing, the occurrence*
> *would be one of the exceedingly rare exceptions to*
> *the second law of thermodynamics.*

For a physicist to state such is, at best, perplexing. A physicist knows there are no known exceptions to any law of thermodynamics.

Sigbjørn Grønås writes in his article, Scientific Weather Prediction: A Newspaper Article on Weather Forecasting by V. Bjerknes that:

> *In both his scientific paper and his newspaper*
> *article, Bjerknes mentions the prognostic*
> *equations and their variables, and sketches how*
> *they could be solved using graphical methods.*[109]

As pointed out by Eliassen (1999), Bjerknes made a mistake

---

[109] http://lib.znate.ru/docs/index-134235.html

when he included the second law of thermodynamics in his set of equations, an error that later was corrected by Richardson (1922), who set up the primitive equations as we know them today.

A physicist, such as LFR, knows one cannot pick and choose which of the laws of thermodynamics apply, and which do not apply, in a given situation. They all apply, all of the time.

The method devised by Richardson, regardless of what it actually calculated, proved to be impractical at the time of its publication. Richardson himself dreamed of the day computers could be used to do the calculating required.

However, being a scientist, he did an experiment. He calculated a weather forecast from a start point. The calculation took in real time about 2 years for him to complete, although Richardson said he did it in his spare time, in 6 weeks' worth of work that was spread over 2 years.

The results of his trial 6 hours ahead forecast were little short of outlandish, not to mention a little behind the weather it was trying to predict. His work was generally interpreted as being far too slow and far too complex to calculate at the time, and it did not give anywhere near the right answer. It seemed of little use or practical application to anyone.

His works as described in his 1922 book were forgotten and regarded as interesting, but massively over-complex and useless.

A Short History Of Radiation Theories—What Do They Reveal About "Anthropogenic Global Warming"?

A paper by Matthias Kleespies.

Introduction

The official, or consensus AGW (Anthropogenic Global Warming) movement has two sides or faces: one, supported by celebrities, governments and the mass media aims to convince the public that AGW is real and threatening; the other, in support of the first, serving as an indispensable base in the attempt to prove that AGW is real on a scientific basis.

The fundamental framework of the basis of AGW is a certain radiation theory claiming that the atmosphere, and in particular certain gases like water vapor, carbon dioxide and methane, absorb the infrared rays emitted from the Earth's surface and then re-emit a fraction of this absorbed radiative energy back to the surface which in turn leads to an increased temperature on the Earth.

This supposed radiative behavior of the atmosphere is referred to as either back radiation or downwelling longwave radiation. Both are said to constitute the natural greenhouse effect which is presented to the public as being the essential factor in warming the Earth above an otherwise hostile "planetary blackbody temperature" of only -18°C. Since carbon dioxide is regarded as a major contributor of "back" or "downwelling longwave" radiation, it is said that we will inevitably face a climate catastrophe if we do not drastically lower our carbon dioxide emissions.

However, something is amiss with the scientific part of AGW and in particular with its radiation hypothesis, in that unexpectedly the Earth temperature does not comply with its laws—a trendline analysis of satellite data clearly shows a maximum of global temperatures in 2010-2011, though worldwide carbon dioxide emissions increased by 45% between 1990 and 2010.

Simply put, it cannot be said that increasing carbon dioxide emissions between 1990 and 2010 cause the increase of Earth's temperature climaxing in 2010/2011. The AGW theory claims that increasing CO_2 leads to an almost proportional increase of average global temperatures. The facts just do not correlate or add up.

It is therefore worthwhile to take a closer look at the history of radiation science so as to provide a better understanding of the development of the currently applied radiation theory to illustrate how, based on historic evidence, the AGW does not hold.

Pictet, Rumford and Prevost

According to ancient Greek and Roman historians, Archimedes already knew about the radiative power of the Sun: during the siege of Syracuse in 212BC, he reportedly set the Roman warships afire with the aid of mirrors.

Later, according to Evans and Popp (1984):

> *References to experiments with radiant heat appear in Italian, English, French, and German publications scattered over a period of 200 years, from 1570, say, to 1770.*

Unless otherwise stated or cited, the following information was taken from the aforementioned source as well.

Until the end of the 18th century experiments were mainly carried out with two objects being placed in the respective foci of two opposite concave mirrors at a distance of several feet apart. In one very popular and dramatic demonstration, a combustible object was ignited at a distance of 20 to 24 feet by the reflection and concentration of the heat of a single coal, the coal being placed at the focus of one mirror and the combustible object at the focus of the other.

It was not until the beginning of the 19th century, or more exactly the summer and fall of 1800, that experiments and research on radiative heat became more focused and structured. Sir Benjamin Thompson, also known as "Count Rumford," in the company of Professors Hope, Playfair and Stewart of the

University of Edinburgh, undertook to repeat an experiment that had been performed originally by Marc-Auguste Pictet of the Academy of Geneva.

In this experiment Pictet investigated what appeared to be the reflection of cold: using two concave mirrors, he placed a flask filled with cold water and snow or ice at the focus of one mirror and a sensitive air thermometer at the other mirror's focus.

When thus placed the thermometer's displayed temperature immediately dropped (AGW claims that an atmosphere colder than the planet's surface does warm the planet). In fact, when the flask was placed *in close proximity to* the mirror's focus, the temperature reading did not change at all.

This apparently intrigued Rumford because following this experiment he presented his first publicly announced opinion on the subject of heat.

In the following years he performed many experiments on this matter, invented new apparatus for use in these experiments, and proffered theoretical explanations for his results. This is covered further on.

One of his most important findings was that a metallic vessel covered with a thin layer of soot cooled more quickly and heated more rapidly than a vessel of the same size and form with a highly polished surface. He thus discovered what is common knowledge today: black coatings are very good emitters (and also absorbers) of heat.

However, it seems he did not draw or come to the above conclusion as he believed in the existence of "calorific" (heat) and "frigorific" (cold) rays, the latter having, to his belief, been clearly demonstrated by the "reflection of cold" in Pictet's experiment.

In another ingenious experiment—with respect to what was known then—he investigated the effect of a heat source applied to one of the hollow balls of his "thermoscope", an instrument of his own devising (please refer to the source mentioned above for clarification of its construction), and a source of "cold" applied to the opposite side of this ball at exactly the same distance as the heat source.

Both radiation sources were metallic tubes; one filled with water at a fixed temperature *above* room temperature and the other with a fixed temperature of the same amount *below* room temperature.

The thermoscope was constructed in such a way that any volume change of air, expansion or compression, inside the hollow ball would be directly visualized.

The results of his experiment were unambiguous: the ball's volume did not change and therefore, Rumford concluded, "calorific" rays were of exactly equal strength as "frigorific" rays. He thus thought he had proven what he believed to be the right explanation for Pictet's "reflection of cold" experiment: the existence of "frigorific" rays.

This assumed misconception of Rumford's, if it is so, is a clear cut example of how a preconceived opinion or concept blocks other rational explanations of the observed facts and we need to keep this in mind when considering why back or downwelling radiation is defended at all cost by its proponents.

Radiation Theories Offered by the Scientists of the Time

There is an ongoing scientific debate—it is in fact still ongoing as will be shown at the end of this article—about the nature of light and/or radiation (at the time scientists thought heat differed from light because ordinary transparent glass was able to block heat for a certain length of time until it was itself heated and thus, in turn, began radiating heat). Two explanations are possible: light is a form of particles (Newton) or waves (Maxwell).

At the time of Pictet, Rumford and Prevost, both theories had their scientific followers. We should remember, however, that these scientists regarded what we now call "empty space" as an invisible fluid, sometimes referred to as the "aether." Waves, according to the received wisdom of the time, required some kind of fluid in which to move. Heat, in particular, was seen as a special igneous fluid.

Equally the "emissionists" thought that "caloric", and therefore also "frigorific", was a form of invisible *particles* emitted by heat or radiation sources.

Pictet's "reflection of cold" experiment had greatly influenced other researchers and in particular Rumford. We'll begin with Pictet's attempts of explanation.

He had been undecided which of two possible fundamental explanations should be favored and claimed it was not possible to choose between the caloric and wave theory of heat on the basis of experimental evidence. However, he inclined through personal preference to the caloric (particle) theory, championed by the French physicists and chemists, and notably by Lavoisier.

Pictet had initially been astounded by the results of his own experiment. On reflection though, he had been able to explain it. He believed the air around the thermometer created a certain *tension* as every warm body does—he also firmly believed that cold did not exist in itself but was a privation of heat. However, this heated air around a thermometer would develop exactly the same tension as the thermometer and would therefore *resist* any further radiation from the thermometer the surrounding air. In this—equilibrium—situation, *tension* and *resistance* were equal and thus no transfer of heat from either body to the other would occur.

Pictet regarded the equilibrium situation as a static balance of tension and resistance.

Therefore, if a cold object was placed at the focus of one mirror, it would, according to Pictet, absorb the heat of the surrounding room including the heat emanating from the thermometer whereby the thermometer itself was cooled. In this regard his experiment would not differ from one in which a heat source would be placed at the focus of the mirror opposite to the mirror holding the thermometer at its focus.

Finally, Pictet remarked that the same explanation would apply if we regard the caloric effect as resulting not from emanation, but from a vibration in the *elastic fluid* (emphasis by the author) *of fire* that fills the space in which the experiment was performed.

> *It is known that these vibrations are susceptible of being reflected according to the same laws as emanations, of which the reflection of sounds affords us daily examples.*

It was already mentioned that Rumford regarded radiant heat as an undulation analogous to sound, and seems to have viewed Pictet's experiment more or less as a case of a driven oscillator This was the explanation he ventured to offer his companions at Edinburgh in 1800...

> *The cold body in one focus compels the warm body (the thermometer) in the other focus to change its note.*

A few years later he gave a much more detailed explanation to further stress and substantiate his undulation theory.

However, Evans and Popp, the authors of the detailed historic outline we reference, point out...

> *...essential difficulty with Rumford's version of the undulationist theory was that he wished to associate the change in temperature experienced by an object solely with the radiation absorbed by it, and denied the temperature-changing effect of the emitted radiation. As a result, Rumford's system suffered from internal inconsistencies that*

did not trouble Prevost's.

According to Prevost's notion of 1818, physicists dealing with the nature of light were divided into three different classes: *les émissionaires, les undulateurs, et les indifférens*—the emissionists, undalationists, and the undetermined.

Evans and Popp remark:

> *A similar division applies very well to physical doctrines on the nature of heat during the 30-year period that concerns us here (1775-1805). If anything, opinion on heat during this period was even more fragmented. Reduced to its most basic terms, the question was this: were the phenomena of heat produced by emissions of a material substance, or were they due to undulations?*

And they conclude:

> *In Saussure and Pictet, we shall see a cautious undulationist and a cautious emissionist, respectively. But in Rumford and Prevost, we shall see two of the most confident and assertive proponents that the two schools of thought ever produced.*

This conclusion may be one of the most important facts in understanding how the present notion of "back" or "downwelling" radiation could develop: *Prevost was a "most confident and assertive" emissionist already before he developed his most influential theory of heat transfer described in the following paragraphs.*

Evans and Popp state:

> *Prevost introduced a mode of reasoning that has*

since become habitual in thermodynamics.

Prevost asserted that fire was a discrete fluid, a fluid believed to consist of particles. Taking this for granted, he came to the following conclusions—again quoted directly from Evans and Popp. This neatly shows why and how proponents of back and downwelling radiation believed this process would occur and why they claimed the science was settled—because Prevost had prepared the basics of this notion already back in 1791, more than 200 years ago.

> *According to Prevost, such equilibrium between two bodies consists in the equal, simultaneous exchanges of fire particles between them. Imagine two cubical portions of space which share a common face, thus forming a rectangular parallelepiped. Let the walls of this rectangular box be of a material perfectly solid and poreless. Into this box, Prevost imagines placing a quantity of free fire. The fire moves freely through the whole of this space. And there is no reason why it should pass with less facility through the empty square that is the boundary between the two cubes than through any other part of this space. There are continual exchanges of particles between the two portions but the quantity of fire in each remains constant. Different particles are ceaselessly found in the same place, but their number and their average separation remain constant. Such is the state of thermometric equilibrium.*

Please note that Prevost believed in the exchange of fire particles between the two bodies. Here was born the theory of heat exchange as the basis of heating via back or downwelling radiation. In our modern science, we believe these particles are photons. But still the whole topic of back radiation is about *particle exchange* between two radiating bodies.

Let us now briefly look at how the scientific debate was led.

Evans and Popp write: "Prevost, it should be noted, treats Pictet with the greatest politeness." ... "And Pictet, for his part, seems to have immediately accepted Prevost's explanation of the experiment."

Rumford, however, whom we see as someone mostly believing only in his own explanations, "does not mention Prevost by name, but he lists Prevost's assumptions so clearly that there can be no doubt whose theory he had in mind." He then "objects that it is impossible to explain how the same body could receive and retain, and reject and drive away, the same substance at one and the same time."

So, it remained unclear whether the observed phenomena could be best explained by undulation or particles.

Application of Radiation Theories to Climate—Tyndall and Arrhenius

The Internet provides a ready source of historical scientific literature sites. One such a site is Timothy Casey's. The following information is taken from this site unless otherwise stated.[110]

Casey has studied (and published) Tyndall's and Arrhenius' original work relating to the GHE. He also gives a translation of Fourier by Burgess (1837). As Arrhenius, the father of the greenhouse effect, defers his work at least in part to Tyndall, we will start with his observations and experimental work.

In 1861, Tyndall wrote a paper titled On the Absorption and Radiation of Heat by Gases and Vapours, and on the Physical Connexion of Radiation, Absorption, Conduction—The Bakerian Lecture. In his preface, he writes:

---

[110] http://greenhouse.geologist-1011.net/

The researches on glaciers which I have had the honour of submitting from time to time to the notice of the Royal Society, directed my attention in a special manner to the observations and speculations of De Saussure, Fourier, M. Pouillet, and Mr. Hopkins, on the transmission of solar and terrestrial heat through the Earth's atmosphere.

This gave practical effect to a desire which I previously entertained to make the mutual action of radiant heat and gases of all kinds the subject of an experimental inquiry.

It may therefore not be surprising that his desire led to false conclusions about the absorption of gases he meant to measure.

Casey writes:

> *It is clear that Tyndall measured opacity and relative opacity, not absorptivity and absorption as he seems to claim.*[111]

In fact, Tyndall uses the terms "opacity" and "absorbing power" interchangeably throughout his work. This is indicative of a fundamental misunderstanding, which is nonetheless studiously avoided by nearly all authors who claim that Tyndall's work proved the Greenhouse Effect.

> *Although historical authors such as Arrhenius generally acknowledge that Tyndall regarded "absorbing" gases as thermal buffers rather than warming agents, contemporary and historical authors alike (Arrhenius, 1896; Weart, 2003, p. 3) fail to acknowledge the fact that Tyndall made absolutely no measurement of actual absorption,*

---

[111] Ibid.

he confused absorption and opacity, and if anything, his differential radiation idea rests heavily on the idea of luminiferous Aether—later refuted by Michelson & Morley (1887).[112]

[Arrhenius] developed a theory to explain the ice ages, and in 1896 he was the first scientist to speculate that changes in the levels of carbon dioxide in the atmosphere could substantially alter the surface temperature through the greenhouse effect.[113]

He was influenced by the work of others, including Joseph Fourier. Arrhenius used the infrared observations of the moon by Frank Washington Very and Samuel Pierpont Langley at the Allegheny Observatory in Pittsburgh to calculate the absorption of infrared radiation by atmospheric CO_2 and water vapor. Using 'Stefan's law' (better known as the Stefan-Boltzmann law), he formulated his greenhouse law.

In its original form, Arrhenius' greenhouse law reads as follows:

...if the quantity of carbonic acid increases in geometric progression, the augmentation of the temperature will increase nearly in arithmetic progression.

In *Worlds in the Making*, he suggested that the human emission of CO_2 would be strong enough to prevent the world from entering a new ice age, and that a warmer Earth would be needed to feed the rapidly increasing population:

---

[112] Ibid.

[113]

https://en.wikipedia.org/wiki/Svante_Arrhenius#Greenhouse_effect

To a certain extent the temperature of the Earth's surface, as we shall presently see, is conditioned by the properties of the atmosphere surrounding it, and particularly by the permeability of the latter for the rays of heat.

That the atmospheric envelopes limit the heat losses from the planets had been suggested about 1800 by the great French physicist Fourier. His ideas were further developed afterwards by Pouillet and Tyndall. Their theory has been styled the hot-house theory, because they thought that the atmosphere acted after the manner of the glass panes of hot-houses.

Here we may see an example of sloppy research by Arrhenius (please also see below) because he cites Fourier "about 1800." However, according to Casey, Fourier published his ideas related to the atmosphere in 1824 at the earliest.

On the other hand, Arrhenius' ideas are most interesting. He believed CO_2 would be BENEFICIAL and NECESSARY to feed the rapidly increasing population. What do the UN IPCC, and many of the scientists referring to Arrhenius, make of that?

But the more important question is: was Arrhenius' theory based on indisputable facts? Or is it merely theory?

Again Casey:

Contrary to what Arrhenius (1896, 1906b) and many popular authors may claim (Weart, 2003; Flannery, 2005; Archer, 2009), Fourier did not consider the atmosphere to be anything like glass. In fact, Fourier (1827, p. 587) rejected the comparison by stipulating the impossible condition that in order for the atmosphere to even remotely resemble the workings of a hotbox or greenhouse, layers of the air would have to solidify without affecting the air's optical properties. What Fourier (1824, translated by Burgess, 1837, p. 12) actually wrote stands in stark contrast to Arrhenius' claims about Fourier's ideas:

> *In short, if all the strata of air of which the atmosphere is formed, preserved their density with their transparency, and lost only the mobility which is peculiar to them, this mass of air, thus become solid, on being exposed to the rays of the Sun, would produce an effect the same in kind with that we have just described. The heat, coming in the state of light to the solid Earth, would lose all at once, and almost entirely, its power of passing through transparent solids: it would accumulate in the lower strata of the atmosphere, which would thus acquire very high temperatures. We should observe at the same time a diminution of the degree of acquired heat, as we go from the surface of the Earth.*

Even worse, according to Casey, Arrhenius[114] still clung to the aether hypothesis, which refers to the unspecified material medium of space. Arrhenius' adherence to this hypothesis remained firm in spite of its sound refutation by Michelson & Morley.[115]

This leaves the conceptual underpinning of radiation in Arrhenius' Greenhouse Effect to Tyndall,[116] who ascribes

---

[114] *Världarnas utveckling, Worlds in the Making: The Evolution of the Universe*, H. Borns [Translation in English Published 1908], Harper & Brs, New York, pp. 154 and 225

[115] Michelson, A. A., & Morley, E. W., 1887, *The Relative Motion of the Earth and the Luminiferous Aether*, American Journal of Science, Vol. 34, p. 333

[116] Tyndall, J., 1864, *Heat Considered as a Mode of Motion: Being a Course of Twelve Lectures Delivered at the Royal Institution of Great*

communication of molecular vibration into the aether and communication of aethereal vibration to molecular motion.

Moreover, Hans Erren points out: [117]

> *The key paper on global warming written by Svante Arrhenius[118] in 1896 relies on the infrared observations of the moon as published by Langley in 1890.[119] The paper of Langley contains errors that were corrected in 1900 by Langley and Abbot[120] but this was after Arrhenius published his theory.[121]*

It is therefore realistic to conclude that Arrhenius' theory is based on misconceptions—aether theory and misunderstanding of Fourier's greenhouse experiments—and flaws in Langley's data upon which his theory is built.

So, Arrhenius' greenhouse effect theory is questionable, to say the least. But nevertheless, modern greenhouse effect theories still largely claim that the atmosphere acts like a greenhouse made of glass, and that CO_2 is a major contributor to this greenhouse effect.[122]

Britain in the Season of 1862, New York, 1864, pp. 264-265; 1867, p. 416

[117] http://members.casema.nl/errenwijlens/co2/langleyrevdraft2.htm

[118] Svante Arrhenius, 1896, *On the Influence of Carbonic Acid in the Air upon the Temperature of the Ground*, The London, Edinburgh, and Dublin Philosophical Magazine and Journal of Science [fifth series] April 1896. vol 41, p237-275

[119] Samuel P. Langley (and Frank W. Very), 1890, *The Temperature of the Moon*, Memoir of the National Academy of Sciences, vol. iv. 9th mem. 193pp.

[120] Langley & Abbot, 1900, Annals of the Astrophysical Observatory of the Smithsonian Institution, Volume I,

[121] http://members.casema.nl/errenwijlens/co2/langleyrevdraft2.htm

[122] There are endless examples, here is one:
https://berkeleysciencereview.com/2016/11/greenhouse-gases-

Robert W. Wood's Refutation of Arrhenius

According to Casey, Arrhenius had misquoted Fourier, "who maintained that closed spaces such as hotboxes (and by extension greenhouses) retained their heat by cutting off circulation with the cooler atmosphere." [123] Perhaps it is thus that it took almost 100 years for another scientist to "rediscover" Fourier's findings and interpretations.

In 1909, Robert W. Wood performed a very simple yet clear-cut experiment to determine why a real greenhouse made of glass is warmer than its surroundings. Wood asked himself:

> *Is it therefore necessary to pay attention to trapped radiation in deducing the temperature of a planet as affected by its atmosphere?* [124]

He answered this question in the following way:

> *The solar rays penetrate the atmosphere, warm the ground which in turn warms the atmosphere by contact and by convection currents. The heat received is thus stored up in the atmosphere, remaining there on account of the very low radiating power of a gas. It seems to me very doubtful if the atmosphere is warmed to any great extent by absorbing the radiation from the ground, even under the most favourable conditions.*

---

versus-glass-greenhouses/

[123] http://geologist-1011.mobi/

[124] http://www.tech-know-group.com/papers/Note_on_the_Theory_of_the_Greenhouse.pdf

Here is a description of Wood's elegant experiment:

> *To test the matter I constructed two enclosures of dead black cardboard, one covered with a glass plate, the other with a plate of rock-salt of equal thickness. The bulb of a thermometer was inserted in each enclosure and the whole packed in cotton, with the exception of the transparent plates which were exposed. When exposed to sunlight the temperature rose gradually to 65° C., the enclosure covered with the salt plate keeping a little ahead of the other, owing to the fact that it transmitted the longer waves from the Sun, which were stopped by the glass.*
>
> *In order to eliminate this action the sunlight was first passed through a glass plate.*
>
> *There was now scarcely a difference of one degree between the temperatures of the two enclosures. The maximum temperature reached was about 55°C. From what we know about the distribution of energy in the spectrum of the radiation emitted by a body at 55°C, it is clear that the rock-salt plate is capable of transmitting practically all of it, while the glass plate stops it entirely. This shows us that the loss of temperature of the ground by radiation is very small in comparison to the loss by convection, in other words that we gain very little from the circumstance that the radiation is trapped.*

Wood's experiment of course does only show that greenhouses *made of glass* do not trap any radiation.

But shouldn't we ask ourselves: if a very solid material like glass does not trap any radiation is it then logical to assume that the turbulent, chaotic mixture of gases comprising our atmosphere, would?

After all, already Fourier refuted such a possibility.

And we should at least stop arguing that the atmospheric greenhouse effect is named in such a way because it resembles the physical mechanisms by which actual greenhouses are warmed. This is definitely wrong.

Wood's experiment was confirmed in great detail by Professor Nasif Nahle in his experiment in 2011.[125]

Kirchhoff's Law

The history of radiation theories of course wouldn't be complete without Kirchhoff's law. Moreover, this law is often stated to prove that back or downwelling radiation heating is real.

Perhaps we should recall the two mechanisms proclaimed to warm the Earth by the action of the atmosphere:

1) Back radiation, as suggested by Kiehl and Trenberth 1997[126] allegedly adds some extra radiation wattage to the Sun's insolation, thereby warming the Earth more than the Sun's radiation alone would do.

2) Back or downwelling longwave radiation acts to slow down cooling of the Earth by acting like a *somewhat* cooler body—cooler with regard to the Earth's surface—which is still *warmer* than outer space and therefore, seemingly, delays cooling of the Earth which in effect leads to a warmer Earth.

Proclamation 1 can easily be seen to contradict the Second law of thermodynamics formulated between 1850 (Clausius) and 1851 (Kelvin), as heat, even radiative heat, cannot flow from the

---

[125] http://principia-
scientific.org/publications/Experiment_on_Greenhouse_Effect.pdf
[126] http://www.cgd.ucar.edu/cas/abstracts/files/kevin1997_1.html

cooler atmosphere (due to convection it is *always* cooler than the Earth's surface) to the warmer surface.

Proclamation 2 is much more tricky. Its proponents say something like:

> *Quantum physics tells us that statistically there are more photons flowing from the warmer body to the cooler body than the other way around but that does not mean that there are NO photons—statistically—moving from the cooler to the warmer body. Only the NET FLOW is decisive. And the net flow, according to the 2nd law of thermodynamics, of course is only from hot to cold. BUT, because—statistically—there are some photons moving from cold to warm, i. e., from the atmosphere to the Earth's surface, the rate of cooling of the Earth is smaller than it would be WITHOUT the somewhat colder body, i.e., the atmosphere.*

It should be easy to see how much this kind of argument is based on nothing more than Prevost's ideas. However, in modern times, Prevost's igneous fluid particles has been replaced by quantum physics or quantitized photons. We will see shortly if quantum physics is something we can really trust, i.e., if it is scientifically undisputed and proven beyond doubt.

Kirchhoff's law states that at thermal equilibrium, the emissivity of a body (or surface) equals its absorptivity. This at first seems logical, a simple matter of energy balance.[127]

However, Dr. Claes Johnson argues…

> *But Kirchhoff's Law concerns emissivity and absorptivity as emission and absorption per unit*

---

time and in this setting it is not at all trivial. The question is why a body capable of absorbing radiation and emitting radiation, must absorb and emit at the same rate? Is it because emission and absorption are simply the reverse of each other with emission simply absorption backwards in time? No, it is not so trivial, because emission and absorption are different physical processes both with an arrow of time which cannot be reversed. Emission and absorption are not the reverse of each other.[128]

What might be worse is yet another fact. Arne Schirrmacher reveals:

David Hilbert told the German physicists at one of their main professional meetings in the morning of September 18, 1912 that they had failed for more than fifty years to provide a proof for one of their most precious laws: Kirchhoff's law on heat radiation that turned involved experimental results into a relation as simple and persuasive like Ohm's law 33 years before, had not even in the simplest special cases been made plausible.[129]

At a later passage in Schirrmacher's text it turns out that Kirchhoff's law is merely based on thought experiments.

Let us be totally clear about that: a law which was never really, EXPERIMENTALLY, i.e., *based on FACTS*, proven is used to prove that back or downwelling radiation must be real

---

[128] http://claesjohnson.blogspot.com/2011/10/who-proved-of-kirchhoffs-law-of.html
[129]

http://www.mzwtg.mwn.tum.de/fileadmin/w00bmt/www/Arbeitspapiere/Schirrmacher_2001_1.pdf

because:

3) according to Kirchhoff's law, all bodies emit the amount of absorbed radiation [in all directions]

4) Prevost's argumentation, disguised as quantum physics in our modern times, says that particles, photons (Planck), emitted by the absorber will travel to another, should the situation arise also warmer, emitter and slow down its emission and thus cooling process.

Of course, Prevost's and even Planck's considerations (see below) are also only theoretical EVEN THOUGH at least Planck's radiation theorem is accepted by the majority of modern physicists.

It may therefore seem justified to state that:

Already the theory of back or downwelling radiation is based on nothing more than other unproven albeit commonly accepted theories.

And, as theory is another word for supposition, in contrast to facts, we may, in keeping with Prevost, Kirchhoff, and Planck, according to the stringent inherent logic of the argument concludes that:

Back or downwelling radiation is mere supposition.

And therefore, the atmospheric greenhouse theory based on downwelling or back radiation of absorbed surface emission by carbon dioxide and other gases, is SUPPOSITION or FICTION.

Pure and simple!

Maxwell

One of the questions discussed in this paper in the light of scientific history is whether light, or heat, is a form of particles (photons) or waves.

Wikipedia neatly summarizes the situation prior to Planck:

> *In most theories up to the eighteenth century, light was pictured as being made up of particles. Since particle models cannot easily account for the refraction, diffraction and birefringence of light, wave theories of light were proposed by René Descartes (1637), Robert Hooke (1665), and Christian Huygens (1678); however, particle models remained dominant, chiefly due to the influence of Isaac Newton. In the early nineteenth century, Thomas Young and August Fresnel clearly demonstrated the interference and diffraction of light and by 1850 wave models were generally accepted. In 1865, James Clerk Maxwell's prediction that light was an electromagnetic wave—which was confirmed experimentally in 1888 by Heinrich Hertz's detection of radio waves—seemed to be the final blow to particle models of light.*
>
> *In 1900, Maxwell's theoretical model of light as oscillating electric and magnetic fields seemed complete. However, several observations could not be explained by any wave model of electromagnetic radiation, leading to the idea that light-energy was packaged into quanta described by $E = h\nu$. Later experiments showed that these light-quanta also carry momentum and, thus, can be considered particles: the photon concept was*

born, leading to a deeper understanding of the electric and magnetic fields themselves.

The Maxwell wave theory, however, does not account for all properties of light. The Maxwell theory predicts that the energy of a light wave depends only on its intensity, not on its frequency; nevertheless, several independent types of experiments show that the energy imparted by light to atoms depends only on the light's frequency, not on its intensity. For example, some chemical reactions are provoked only by light of frequency higher than a certain threshold; light of frequency lower than the threshold, no matter how intense, does not initiate the reaction. Similarly, electrons can be ejected from a metal plate by shining light of sufficiently high frequency on it (the photoelectric effect); the energy of the ejected electron is related only to the light's frequency, not to its intensity.[130]

We can learn the following from the above:

- Before 1850, particle models remained dominant, chiefly due to the influence of Isaac Newton.

- By 1850 wave models were generally accepted and in 1865, James Clerk Maxwell's prediction that light was an electromagnetic wave...seemed to be the final blow to particle models of light.

- The Maxwell wave theory, however, does not account for all properties of light. The Maxwell theory predicts that the energy of a light wave depends only on its intensity, not on its frequency... Furthermore, electrons can be ejected from a

---

[130] https://en.wikipedia.org/wiki/Photon

metal plate by shining light of sufficiently high frequency on it (the photoelectric effect); the energy of the ejected electron is related only to the light's frequency, not to its intensity.

Please keep this in mind when we now turn to Planck's radiation law and a new approach to solve the mystery of radiation.

Planck

Here's how the genesis of Planck's (radiation) law is described:

> *In 1894 Planck turned his attention to the problem of black-body radiation.*
>
> *Planck's first proposed solution to the problem in 1899 followed from what Planck called the "principle of elementary disorder", which allowed him to derive Wien's law from a number of assumptions about the entropy of an ideal oscillator, creating what was referred-to as the Wien-Planck law. Soon it was found that experimental evidence did not confirm the new law at all, to Planck's frustration. Planck revised his approach, deriving the first version of the famous Planck black-body radiation law, which described the experimentally observed black-body spectrum well. It was first proposed in a meeting of the DPG on October 19, 1900 and published in 1901. This first derivation did not include energy quantization and did not use statistical mechanics, to which he held an aversion. In November 1900, Planck revised this first approach, relying on Boltzmann's statistical interpretation of the second law of thermodynamics as a way of gaining a more fundamental understanding of the principles*

behind his radiation law. As Planck was deeply suspicious of the philosophical and physical implications of such an interpretation of Boltzmann's approach, his recourse to them was, as he later put it, "an act of despair...I was ready to sacrifice any of my previous convictions about physics.[131]

The central assumption behind his new derivation, presented to the DPG on 14 December 1900, was the supposition, now known as the Planck postulate, that electromagnetic energy could be emitted only in quantized form.

In other words, the energy could only be a multiple of an elementary unit $E = h\nu$, where h is Planck's constant, also known as Planck's action quantum (introduced already in 1899), and ν (the Greek letter nu, not the Roman letter v) is the frequency of the radiation.

Note that the elementary units of energy discussed here are represented by $h\nu$ and not simply by h.

Physicists now call these quanta photons and a photon of frequency ν will have its own specific and unique energy.

Again, we would like to point out what seems most important from the above quote:

Planck was deeply suspicious of Boltzmann's statistical interpretation of the second law of thermodynamics. Therefore, his "recourse to them was, as he later put it, "an act of despair ..."

An act of despair...

Physicists now call these quanta photons...

As an outcome of Planck's theorem, modern radiation

---

[131] https://en.wikipedia.org/wiki/Max_Planck

physics now has to live with the wave-particle duality of light.[132]

But does it really have to?

We will see shortly.

Summary of Historical Approaches to Explain the Nature of Light or Radiation

You might ask yourselves: 'Why is it important to contemplate the nature of light with respect to radiation? What's the difference for any radiative effect to be exerted as photon (particle) or wave?'

We will solve this puzzle soon.

The different historical views of the nature of radiation or light can be summarized as follows:

- Pictet was uncertain and thought both a wave or particle model might explain his observed reflection of cold. However, he preferred the particulate approach.

- Rumford was a strict undulationist—a proponent of the claim that only waves could explain what was observed.

- Prevost again was just as strictly adhering to his particle model.

- Due to Newton's influence, particle models dominated until 1850.

- By 1850 wave models were generally accepted and after Hertz's experimental confirmation of Maxwell, his wave model again dominated.

---

[132] https://en.wikipedia.org/wiki/Wave%E2%80%93particle_duality

- After 1900 photons, the wave-particle duality and quantum physics are dominating physics and radiation theories.

If this summary can show us one thing then it is that the wave-particle duality played a wicked game throughout the history of modern science. Like a huge pendulum the attempts to explain the nature of radiation and light were deflected from one side to the other until the concept of wave-particle duality seemingly stopped the pendulum at a resting point and finally harmonized two fundamentally different concepts in a third and hitherto unknown theoretical approach.

But did this harmonization bring peace of mind?

Albert Einstein, whom some call the greatest physicist and genius of all time, was never truly satisfied with Planck's findings, as some of his quotes show—respective emphasis, if any, are by the author.

> *In the year nineteen hundred, in the course of purely theoretical (mathematical) investigation, Max Planck made a very remarkable discovery: the law of radiation of bodies as a function of temperature could not be derived solely from the Laws of Maxwellian electrodynamics.*[133]

Please note what is most important in the above quote: ...in the course of purely THEORETICAL investigation.

Therefore, it is ONLY a theory with NO evidence based on experiments.

> *This discovery became the basis of all twentieth-century research in physics and has almost entirely conditioned its development ever since. Without*

---

[133] http://www.spaceandmotion.com/quantum-theory-albert-einstein-quotes.htm

this discovery it would not have been possible to establish a workable theory of molecules and atoms and the energy processes that govern their transformations. Moreover, it has shattered the whole framework of classical mechanics and electrodynamics and set science a fresh task: that of finding a new conceptual basis for all physics. Despite remarkable partial gains, the problem is still far from a satisfactory solution.[134]

And finally:

All these fifty years of conscious brooding have brought me no nearer to the answer to the question, 'What are light quanta?' Nowadays every Tom, Dick and Harry thinks he knows it, but he is mistaken.[135]

Can we therefore really trust Planck's law?

Dr. Claes Johnson

In 2010, Professor Claes Johnson[136] developed and published a completely new mathematical approach to solve the problem of blackbody radiation and the photoelectric effect.[137] which required quantum physics by Planck and Einstein, respectively, before, on the basis of a unified set of equations which now again rely on *waves* only.[138]

---

[134] Albert Einstein, 1950
[135] Albert Einstein, 1954
[136] http://claesjohnson.blogspot.com/
[137] http://claesjohnson.blogspot.com/2011/02/photoelectric-effect-photons-and-nobel.html
[138] http://www.stairwaypress.com/bookstore/slaying-the-sky-dragon-death-of-the-greenhouse-gas-theory/

Johnson calls his approach deterministic finite precision computational wave mechanics.[139]

According to Johnson:

> *A blackbody acts like a transformer of radiation which absorbs high frequency radiation and emits low-frequency radiation. The temperature of the blackbody determines a cut-off frequency for the emission, which increases linearly with the temperature: The warmer the blackbody is, the higher frequencies it can and will emit. Thus only frequencies below cut-off are emitted, while all frequencies are being absorbed.*
>
> *A blackbody thus can be seen as a system of resonators with different eigen-frequencies which are excited by incoming radiation and then emit radiation. An ideal blackbody absorbs all incoming radiation and re-emits all absorbed radiation below cut-off.*
>
> *Conservation of energy requires absorbed frequencies above cut-off to be stored in some form, more precisely as heat energy thus increasing the temperature of the blackbody.*

While already this view of a blackbody is theoretically interesting and new, Johnson's conclusions from his model are even more interesting:

> *Radiative heat can be transmitted by electromagnetic waves from a warm blackbody to a colder blackbody, but not from a cold to a warmer, thus with a one-way direction of heat energy, while the electromagnetic waves*

---

[139] http://www.csc.kth.se/~cgjoh/ambsblack.pdf

propagate in both directions. We thus distinguish between two-way propagation of waves and one-way propagation of heat energy by waves. A cold body can heat up by eating/absorbing high-frequency, high temperature, coherent waves in a catabolic process of destruction of coherent waves into incoherent heat energy. A warm body cannot heat up by eating/absorbing low-frequency low-temperature waves, because catabolism involves destruction of structure. Anabolism builds structure, but a black-body is only capable of destructive catabolism (the metabolism of a living cell consists of destructive catabolism and constructive anabolism).

Again, we would like to stress Johnson's most important point of argumentation:

We thus distinguish between two-way propagation of waves and one-way propagation of heat energy by waves.

What does this mean?

If you read at least the shorter of Johnson's articles, you will understand that electromagnetic waves can flow from both the warmer to the colder body and vice versa but HEAT can ONLY be transferred from the *warmer* to the *colder* body as required by the 2nd law of thermodynamics.[140]

Proponents of AGW choose to argue that downwelling longwave radiation (DLR) is real because it can be *measured*. There are many government funded programs to measure DLR.[141]

---

[140] http://www.csc.kth.se/~cgjoh/blackbodyslayer.pdf
[141] http://claesjohnson.blogspot.com/2011/08/who-invented-downwelling-longwave.html

However, with respect to AGW the question is not if one can measure the temperature of the atmosphere by means of radiation—which is basically what is done when DLR is measured from Earth's surface.

The one and only important question is whether DLR transports heat from the *colder* atmosphere to the *warmer* ground.

Particle-based radiation models, like Planck's, inevitably suggest to someone ready to believe such a suggestion that heat bound to particles (quantitized photons) is transported—at least statistically—from cold to warm, thereby violating the 2nd law of thermodynamics.

Johnson avoids this violation of the 2nd law.

With Johnson's proposed mechanism it is OF COURSE possible to *measure* the temperature of the—colder—atmosphere standing on the Earth's surface with appropriate devices like e. g. a pyrgeometer,[142] but any downwelling radiation cannot transport HEAT from the colder atmosphere to the warmer Earth surface and thus can neither warm the surface nor reduce its cooling rate *by means of downwelling radiation.*

Note: of course, the presence of an absorbing/emitting atmosphere can change a planet's temperature and the cooling rate must be the same as the insolation in stationary state, but the temperature gradient and thus surface temperature can change with changing atmospheric properties. The above statement therefore *only* refers to a change of cooling rate by back or downwelling radiation.

Is Johnson's mathematical and theoretical approach less (or more) credible than Planck's and Einstein's in the first place?

Unlikely! Planck's and Einstein's proofs were as purely mathematical and theoretical as is Claes Johnson's.

From this point of view, Johnson's approach has to be regarded as equally valid as Planck's.

---

[142] https://en.wikipedia.org/wiki/Pyrgeometer

However, the implications with regard to back or downwelling radiation suppositions are huge.

Whereas particle (photon) statistics implies the delusion of added heat or reduced rate of planetary cooling imposed by the atmosphere, Johnson rejects this supposition as fiction.

Conclusions

The history of radiation theories reflects the history of science: concepts, or theories, are born and discarded as further research and further observation failed to cohere with old concepts. What was initially a valid concept accepted by all or the majority of scientists for a time can cease to hold with the emergence of new knowledge and eventually become recognized as a misconception.

A telling example of this is Rumford's "frigorific" waves.

Tyndall thought he had measured absorption when he experimented with different gases (among them carbon dioxide and air free of carbon dioxide) but had apparently only measured opacity which, in contrast to absorption, still includes a measure of reflected radiation.

Other scientists, like Arrhenius, appear to have misunderstood Tyndall and also Fourier and additionally relied on inappropriate data sets to develop their theory.

Arrhenius' theory of carbon dioxide as major warming agent of the atmosphere due to absorption and back radiation of heat is thus not credible.

Additionally, his belief of a greenhouse being heated by trapped radiation was clearly refuted by Wood only some years after Arrhenius' proposal. Arrhenius emerges as seemingly not as noble as his involvement in setting up the Nobel committee implied:

> *About 1900, Arrhenius became involved in setting up the Nobel Institutes and the Nobel Prizes. He was elected a member of the Royal Swedish*

Academy of Sciences in 1901. For the rest of his life, he would be a member of the Nobel Committee on Physics and a de facto member of the Nobel Committee on Chemistry. He used his positions to arrange prizes for his friends (Jacobus van't Hoff, Wilhelm Ostwald, Theodore Richards) and to attempt to deny them to his enemies (Paul Ehrlich, Walther Nernst, Dmitri Mendeleev).[143]

Thus, for over a quarter century (he died in 1927), Arrhenius exerted his enormous bias in all Nobel Prize winners of that time.

All in all, it is most remarkable that Arrhenius' flawed theory could have survived for as long as it did and be the historical basis of today's AGW religion.

This may be because Arrhenius was awarded the Nobel Prize and Wood was not.

However, Arrhenius did not receive a Nobel Prize for his climate theory but for his discovery of ions dissolved in aqueous solutions, the fundamental difference being that Arrhenius' discovery of ions was based on EXPERIMENTS unlike his climate theory which was only a theory based on someone else's —flawed—data set.

The historical development of radiation theories clearly showed that heat transported from the atmosphere to the Earth's surface by back or downwelling radiation is incorrect for a very simple and indisputable reason: Both Prevost's and Planck's particle-based theories are just that: theories. There is and has been NO factual evidence for their validity. Just as there is NOT A SINGLE shred of factual proof for downwelling radiation warming the Earth or retarding its cooling.

Thus the basis of AGW remains unproven and highly suspect.

To capitalize on the above: there are two possibilities for a

---

[143] https://en.wikipedia.org/wiki/Svante_Arrhenius#Middle_period

scientific proof. The hard proof involves experimental results reproducible and reproduced by other scientists. Ohm's law is a classic example of such a law proven by experiments. Even a non-scientist, can verify Ohm's law with simple experiments and measurements.

The other, weaker, proof is one which arises from conviction and *common acceptance* or *scientific consensus*: a theory is most convincing for other scientists to explain certain observations which cannot be easily measured or not measured at all with the instrumentation available at a given time.

Prevost could not measure particles flowing from one body to the other in his igneous fluid—just as Kirchhoff could not measure and verify that in-going and out-going radiation of a blackbody were equal (therefore, he had to rely on thought experiments only). Equally, Planck could not measure his proposed quantified photons.

These latter, weaker, proofs tend to have a limited half-life—depending on the duration in which they remain unchallenged. The Ptolemaic model of the Sun and stars revolving around the Earth was accepted by almost everyone for some 14 centuries. Initially Copernicus, then Bruno and eventually Galileo challenged this proven theory and the rest is history.

111 years ago, Planck formulated his radiation law which led to the birth of quantum mechanics or quantum physics. This, in turn, led to completely new branches of physics and what is called "modern" theoretical physics.

It is illogical to accept that the theoretical development of physics ended 111 years ago and that there would be no further developments.

Initially as Earth's temperature was increasing along with increasing emissions of carbon dioxide there had been a *certain* justification for the AGW stance in assuming that this simple proportional correlation could prove correct even though correlations do not in itself constitute proof.

Now that the very little increase of Earth's average atmosphere temperature—less than 0.4°C measured by 11 different NOAA satellites between 1984 and 2010-2011—has achieved a preliminary maximum, this correlation and the AGW theory has failed.

This should be the time to reconsider the theoretical basis of AGW and the theoretical explanations given for back or downwelling radiation by many scientists all over the world.

Measuring DLR does not prove anything except that any temperature—and thus also the temperature of the atmosphere—can be measured by means of radiation which is nothing new. All the rest derived from these measurements is only theory or supposition.

While it is the right of any scientist to believe in a theory, this alone is not scientific. The spirit of science requires sustained reconsideration of one's own theoretical beliefs and convictions in conjunction with reality and other emerging and eventually more convincing theories.

Now that Planck's and Einstein's theories have been challenged by Claes Johnson, the consensus has been broken and they are no longer undisputed and thus not entirely credible.

A new and probing scientific discussion about the nature of radiation and the photoelectric effect needs to take place. With the credibility of AGW under the spotlight, such a discussion could lead to a deeper understanding of radiation and the photoelectric effect and thus draw us closer to understanding the true nature of the world we live in.

It could serve to offset the billions of government funds spent on dubious science worldwide over the past 20 years and ultimately lead humanity to a more reasoned outcome.

Chapter 6—Seminal Sky Dragon Slayer Papers—Chilingar

Confidence comes not from always being right but from not fearing to be wrong.
—Peter McIntyre

What the Slayers Got Wrong

WE KNOW THERE are complexities and nuances in a subject as intently studied and debated as hotly as man-made global warming. This is especially so when considering the increasing contentiousness of the cornerstone of consensus climate science, the radiative greenhouse gas hypothesis.

In the spirit of fellowship and integrity, here we will list the proven errors made by the original *Slaying the Sky Dragon* authors.

Crickets—The Sound of Dead Silence

After publication of our first book in 2011, we soon understood we had not gone far enough in our assessment that carbon dioxide did not and cannot cause global warming.

Indeed, as each year passed, we collectively found more and more credible scientific empirical evidence that CO_2 was actually cooling the atmosphere. If we had dared make such a bold statement a decade ago, we would have been ridiculed and ostracized more than we were.

But now we can be bolder. Our assessment is based on the most reliable empirical evidence comporting with what the laws of science tells us. Atmospheric CO_2 cools.

Explanation is most eloquently set out by PSI's Chief Scientific Officer, George V. Chilingar, one of the most eminent and internationally respected American scientists of our time. Among his numerous achievements and awards is his appointment as Knight of Arts and Sciences by the Russian Academy of Natural Sciences. Chilingar slays the sky dragon with his superb papers.

Chilingar's 2008 paper, *Cooling of Atmosphere Due to CO_2 Emission* (co-authored by L. F. Khilyuk and O. G. Sorokhtin) remains unrefuted in any peer-reviewed scientific journal.[144]

The paper's authors investigated the effect of CO_2 emission on the temperature of our atmosphere. Their computations, based on the adiabatic theory of greenhouse effect, shows that increasing CO_2 concentration in the atmosphere results in cooling rather than warming of the Earth's atmosphere.

The paper correctly identifies that when infrared radiation is absorbed by atmospheric molecules of 'greenhouse gases', its energy is transformed into thermal expansion of air.

This, in turn, causes convective fluxes of air masses which restore the adiabatic distribution of temperature in the troposphere. As such, Earth's atmosphere is a self-regulating system and 'greenhouse gases' act as the safety valve to ensure temperatures remain extremely stable despite variances in energy

---

[144] https://greatclimatedebate.com/wp-content/uploads/CO2-Cooling-Chilingar.pdf

in the system.

We summarize this paper here.

Introduction

Traditional anthropogenic theory of currently observed global warming states that release of carbon dioxide into atmosphere (partially as a result of utilization of fossil fuels) leads to an increase in atmospheric temperature because the molecules of CO_2 (and other greenhouse gases) absorb the infrared radiation from the Earth's surface. This statement is based on the Arrhenius hypothesis, which was never verified (Arrhenius, 896). The proponents of this theory take into consideration only one component of heat transfer in atmosphere, i.e., radiation. Yet, in the dense Earth's troposphere with the pressure $p_a > 0:2$ atm, the heat from the Earth's surface is mostly transferred by convection (Sorokhtin, 2001a). According to our estimates, convection accounts for 67%, water vapor condensation in troposphere accounts for 25%, and radiation accounts for about 8% of the total heat transfer from the Earth's surface to troposphere. Thus, convection is the dominant process of heat transfer in troposphere, and all the theories of Earth's atmospheric heating (or cooling) first of all must consider this process of heat (energy)-mass redistribution in atmosphere.[145]

When the temperature of a given mass of air increases, it expands, becomes lighter, and rises. In turn, the denser cooler air of upper layers of troposphere descends and replaces the warmer air of lower layers. This physical system (multiple cells of air convection) acts in the Earth's troposphere like a continuous surface cooler. The cooling effect by air convection can surpass considerably the warming effect of radiation.

The most important conclusion from this observation is that the temperature distribution in the troposphere has to be close

---

[145] Sorokhtin, 2001a, 2001b; Khilyuk and Chilingar, 2003, 2004

to adiabatic because the air mass expands andcools while rising and compresses and heats while dropping. This does not necessarily imply that at any particular instant distribution of temperature has to be adiabatic. One should consider some averaged distribution over the time intervals of an order of months.

Key Points of the Adiabatic Theory of Greenhouse Effect

By definition, the greenhouse effect is the difference T between the average temperature of planet surface T_s and its effective temperature T_e (which is determined by the solar radiation and the Earth's albedo):

$$\Delta T = T_s - T_e \quad (1)$$

The present-day average surface temperature $T_S \approx 288$ ·K and effective temperature $T_e \approx 255$ K. Therefore, the present-day greenhouse effect is approximately equal to $+33°C$. The term "greenhouse effect" is confusing from the physical point of view and leads the general public astray.

According to the Arrhenius hypothesis, the atmosphere, containing "greenhouse gases," is transparent to the short-wave solar radiation but absorbs the long-wave (infrared) radiation emitted from the heated Earth's surface thus reducing the losses of Earth's heat into space. The latter is considered to be the main cause of atmospheric warming: the greater the concentration of "greenhouse gases" in atmosphere, the higher its global temperature.

The term "greenhouse effect" was coined by analogy with the glass greenhouses, because glass is transparent for the visible part of solar spectrum but absorbs the infrared radiation. The main heating effect in the greenhouse, however, is due to the isolation of air volume contained in the greenhouse and preventing it from mixing with outside air.

As soon as the greenhouse windows are opened, convection occurs and the greenhouse effect disappears.

In the Earth's troposphere, the convective component of heat transfer dominates. When the infrared radiation is absorbed by the greenhouse gases, the energy of radiation is transformed into oscillations of gas molecules (i.e., heating of exposed volume of gas mixture). As a result, the heated gas expands, becomes lighter, and rises rapidly to the upper layers of troposphere, where heat is emitted into space by radiation. As the gas cools down, it descends to the Earth's surface, where the previous (or even lower) surface temperatures are restored. Analogous situation is observed with heating of air due to the condensation of water vapor.

The effective radiation temperature is determined by the Stefan-Boltzmann law:

T_e is the radiation temperature

$\sigma = 5.67 * 10^{-5} \frac{ergs}{cm^2} * S^{-1} * K^{-4}$ the Stefan-Boltzmann constant

S is the solar constant at the distance from the Earth to the Sun = $1.367 * 10^6 ergs/cm^2/seconds$

S is albedo, determined mostly by cloud cover (for the Earth, $A \approx 0.3$)

(2)

According to Eq. (2), the effective temperature T_e is equal to 255 K (or 18°C). Therefore, the present-day greenhouse effect for the Earth should be equal to 33°C.

The water vapor condensation in troposphere begets clouds, which to a considerable degree determine the reflective properties of the planet, i.e., its albedo A.

The latter gives rise to a strong negative feedback between the surface temperature T_s and the temperature of "absolutely black body" T_{bb}, which is determined by the solar radiation S reaching the Earth's surface at its distance from the Sun.

Indeed, any increase in surface temperature intensifies the water evaporation and increases the Earth's cloudiness, which, in turn, increases the Earth's albedo.

As a result, the reflection of solar heat from the clouds into space increases and the heat influx to the Earth's surface decreases and the average surface temperature decreases to the previous level. Strong negative feedback in any system leads to linear dependence of system's output on its input.

The latter implies that the surface temperature T_S (as well as the temperature T at any elevation in troposphere) is proportional to the effective radiation temperature T_e, which is determined by the solar radiation at a distance of Earth from Sun.

For adiabatic process, the absolute temperature of gas T is a function of pressure p.[146]

$$T = Cp^\alpha$$

C is constant, which can be determined using theoretical considerations or using experimental data. Using previous theoretical considerations, Equation 3 can be rewritten in the following form:

$$T = b^\alpha * T_e (\frac{p}{p_0})^\alpha$$

Where...

p is the atmospheric pressure at a certain elevation

p_0 is the atmospheric pressure at sea level, $p_0 = 1$

α is the adiabatic exponent $= \frac{c_p - c_v}{c_p}$ where c_p and c_v are specific heats of air gaseous mixture at a constant pressure and a constant volume, respectively

b is a scaling coefficient, $b = (\frac{1}{\sqrt[4]{1-A}})^{\frac{1}{\alpha}}$

(3) (4)

---

[146] Landau and Lifshitz, 1979

Adiabatic exponent α, a function of atmospheric composition and humidity, can be determined using:

$$\alpha = \frac{R}{\mu(c_p + c_w + c_r)}$$

$$c_p = \frac{[p(N_2)c_p(N_2) + p(O_2)c_p(O_2) + p(CO_2)c_p(CO_2) + p(AR_2)c_p(AR_2)]}{p}$$

$R = 1.987 \frac{cal}{mol} \cdot C$ the universal gas constant

μ = the molecular weight of air mixture (for the Earth, $\mu \approx 29$);
$p(N_2) \approx 0.7551;\ p(O_2) \approx 0.2315;\ p(CO_2) \approx 0.00046;\ p(Ar) \approx 0.0128$ atm are the partial atmospheric pressures of nitrogen, oxygen, carbon dioxide and Argon, respectively.

$p \approx 1\ atm$ is the total atmospheric pressure, $c_p(N_2) = 0.248, c_p(O_2) = 0.218, c_p(CO_2) = 0.197,$

$c_p(Ar) = 0.124 \frac{cal}{g} \cdot C$ are the specific heats of nitrogen, oxygen, carbon dioxide and argon (at constant pressure, respectively)

c_w and c_r are corrective coefficients considering the heating effects of water condensation and absorption of infrared radiation by the greenhouse gases, respectively

(5) [147] (6)

From Eq. (5) one obtains:

$$C_w + C_r = R/\mu \cdot \alpha - c_p \tag{7}$$

The best fit of the theoretical temperature distribution (Eq. (4)) to the averaged experimental data in the Earth's troposphere occurs at $a = 0.1905$. For the dry air mixture of Earth's atmosphere, $c_p = 0.2394$ cal/g°C. On substituting these data into Eq. (7), one obtains $C_w + C_r = 0.1203$ cal/g°C.

To determine the components C_w and C_r separately, one needs to use the surface (T_s) and effective (T_e) temperatures of the planet. [148]

$$C_r = R(T_s - T_e)/\mu \cdot \alpha \cdot T_s \tag{8}$$

$$C_w = RT_e/\mu \cdot \alpha \cdot T_s - c_p \tag{9}$$

On substituting the parameters of Earth's atmosphere ($a =$

[147] Voytkevitch et al, 1990
[148] Sorokhtin, 2001a, 2001b

0.1905, $\mu \approx 29$, $c_p = 0.2394$ cal/g°C, $T_S = 288.2$ K, $T_e = 263.6$ K, and $R = 1.987$ cal/mole°C) into Eqs. (8) and (9), one obtains $C_r = 0.0307$ cal/g°C, $C_w = 0.0896$ cal/g°C, and $C_w + C_r = 0.1203$ cal/g°C, which is exactly the same as the previously determined value. The obtained estimates for the components of specific heat of air mixture allow one to compare relative effects of various processes of heat transfer in the Earth's atmosphere: convection accounts for about 67%, water vapor condensation accounts for 25%, and radiation accounts for about 8%.

Substitution of T_e determined by Eq. (2) into Eq. (4) results in the following relations:

$$T = b^{\alpha}[(1 - A)S/4\sigma]^{1/4}(p/p_0)^{\alpha} \quad (10)$$

It is noteworthy that in Eq. (10) the solar constant S is divided by 4 because the area of Earth's disk insolation is 4 times lower than the total illuminated area of Earth. Equation (10) is valid only if the axis of rotation of planet is strictly perpendicular to the ecliptic plane, i.e., the angle of precession is equal to zero.

The angle of inclination of equatorial plane to the ecliptic plane is not equal to zero and is changing in time.

Therefore, each of the Earth's polar regions is insolated during half a year only. In another half a year, it is deprived of the influx of solar energy. When one polar region is insolated, the other is situated in the shadow of Earth's body and does not receive the solar energy. The rest of Earth's surface receives its portion of solar energy on a regular basis and, consequently, Eq. (10) is valid for calculation of temperature of air.

Therefore, in computing the average temperature of "inclined" planet at high latitudes (polar regions), one needs to divide the solar constant by 2 (not by 4).

In addition, one has to take into consideration the spherical shape of polar region. As a result, the solar constant in Eq. (10) has to be divided by a number N, which lies between 2 and 4.

Taking all of the above into consideration and assuming that the precession angle is relatively small, one can derive the following equation for the distribution of average temperature in troposphere:

$$T = b^\alpha \left[\frac{S \cdot (1 - A)}{\sigma \left(\dfrac{4(\pi/2 - \psi)}{\pi/2} + \dfrac{4\psi}{\pi/2 \cdot (1 + \cos \psi)} \right)} \right]^{\frac{1}{4}} (p/p_0)^\alpha \tag{11}$$

...where ψ is the Earth's precession angle; p is the atmospheric pressure at a given altitude (0.2 atm $< p <$ p_0), and $p_0 = 1$ atm.

For the present-day Earth's angle of inclination ($\psi \approx 23.44°$), the average surface temperature at sea level Ts $\approx$ 288.2 K and the coefficient b is equal to 1.597.

For the nitrogen-oxygen atmosphere $b^a = 1.093$. If the albedo is constant, then the coefficient b is constant, whereas the value b^a varies with the value of a which, in turn, depends on the composition of atmosphere.

The convective component of heat transfer dominates in the troposphere. When infrared radiation is absorbed by the greenhouse gases, the radiation energy is transformed into the oscillations of gas molecules, i.e., in heating of the exposed volume of gaseous mixture. Then the further heat transfer can occur either due to diffusion or by convective transfer of expanded volumes of gas. Inasmuch as the specific heats of air are very small (about 5.3 x 10^5 cal/cm s°C), the rates of heat transfer by diffusion do not exceed several cm/s, whereas the rates of heat transfer by convection in the troposphere can reach many meters per second. Analogous situation occurs upon heating of air as a result of water vapor condensation: the rates of convective transfer of heated volumes of air in the troposphere are many orders of magnitude higher than the rates of heat transfer by diffusion.

Equation (11), (the adiabatic model of atmospheric temperature) can be applied for computation of atmospheric temperature distribution for any planet possessing a dense atmosphere (with atmospheric pressure higher than 0.2 atm) and also for various geologic periods of Earth's development. To modify the adiabatic model for different conditions, one needs to specify the value of solar constant S, the angle of precession of planet, and the value of adiabatic exponent a.

The adiabatic model of greenhouse effect was verified by comparison of the theoretical temperature distribution in the troposphere of Earth (constructed based on Eq. (11)) with the standard model based on experimental data. For the Earth, the parameters of adiabatic model were chosen as follows:

$$S = S_0 = 1.367 \text{ erg/cm*s}; \ \psi = 23.44°;$$
$$\text{and } a = 0.1905$$

The computations by Sorokhtin[149] showed that the theoretical temperature distribution based on Eq. (11) was identical to the standard temperature distribution of Earth[150] with the precision of 0.1%. The standard model of Earth's atmospheric temperature gives averaged (over the Earth's surface) values of temperature and pressure as the function of elevation above sea level. This model (with the temperature gradient of 6.5 K/km) is applied worldwide for calibration of aircraft gauges and barometers, which are used for weather observations.

The adiabatic model was further verified by comparison of theoretical temperature distribution in the dense (consisting mostly of carbon dioxide) troposphere of Venus with experimental data. For Venus, $\psi = 3°$, $a = 0.179$, $\mu = 43.5$, $c_p = 0.2015$ cal/g°C; $T_s = 735.3$ K, and $T_e = 228$ K, and, therefore, $C_r = 0.177$ cal/g°C, $C_w = -0.122$ cal/g°C, and $C_w +$

---

[149] Sorokhtin, 2001a, 2001b

[150] Bachinskiy et al., 1951

$C_r = 0.055$ cal/g°C.

The increased value of parameter C_r, which is a measure of the radiation component of heat transfer, most probably can be explained by the extremely hot condition of the troposphere of Venus. The fact that $C_w < 0$ means that in the troposphere of Venus (especially in its lower and middle layers) the endothermic reactions of dissociation of some compounds dominate (for example, dissociation of sulfuric acid H_2SO_4 into SO_3 and H_2O).

Meantime, in the upper layers of troposphere of Venus, at the altitudes of 40 to 50 km and above the altitude of 60 km, the parameter $Cw > 0$. Thus, the exothermic reactions of formation of chemical compounds (sulphuric acid, for example) dominate there. In addition, the water vapour condensation in the clouds of Venus heats its atmosphere.

For the Venus atmosphere, $p_s = 90.9$ atm and $S = 2.62\ 10^6$ erg/cm^2 s. [151] On substituting all these values into Eq. (11), one can construct the temperature distribution for the atmosphere of Venus. The results of testing the adiabatic model (Eq. (11)) showed a good agreement between the theoretical and experimental data (1% precision for Venus).

Anthropogenic Impact on the Earth's Climate

The adiabatic theory allows one to evaluate quantitatively the influence of anthropogenic emission of carbon dioxide on the Earth's climate. The carbon content in the atmosphere was increasing by approximately 3 billion tons per year at the end of Century. The rate of the total human-induced CO_2 emission to the Earth's atmosphere is currently about 5-7 billion tons per year,[152] or about 1.4-1.9 billion tons of carbon per year. This amount of carbon dioxide slightly increases the atmospheric

---

[151] Marov, 1986; Venus, 1989
[152] Schimel, 1995; Robinson et al., 1998

pressure.

To evaluate the effect of anthropogenic emission of carbon dioxide on global temperature, one can use the adiabatic model together with the sensitivity analysis.[153] At sea level, if the pressure is measured in atmospheres, then $p = 1$ atm and...

$$\Delta T \approx T\alpha\Delta p \quad (12)$$

If, for example, the concentration of carbon dioxide in the atmosphere increases two times (from 0.035% to 0.07%), which is expected by the year of 2100, then the atmospheric pressure will increase by $\Delta p \approx 1.48 \ 10^{-4}$ atm.[154] After substitution of $T = 288$ K, $a = 0.1905$, and $\Delta p = 1.48 \times 10^{-4}$ atm into Eq. (13), one obtains $\Delta T = 8.12 \times 10^{-3}$°C. ΔT will be slightly higher at the higher altitudes.[155] Thus, the increase in the surface temperature at sea level caused by doubling of the present-day CO_2 concentration in the atmosphere will be less than 0.01°C, which is negligible in comparison with natural temporal fluctuations of global temperature.

From these estimates, one can deduce a very important conclusion that even considerable increase in anthropogenic emission of carbon dioxide does not lead to noticeable temperature increase. Thus, the hypothesis of current global warming as a result of increased emission of carbon dioxide (greenhouse gases) into the atmosphere is not true.

In addition, evaluating the climatic consequences of anthropogenic CO_2 emission, one has to take into consideration the fact that emitted carbon dioxide dissolves in oceanic water (according to the Henry's Law) and then is fixed into carbonates. In this process, together with carbon, a part of atmospheric oxygen is also transferred into the carbonates.

---

[153] Sorokhtin, 2001; Khilyuk and Chilingar, 2003, 2004
[154] Sorokhtin, 2001
[155] Khilyuk and Chilingar, 2003

Therefore, instead of a slight increase in the atmospheric pressure, one should expect a slight decrease with a corresponding insignificant cooling of climate. In addition, part of carbon dioxide is reduced to methane in the process of hydration of oceanic crust rocks. Because formation of carbonates and generation of methane, about 2.3×10^8 tons/year of CO_2 are removed from the atmosphere; the potential consumption of CO_2 in the process of hydration, however, is considerably higher. Although the period of this geochemical cycle is over 100 years, the effect of CO_2 consumption is additive.

Together with the anthropogenic CO_2, part of O_2 is also removed from the atmosphere (about 2.3 g per 1 g of carbon). If the ocean and plants consume all this additional CO_2, after the year of 2100 this would lead to a reduction in atmospheric pressure by approximately 0.34 mbar and cooling of the climate by $-8.2 \ 10^{-2}$°C ≈ 0.01°C.

Actually, the metabolism of plants should almost completely compensate for the disruption of equilibrium by mankind and restore the climatic balance.

Global Atmospheric Cooling due to Increase in CO_2 Content

Increase in CO_2 content leads to global cooling of atmosphere. This paradoxical, at first sight, conclusion can be inferred from the adiabatic theory of heat transfer. To compare the temperature characteristics of a planet at various compositions of its atmosphere, one can use Eq. (11).

If one assumes that the existing nitrogen-oxygen atmosphere of Earth is replaced entirely by an imaginary carbon dioxide atmosphere with the same pressure of 1 atm and adiabatic exponent of $a = 0.1428$, then the value of $b^a = 1.597^{0.1428} = 1.069$ and the near-surface temperature would decline to 281.6 K. Thus, the atmospheric temperature would decreases by 6.4°C, instead of increasing according to the traditional theory.

Constructing the distributions of temperature in the carbon dioxide atmosphere, one should take into consideration the fact that for the same pressure the corresponding elevation above sea level is lower than that for the nitrogen-oxygen atmosphere of Earth: $h(CO_2) = h(N_2 + O_2) \times 29/44$, where h is the elevation, and 29 and 44 are the molecular weights of nitrogen-oxygen and carbon dioxide atmospheres, respectively.

Such temperature distributions are shown in Figure 1. In this figure, the graph of temperature distribution for the carbon dioxide troposphere lies below the graph of distribution for the nitrogen-oxygen atmosphere. Thus, the near-surface temperature for the carbon dioxide atmosphere is 6.4°C lower than that for the nitrogen-oxygen atmosphere and not considerably higher as some scientists continue to believe.

Therefore, the accumulation of carbon dioxide in great amounts in atmosphere should lead only to the cooling of climate, whereas insignificant changes in the partial pressure of CO_2 (few hundreds of PPM) practically would not influence the average temperature of atmosphere and the Earth's surface.

Similarly, if one assumes that the existing carbon dioxide atmosphere of Venus is entirely replaced by the nitrogen-oxygen atmosphere at the same pressure of 90.9 atm, then its surface temperature would increase from 735 to 796 K.

Thus, increasing the saturation of atmosphere with carbon dioxide (despite its radiation absorbing capacity), with all other conditions being equal, results in a decrease and not an increase of the greenhouse effect and a decrease in average temperature of planet's atmosphere.

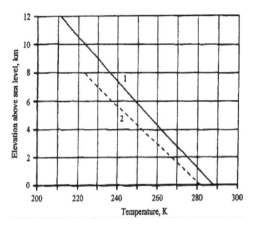

Figure 1. Relationship between the temperature and elevation above sea level for (1) existing nitrogen-oxygen atmosphere on Earth, and (2) hypothetical carbon dioxide atmosphere. |

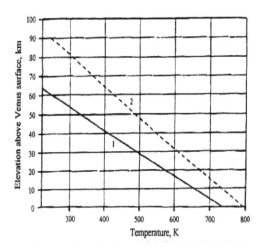

Figure 2. Relationship between temperature and elevation above Venus surface for (1) existing carbon dioxide atmosphere, and (2) hypothetical nitrogen-oxygen atmosphere.

The averaged temperature distributions for the existing carbon dioxide and hypothetical nitrogen-oxygen atmosphere on Venus are shown in Figure 2.

Conclusions

During the latest three millennia, one can observe a clear cooling trend in the Earth's climate.[156] During this period, deviations of the global temperature from this trend reached up to 3°C with a clear trend of decreasing global temperature by about 2°C. Relatively short-term variations in global temperature aremainly caused by the variations in solar activity and are not linked to the changes in carbon dioxide content in atmosphere.

Accumulation of large amounts of carbon dioxide in the atmosphere leads to the cooling, and not to warming of climate, as the proponents of traditional anthropogenic global warming theory believe.[157] This conclusion has a simple physical explanation: when the infrared radiation is absorbed by the molecules of greenhouse gases, its energy is transformed into thermal expansion of air, which causes convective fluxes of air masses restoring the adiabatic distribution of temperature in the troposphere. Our estimates show that release of small amounts of carbon dioxide (several hundreds PPM), which are typical for the scope of anthropogenic emission, does not influence the global temperature of Earth's atmosphere.

References

Arrhenius, S. 1896. On Influence of Carbonic Acid in the Air upon the Temperature of the Ground, Phil. Mag. 41:237-276.
Aeschbach-Hertig, W. 2007. Rebuttal of On Global Forces of Nature Driving the Earth's Climate. Are Humans Involved?, L. F. Khilyuk and G. V. Chilingar. Env. Geol.
Bachinskiy, A. I., Putilov, V. V., and Suvorov, N. P. 1951 Handbook of Physics. Moscow: Uchpedgiz, 380 pp.

---

[156] Keigwin, 1996; Sorokhtin and Ushakov, 2002; Gerhard, 2004; Khiyuk and Chilingar, 2006; Sorokhtin et al., 2007
[157] Aeschbach-Hertig, 2006

Gerhard, L. C. 2004. *Climate Change: Conflict of Observational Science, Theory,* and Politics, Am. Assoc. Petrol. Geol. Bull. 88:1211-1220.

Keigwin, L. D. 1996. The Little Ice Age and Medieval Warm Period in the Sargasso Sea, Science 274:1504-1508.

Khilyuk, L. F., Chilingar, G. V., Endres, B., and Robertson, J. 2000, *Gas Migration,* Houston: Gulf Publishing Company, 389 pp.

Khilyuk, L. F., and Chilingar, G. V. 2003, *Global Warming: Are we Confusing Cause and Effect?,* Energy Sources 25:357-370.

Khilyuk, L. F., and Chilingar, G. V. 2004, *Global Warming and Long-term Climatic Changes: A Progress Report,* Environ. Geol. 46:970-979.

Khilyuk, L. F., and Chilingar, G. V. 2006, On Global Forces of Nature Driving the Earth's Climate. Are Humans Involved? Environ. Geol. 50:899-910.

Landau, L. D., and Lifshits, E. M. 1979, *Statistical Physics,* Moscow: Nauka, 559 pp. Marov, M. Ya. 1986, *Planets of Solar System,* Moscow: Nauka, 320 pp.

Robinson, A. B., Baliunas, S. L., Soon, W., and Robinson, Z. W. 1998, *Environmental Effects of Increased Atmospheric Carbon Dioxide*

Schimel, D. S. 1995, *Global Change Biology,* 1:77-91.

Sorokhtin, O. G. 1990. The Greenhouse Effect of Atmosphere in Geologic History of Earth, Doklady AN SSSR 315:587-592.

Sorokhtin, O. G. 2001a, *Greenhouse Effect: Myth and Reality,* Vestnik Russian Academy of Natural Sciences 1:8-21.

Sorokhtin, O. G. 2001b, *Temperature Distribution in the Earth,* Izvestiya RAN, Physics of Earth 3:71-78.

Sorokhtin, O. G., and Ushakov, S. A. 2002, *Evolution of the Earth,* Moscow: Moscow Univ. Publishers, 560 pp.

Sorokhtin, O. G., Chilingar, G. V., and Khilyuk, L. F. 2007, *Global Warming and Global Cooling. Evolution of Climate on Earth.* Amsterdam: Elsevier, 313 pp.

Sorokhtin, O. G., Chilingar, G. V., Khilyuk, L. F., and Gorfunkel,

M. V. 2006, *Evolution of the Earth's Global Climate*, Energy Sources 29:1-19.

Venus (Atmosphere, Surface and Ecosystem), 1989. Moscow: Nedra, 482 pp.

Voytkevitch, G. V., Kokin, A. V., Miroshnikov, A. E., and Prokhorov, V. G. 1990, *Handbook of Geochemistry*, Moscow: Nedra, 480 pp.

> *Climate change knows three realities. Science reality, which is what working scientists deal with on a daily basis. Virtual reality, which is the wholly imaginary world inside computer climate models. And public reality, which is the socio-political system within which politicians, business people and the general citizenry work.*[158]
> —Robert M. Carter

More about George Chilingar

We cannot emphasize enough the very high scientific standing of George Chilingar—a longtime champion of international partnerships with resource-rich and resource-poor nations. Born in Russia of Russian and Armenian descent, he was the first American petroleum geologist to be elected to the Russian Academy of Sciences. He is considered an ambassador of goodwill by many nations.

George certainly stands among the world's leading applied scientists. His mastery of empirical science is such that he has been a specialist adviser to the United Nations from 1967 to 1969, and then again from 1978 to 1987. Chilingar's list of honors is long and includes Crown and Eagle Medal of Honor from the Russian Academy of Natural Sciences, 2000, Gold

---

[158] https://www.govinfo.gov/content/pkg/CHRG-109shrg52324/pdf/CHRG-109shrg52324.pdf

Medals of Honor from Iran, Thailand, Taiwan, Honduras, El Salvador, Armenia and Russia. He has published 72 books and over 500 of articles on geology, petroleum engineering and environmental engineering.

We are honored to have him as Principia Scientific International's Chief Scientist and we recommend readers seeking a rational assessment of recent heatwaves to read his recent paper on the subject, *Accumulation of Carbon Dioxide and Methane in the Earth's Atmosphere is not responsible for the Recent Worldwide Heat Wave*[159]

The key finding of the paper, confirming those separate and independent research findings by other PSI and non-PSI researchers, is that *more CO_2 in the atmosphere leads to cooling* due to accelerating the air mass convection process.

The current year of 2019 was not an exceptionally warm one, but records were broken in several countries—which caught the attention of the alarmist mainstream media.

It was hot (very hot) in the most of Europe and North America and also in Australia, India, and Pakistan. Some samples of the record high temperatures (Yahoo News, July 26, 2019): 42.6°C (108.7 F) in Paris, 39.9°C (103.8 F) in Belgium, 40.5°C (104.9 F) in Germany, and 38.8°C (101 F) in Netherlands. Even in Alaska the heat wave drove temperature to the astonishing record 90°F (with the historic average high temperature of 75°F).

The above referenced paper tells us:

Significant releases of anthropogenic carbon dioxide and methane into the atmosphere do not change average parameters of the Earth's thermal regime and have no effect on the Earth's global warming. Moreover, based on the adiabatic model of heat

---

[159] L.F. Khilyuk, and G.V. Chilingar, Russian Academy of Natural Sciences, US Sections, Los Angeles, USA

transfer in the atmosphere, the writers showed that additional releases of CO_2 and CH_4 lead to cooling of the Earth's atmosphere (accelerating the air mass convection process) and not warming [1]. Our model was proved to be correct by testing on empirical data [2].

The persistent trend of global warming has been observed for the last 150 years (when people actually have regular records of atmospheric temperature data) and resulted in about 1 K increase in the global average terrestrial temperature. This increased temperature caused various environmental and economic problems in the lower and middle latitude countries of the Northern hemisphere.

To understand causes of currently observed global warming, one needs to analyze the evolution of global forces of nature driving the Earth's Climate. Solar irradiation is a dominant energy supplier to the atmosphere and hydrosphere. Outgassing is a dominant gaseous matter supplier to the atmosphere and hydrosphere. The microbial activities at the interface of lithosphere and atmosphere influence considerably the atmospheric composition [2, 3, 4]. In explaining the persistent global warming (during the last 150 years), one should analyze and evaluate the historic solar activity and the quantities of solar irradiation reaching the Earth's surface, i.e., terrestrial solar irradiance (TSI).

Physical explanation of current heat wave came just in time with the brilliant, recently published paper: *Oscillations of the Baseline of Solar Magnetic Field and Solar Irradiance on a Millennial Time Scale* by Valentina Zharkova and associates [5]. They discovered the Terrestrial Solar Irradiance (TSI) super cycle with a period of about 2000 years. The last minimum of super cycle occurred about 1620 coinciding with the beginning of the Maunder Minimum of Solar Activity (MMSA).

The MMSA happened in the middle of medieval Little Ice Age, during which all water bodies of contemporary Europe were mostly frozen, agriculture was unsustainable due to crop failures, and populations suffered significant declines because people were either dying from disease, starvation and hypothermia or displaced as they migrated south.

The maximum of TSI super cycle should fall in around 2600. On the preceding 1000-year interval, the TSI is gradually increasing. Professor Zharkova and associates attributed these "2000-year periodic TSI oscillations to the long-term solar inertial motion about the barycenter of solar system" and noted that they are "closely linked to an increase of solar irradiance and terrestrial temperature in the past two centuries" [5].

This TSI cycle explains global warming trend observed during the last 150 years (1 K increase in the global average Earth's temperature) and predicates continuous perilous ascent of the global average temperature to an increase of solar irradiance and atmospheric temperature until the year of 2600 (with about 3% increase in TSI). The latter implies long-lasting extremely hot summers and slushy winters in the Northern hemisphere of the Earth until the year 2600.

> *By very conservative extrapolation we expect an increase of the terrestrial temperature in the Northern hemisphere by 2.5 C or slightly higher.*[160]

The expected 3% increase in TSI translates into 2.3 K increase in global average atmospheric temperature by the year of 2600 (year of the TSI cycle maximum). This global average temperature increase is well correlated with the rate of linear approximation of a 0.5 K/100 years of global average atmospheric temperature curve in the Northern hemisphere from the Maunder minimum to the beginning of the 21th Century (Akasofu rate, [6]).

The ongoing global atmospheric warming is a result of

---

[160] Zharkova, V.V., Shepherd, S.J., Zharkov, S.I., and Popova, S., 2019, *Oscillations of the Baseline of Solar Magnetic Field and Solar Irradiance on a Millennial Timescale*, Scientific Reports, 9, Article 9197

increasing TSI on the rising half a period of the 2000-year super TSI cycle at the current rate of approximately 0.5 K/100 years. This increase is expected to be compensated by the reduction of 0.3 K-0.5 K in the period between the years 2020 and 2055 (about three of 11-year cycles) due to the coming grand minimum of solar activity. After this period the global atmospheric warming will probably continue unmitigated on the upswing of the 2000-year cycle of TSI until 2600 (estimated time of the maximum of the TSI super cycle).

Conclusion

The proponents of any anthropogenic theory of the currently observed global atmospheric warming need to acknowledge that people are not responsible for and are not able to prevent natural solar irradiance increase.

> *Any attempts to mitigate undesirable climatic changes using restrictive regulations are condemned to failure, because the global natural forces are at least 4-5 orders of magnitude greater than the available human controls.*[161]

Climate will continue changing on various time scales with or without human interference. In the long run, it is more promising to expect some natural atmospheric cooling due to nitrogen consuming bacteria activities or natural relief in the form of strong volcano eruptions releasing large volumes of volcanic dust and forming sulfuric acid aerosol screen in the upper layers of atmosphere. It is rather unrealistic to assume that any climatic engineering group could successfully design and execute some futuristic technologies to combat nature's cycles.

---

[161] Khilyuk, L.F. and Chilingar, G.V., 2006, *On Global Forces of Nature Driving the Earth's Climate. Are Humans Involved?*, Environmental Geology, 50, 899-910

References

[1] Chilingar, G.V., Sorokhtin, O.G., Khilyuk L.F., and Lui, M., 2014, *Do Increasing Contents of Carbon Dioxide and Methane in the Atmosphere Cause Global Warming?*, Atmospheric and Climate Science, 4, 819-827

[2] Sorokhtin, O.G., Chilingar, G.V., and Sorokhtin, N.O., 2010, *Theory of Earth Evolution*, Moscow, Nauka, 751p. (in Russian)

[3] Khilyuk, L.F. and Chilingar, G.V., 2006, *On Global Forces of Nature Driving the Earth's Climate. Are Humans Involved?*, Environmental Geology, 50, 899-910

[4] Robertson, J.O., Chilingar, G.V., Sorokhtin, O.G., Sorokhtin, N.O, and Long, W., 2018, *The Evolution of Earth's Climate*, Scrivener-Wiley, 282 p.

[5] Zharkova, V.V., Shepherd, S.J., Zharkov, S.I., and Popova, S., 2019, *Oscillations of the Baseline of Solar Magnetic Field and Solar Irradiance on a Millennial Timescale*, Scientific Reports, 9, Article 9197

[6] Akasofu, P., 2010, *On the Recovery from the Little Ice Age*, Natural Science, 2, pps 1211-1224

Chapter 7—A Seminal Sky Dragon Slayer Paper by Professor Nahle

See now the power of truth; the same experiment which at first glance seemed to show one thing, when more carefully examined, assures us of the contrary.
—Galileo Galilei

Observations on Backradiation during Nighttime and Daytime

A paper by Professor Nasif Nahle, Scientist; University Professor; Scientific Research Director at Biology Cabinet.

Abstract

THROUGH A SERIES of instantaneous measurements of thermal energy of the atmosphere and surface materials during nighttime and daytime, I demonstrate that the effect of backradiation emitted from Earth's atmosphere on surface temperature is not real.

235

Introduction and Theoretical Work

Depicting the Earth's energy budget is a complicated task because many processes and phenomena derived from thermal energy transfer in the system atmosphere-surface have not been analyzed in climatology.

Oceans, atmospheric water vapor, surface and subsurface materials store thermal radiation during prolonged periods of time and are the real drivers of climate on Earth. Oceans have always been considered as thermostats of Earth's climate.

The complexity of depicting Earth's energy budget is boosted up by many assumptions that modellers have had to introduce, giving place to contradictions regarding laws of thermodynamics.

Some scientists start by averaging a solar power flux through 24 hours (one terrestrial day) and over the entire surface area of the Earth all at once. This cannot be averaged because it is already an average of satellite measurements along the trajectory of the Earth around the Sun and where night cannot exist because it is an imaginary sphere (outer sphere) whose surface area is calculated geometrically by taking into account the track of Earth's translational motion as the perimeter of an egg-shaped sphere and the distance from Earth to Sun as the maximum radius of such ellipsoidal sphere.

The incident solar power flux impinging on Earth's *surface* is ~ 1000 W/m^2 (better known as insolation) and this is already an average during daylight that cannot be averaged once again.[162] The result obtained from averaging insolation twice is an unphysical average of solar power flux impinging on the outer sphere by means of dividing the annual average of incident solar power flux on each square meter of the outer sphere by 4:

---

[162]

http://education.gsfc.nasa.gov/experimental/July61999siteupdate/in v99Project.Site/Pages/solar.in solation.html

$$1360 \text{ W/m}^2 / 4 = 340 \text{ W/m}^2$$

Problems found on the calculation above:

- It considers the solar thermal radiation is 49%.

- It multiplies the supposed coefficient of thermal radiation, 0.49, by the coefficient of mitigation of solar radiation by the atmosphere, 0.51, to obtain an unreal coefficient of 0.25.

- It multiplies the total incident solar radiation on top of the atmosphere by the artificial coefficient, 0.25, to obtain a supposed incoming solar thermal radiation impinging on the surface:

$$1360 \text{ W/m}^2 * 0.25 = 340 \text{ W/m}^2$$

- It multiplies the resultant incoming solar radiation by 0.48 to obtain an unreal thermal radiation absorbed by the surface:

$$340 \text{ W/m}^2 * 0.48 = 163 \text{ W/m}^2$$

- It introduces a novel unreal effect of accumulation of thermal radiation by the atmosphere which is 5.7 times higher than real atmospheric thermal radiation:

$$60 \text{ W/m}^2 * 5.7 = 342 \text{ W/m}^2$$

Following this series of erroneous calculations, as the Sun is the main source of thermal radiation to Earth, the flux of solar thermal radiation on the Earth's surface would forcibly be 1938 W/m^2, which is erroneous, and the atmosphere would be, forcibly, at 143 °C:

$$T = Q/(e * ?)$$

$$= 342 \ \text{W/m}^2 \ /(0.201 * 5.6697 \times 10^{-8} \ \text{W/m}^2 \ \text{K})$$
$$= 416 \ \text{K} = 143 \ °\text{C}$$

Notice the term e in the equation, which is for total emittance of the absorber system, the air in this case. We cannot disregard total emittance of the absorber system because we are calculating real magnitudes, not blackbody approximations.

Blackbodies do not exist in the known universe, so we must introduce total emittance of the absorber because it is a gray body, not a blackbody.

The observed and measured total emittance of air is 0.201. Other values are incorrect, whether they are prejudiced or damaged. For example, the total absorptance of air must be altered to obtain the multiplication of energy by the atmosphere.

Following the much damaged calculations of thermal radiation budget, if we had a surface of Earth absorbing 160 W/m^2, the atmosphere must have a total emittance 5.7 times as greater than the total emittance of a black body. Actually, the amount of thermal radiation that the atmosphere would absorb, from thermal radiation emitted by the surface, would be:

$$160 \ \text{W/m}^2 * 0.201 = 32.16 \ \text{W/m}^2$$

...which is absolutely false.

Annual average of incident power flux on the surface area of the outer sphere, 1360 W/m^2, divided by 4 gives 340 W/m^2. NASA-CERES scientists have taken this amount of solar power (340 W/m^2) as incoming solar "energy", as well as "backradiation" from atmosphere.[163]

From here, we see that it is not what happens in our planet because the Earth's surface does not receive 340 W/m^2 during daytime but around 1000 W/m^2. Therefore, 340 W/m^2 is not

---

163

http://mynasadata.larc.nasa.gov/docs/earth_radiation_budget_17.pdf

the solar constant and it has never been registered by satellites on top of the atmosphere.[164]

From 340 W/m^2, those scientists discount the solar power reflected and absorbed by the atmosphere, and reflected by the surface; therefore, they get another unreal power absorbed by the surface of 163 W/m^2:

$$340 \text{ W/m}^2 * 0.48 = 163 \text{ W/m}^2$$

Actual annual average of incident solar thermal radiation on top of the atmosphere (TOA) is ~698.15 W/m^2 (1365 W/m^2 * 0.51), while backradiation from the atmosphere depends on the atmosphere's content of thermal energy, which always is lower than the surface's content of thermal energy.

The remaining 49% of the solar constant, i.e. 667 W/m^2, is not thermal radiation, but other forms of radiation, like gamma Ray, X-Ray, L-UV, FIR, radio, microwave, etc.[165]

Real solar thermal radiation absorbed by the surface and the temperature derived from such amount of absorbed solar thermal radiation are calculated from measurements as follows: solar thermal radiation absorbed and reflected by the atmosphere (mainly by water vapor, condensed water vapor in clouds and dust), and reflected by the surface:

$$1365 \text{ W/m}^2 * 0.51 = 696.15 \text{ W/m}^2$$

The factor 0.51 represents the mitigating effect by the atmosphere on the net flux of solar radiation, not the total solar irradiance on top of the atmosphere, which is 1365 W/m^2 in average.

---

[164] Ibid.,
http://education.gsfc.nasa.gov/experimental/July61999siteupdate/inv99Project.Site/Pages/solar.in solation.html
[165] Pitts, Donald and Sissom, Leighton, *Heat Transfer*, 1998, McGraw-Hill, pp. 289-311

The factor 0.51 is obtained from the sum of the thermal radiation absorbed by the atmosphere before it strikes the surface (30%), the thermal radiation reflected by clouds (14%), and the thermal radiation reflected by the surface (7%).[166]

Total incident solar thermal radiation on the surface after mitigation by atmospheric water vapor, condensed water vapor in clouds, dust, and surface:

$$1365 \text{ W/m}^2 - 696.15 \text{ W/m}^2 = 668.85 \text{ W/m}^2$$

An average of incident solar thermal radiation on the surface of 668.85 W/m^2 is absolutely coherent with measurements of thermal radiation impinging on Earth's surface (insolation), which could fluctuates around the average of insolation of 1000 W/m^2.[167]

In average, the surface of Earth, land and oceans, absorb:

$$668.85 \text{ W/m}^2 * 0.7 = 535.1 \text{ W/m}^2$$

0.7 is an average of total absorptance of Earth's surface. NASA-CERES scientists introduce 0.8 as total absorptance of Earth's surface.[168]

From these calculations, taking into account average measurements, we find that the rate 163 W/m^2 for absorbed solar thermal radiation by the surface is a flawed value. The real average of solar thermal radiation absorbed by the surface during daytime is 535.1 W/m^2.

During daytime, from 535.1 W/m^2 of thermal radiation,

---

[166] Peixoto, José P., Oort, Abraham H. 1992, *Physics of Climate*, Springer-Verlag New York Inc. New York.

[167] Ibid.,

http://education.gsfc.nasa.gov/experimental/July61999siteupdate/inv99Project.Site/Pages/solar.in solation.html

[168] Ibid.,

http://mynasadata.larc.nasa.gov/docs/earth_radiation_budget_17.pdf

309.43 J are stored by the surface as static thermal energy causing a global temperature of 24°C. From the remaining 225.67 J, a portion is transferred to the atmosphere by convection, sensible flux of thermal radiation and enthalpy of evaporation; another portion is transferred to heat sinks, especially to outer space and gravity field (static energy).

When we measure the surface temperature at day and night we find its average is 24°C. The standard ambient temperature of Earth, scientifically correct and accepted, is 298.8 K (25°C).[169]

To argue that the standard ambient temperature of Earth is -18°C is unscientific because it does not coincide with reality and proper calculations.

The temperature of air fluctuates according to the temperature of the surface, not the opposite.

Now let us examine the issue on radiometers and infrared thermometers.

When we place a pyrometer on the floor, under direct sunlight with its sensors facing up, and measure the solar power flux during daytime, we record an amount of solar thermal radiation which is close to:

$$1000 \text{ W}/\text{m}^2, \text{ not to } 340 \text{ W}/\text{m}^2$$

If we place the same pyrometer on the floor, adjusted to longwave thermal radiation, during nighttime, the recorded power flux will be around 60 W/m^2. Nevertheless, the proponents of the greenhouse effect argue that backradiation is 340 W/m^2, day and night.[170] [171]

If we measure the power flux from the surface to the atmosphere during nighttime, we will record around 310 W/m^2. This is five times higher as the power flux recorded from the

[169] http://www.taftan.com/thermodynamics/SATP.HTM
[170] http://asd-www.larc.nasa.gov/SCOOL/energy_budget.html
[171] Ibid.,
http://mynasadata.larc.nasa.gov/docs/earth_radiation_budget_17.pdf

atmosphere.

As the solar power flux on the surface area of the Earth calculated by those scientists did not coincide with reality, those scientists had to invent another process that could permit them to obtain a matching amount of power absorbed by the surface, the "greenhouse effect".

The original hypothesis of the greenhouse effect, which assumed that the Earth was warmed up because of "trapped" longwave thermal energy, was debunked through experimentation and observation,[172] and from already measured states.[173] The assumed "greenhouse gases", with exception of water vapor, were found not being capable of "accumulating" longwave radiative energy as it had been assumed.

As a consequence of the scientific demonstration that the "greenhouse effect" by "trapped" longwave radiative energy is imaginary,[174] proponents of the inexistent "greenhouse effect" are resorting to another explanation that you will not find in any serious scientific literature; they argue about a process of warming a warmer surface by a cooler atmosphere through backradiation derived from thermal energy which has been impossibly accumulated by a cooler atmosphere that in the real world does not reach such average of thermal energy content.

They explain this hypothesis saying that it is backradiation emitted from the atmosphere what warms up the warmer surface, as if the atmosphere were a duplicator of thermal energy. As a consequence, the second law of thermodynamics that determines the specific flow of thermal radiation from warmer to cooler is dismissed.

That is the reason by which we decided to conduct a

---

[172] http://principia-scientific.org/publications/Experiment_on_Greenhouse_Effect.pdf
[173] http://principia-scientific.org/publications/The_Model_Atmosphere.pdf
[174] Ibid., http://principia-scientific.org/publications/Experiment_on_Greenhouse_Effect.pdf

scientific experiment, based on direct observations of nature, to find the true science behind the phenomenon.

The above explanation is only a theoretical explanation. The following section is a brief description of terminology and symbols that I have used on this report. Soon after, I will describe the experiment that demonstrates that backradiation from a cooler atmosphere warming up a warmer surface is unphysical.

Terminology and Symbols

Refer to this section whenever you find incomprehensible concepts or units.

- **Cp** is the symbol for heat capacity at constant pressure. Heat capacity refers to the amount of thermal radiation needed to raise the temperature of a given mass of a substance in one degree Kelvin (K) or degree Celsius (°C).

- **W (Watt)** is the symbol for power. Power is speed at which work is performed or energy is transferred or transformed. Power can be expressed also in J/s (Joule per second); 1 J/s = 1W.

- **J (Joule)** is units of energy. Energy is the capability to perform or exert work. It can be expressed also in W*s (Watt per second); 1 J = 1 Watt-seconds.

- **T** is symbol of temperature. Temperature is static internal kinetic energy. The term static refers to any state function, i.e. energy that is not in process of being transferred or exerted on a system.

- **ΔT** is for difference of temperature, fluctuation of temperature, or change of temperature. It could be related with other functions of thermodynamic systems.

- **Q or q** is the symbol of heat. Heat is energy in transit, i.e. energy in the very moment of being transferred from a system at higher temperature to another system at lower temperature.

- **Thermal Energy** is the amount of energy contained by a thermodynamic system in virtue of its temperature. For example, the thermal energy of 10 liters of water at Ti = 17 °C (290.15 K), which temperature increases to Tf = 100 °C (373.15 K), is:

4190 J/kg °C * 83 °C * 10 kg = 3.48 x 10J, or 831.2 kcal

If the same volume of water is at thermal equilibrium and its temperature does not change, -23, but Ti remains constant at 290.15 K, its thermal energy will be:

$$Q = 1.5 * (1.3806503 \times 10 \, J/K * 290.15 \, K) = 6.01 \times 10\text{-}21 \, J,$$
$$\text{or } 1.44 \times 10\text{-}24 \text{ kcal.}$$

- **Thermal Radiation** is the fraction of the electromagnetic spectrum between wavelengths 0.1µm and 100 µm.

Thermal Radiation includes visible spectrum, almost the whole ultraviolet spectrum (Vacuum UV, Far UV, C-UV, Middle UV, B-UV, Near UV, and A-UV. Low UV is excluded), and almost the whole infrared (IR) spectrum, except the portion of the spectrum corresponding to wavelengths of Far-IR, from 101µm to 1000µm.

The remaining segments of the electromagnetic spectrum do not correspond to thermal radiation and cannot be considered on calculations of thermal radiation transfer. The proportion of the spectrum concerning thermal radiation is about 51% of the whole spectrum.

Thermal radiation is dynamic energy, which is a process, not a state.

- **Solar Constant** is the amount of energy emitted from the Sun, at all wavelengths of the whole electromagnetic spectrum, impinging on the surface area of a virtual ellipsoidal sphere, known as the outer sphere, whose semi-major axis is twice the distance from Sun to Earth (average of 1.49597871 x 108 km, or 1 Astronomical Unit, i.e. 1 AU), and its major perimeter is traced by the orbit of the Earth moving around the Sun.

Solar Constant to Earth system is 1365 W/m^2, which is the annual average of measurements by satellite.

- **Insolation** is the amount of solar power impinging on a given surface area of a planet. It is ~1000 W/m^2 on Earth.

Over real situations and locations, the energy absorbed and reflected by the atmosphere, and the amount of energy reflected by the surface are discounted from the total solar irradiance impinging on top of the atmosphere. It gives a theoretical value of 668.85 W/m^2. However, this value fluctuates due to the incident solar angle; therefore, a real measurement could be higher or lower than 668.85 W/m^2.

From 668.85 W/m^2, only 535.1 W/m^2 is thermal radiation absorbed by the surface, from which 56% is stored by surface and subsurface materials, i.e. 309.43 W/m^2, which causes a surface temperature of 24°C.

- **Back Radiation** is supposed thermal radiation emitted or reflected by a thermodynamic system towards the primary source of thermal radiation.

As a system absorbs thermal radiation, it immediately emits the absorbed radiation in all directions. If we imaginarily divide an absorber system into two identical symmetrical subsystems, the amount of radiation emitted from one subsystem will be always a fraction equal to 0.5 of total emissions.

For example, a system emitting a total amount of 100 J to all directions would emit 50 J from the upper subsystem and 50 J from the lower subsystem.

Backradiation would be thermal radiation emitted by any subsystem towards the radiating source.

- **Greenhouse Effect**, if it were real, would be the result of backradiation absorbed by the source of primary thermal radiation, in opposition to the universal trajectory of events, i.e. against natural spontaneous progression of entropy, from low level to high level.

- **Entropy** is the trajectory that any process or event happening in the known universe follows, which is related to availability of energy microstates of thermodynamic systems.

Entropy is considered to be irreversible, that is, that once the universe has increased its entropy, there is no way to revert such increase of entropy.

Universe's entropy can never diminish. Decreases of entropy have never been observed in the known universe. The entropy of any thermodynamic system can remain constant ($\Delta S = 0$) or increase ($\Delta S > 0$), but can never decrease.

- **Static Energy** is stationary energy contained by a system. It is not transitional energy, i.e. it is not a process, but a property of the system.

  Thermal energy is static energy, i.e. it is a property of thermodynamic systems (state function).

- **Dynamic Energy** is energy in transit from one system to another system.

  Heat, work, and heat transfer are dynamic energy; therefore, they are not properties of thermodynamic systems, but process functions.

  Heat and work cease to exist as they are taken in by thermodynamic systems and they are transformed into any form of static energy.

- **Enthalpy** is a state function and an extensive property which includes the total energy that a thermodynamic system contains, including thermal energy, potential energy, kinetic energy, electromagnetic energy, displacement energy, chemical energy, and deformation energy.

- **Deformation Energy** is the energy spent on change in shape and/or dimensions of a system due to a force exerted (transfer of work) or to changes of temperature (heat transfer).

- **Chemical Energy** is a form of energy related to the structural configuration of systems that can be changed to other forms of energy through chemical, biochemical, or electrochemical processes.

  Static Energy (U) of air at 300 K is 2.141 x 105 J/kg.

Enthalpy (H) of air at 300 K is 3.002 x 105 J/kg.

Experiment, Problems, Underlying Principle and Results

Summary of the Experiment:

- September 9, 2011; it is 15:00 hrs UTC. I point my radiometer towards a clear sky in an angle of 90° with respect to ground surface and stand waiting during 30 seconds until the instrument calculates the average of a set of records of thermal radiation received on its sensors each one second. Recorded Thermal Radiation = 61.93 W.

- September 9, 2011; it is 15:15 hrs UTC. I point my thermometer-radiometer towards the soil in an angle of 90° with respect to the plane of the ground surface area. Stand waiting for 30 seconds until the instrument gets stable and calculates the average of a series of records of thermal radiation received on its sensors each one second. Recorded Thermal Radiation from Soil = 308.2 W.

- September 10, 2011; it is 10:00 hrs UTC. I point my radiometer towards a clear sky in an angle of 90° with respect to ground surface and stand waiting during 30 seconds up to the instrument calculates the average of a set of records on thermal radiation received on to its sensors each one second. Recorded Thermal Radiation = 65.96 W.

- September 10, 2011; it is 10:15 hrs UTC. I point my radiometer towards the soil in an angle of 90° with respect to the plane of the ground surface area. Stand waiting for 30 seconds until the instrument stabilizes and records the average of a set of records of thermal radiation received on its sensors each one second. Recorded Thermal Radiation =

336 W.

Summarized Dataset

Time (UTC)	Nighttime	Daytime	Diff. ThR $_{day}$ – ThR $_{night}$	Correlation Factor ThR/ThR $_{day}$ Diff	Correlation Factor ThR/ThR $_{night}$ Diff
Thermal Radiation (ThR) from Soil	308.2 W	336 W	27.8 W	0.083	0.09
Thermal Radiation (ThR) from Atmosphere	61.93 W	65.96 W	4.03 W	0.061	0.065
ThR $_{soil}$ – ThR $_{atm}$	246.27 W	207.04 W	-39.23 W	-0.189	-0.159

From this database, a problem arises.

The problems:

- Does thermal radiation emitted by a cooler atmosphere warm up a warmer surface by backradiation?
- What are infrared thermometers, radiometers, pyrgeometers and pyrometers measuring when they are pointed up towards the sky?

The Underlying Principle

Power emitted by the surface during nighttime at 15:15 h UTC = 308.2 W. Equivalence in absolute temperature: 296.8 K.

The load of heat transferred from surface to atmosphere during nighttime, at 15:15 h UTC, decreases as night advances and it is followed by the amount of heat transferred by the atmosphere, not the opposite.

The power emitted by the surface before sunrise (10:00 hrs UTC) is 280 W, which are equivalent to an absolute temperature of 290 K (16.85°C).

The total change of temperature (ΔT) of ground in seven hours during nighttime is -7.04 K.

Power emitted downwards by an inverted conical volume of atmosphere during nighttime, at 15:15 h UTC = 61.93 W. Equivalence in absolute temperature: 271.51 K (-1.64°C).

The load of heat transferred from the atmosphere during nighttime decreased as the load of thermal radiation from the surface decreased as night advanced. The power emitted by an inverted conical volume of the atmosphere towards the surface before dawn (22:00 hrs UTC) is 60.36 W, which is equivalent to an absolute temperature of 244.1 K (-29.05°C).

The total change of temperature of the atmosphere between the first hours of night and last hours of night was -19 K.

The total change of temperature in the atmosphere was 12 K higher than the total change of temperature of the surface. This means that the atmosphere temperature decreases faster than the surface temperature.

It happens because the surface contains more thermal energy than the atmosphere and the load of heat transferred from surface to atmosphere remains constant while the lost of heat from the atmosphere towards the outer space increases in time.

Consequently, an atmosphere that increasingly cools absorbs each time a higher amount of thermal radiation from the surface, i.e. the difference between the thermal energy contained by the surface and the thermal energy contained by the atmosphere decreases.

The thermal nonequilibrium is sustained and the difference of temperature between the interacting systems decreases; however, thermal equilibrium between the interacting systems is never reached because the change of temperature of the atmosphere is always higher after each thermal interaction between soil and atmosphere due to a higher lost of thermal energy from the atmosphere. This is the underlying principle.

Before the nocturnal hemisphere runs out of energy, insolation starts again and the cycle restarts on this hemisphere.

The Experiment

We choose a completely clear day with Relative Humidity of 33% - 42% during the hours of observations to avoid nebular atmosphere. We performed the experiment on September 9, 2011, starting at 15:00 hrs UTC and finishing at 22:15 hrs UTC.

The field of view of our radiometers is a three-dimensional cone-like field with a volume of 7.86 x 1011 m3 with radius of 30 km; consequently, our radiometers are measuring the thermal energy contained by a volume of air which is 30 km high.

Radiometers are adjusted to record thermal radiation emitted by the target. The target during this experiment was the atmosphere.

For example, pointed in a straight perpendicular line towards the Sun in the zenith, they recorded 797.5W, which was insolation at floor level; this means the sensors have "felt" the total solar thermal radiation received on the lowest cubic meter of air buoying exactly over the surface, at 1 m in height, not at 30,000 meters in height, after being mitigated by the atmosphere. This globule of air, which is not square, but amorphous, is what we know as boundary layer.

The same thing occurs during nighttime. The radiation detected by the radiometer sensors is the total thermal radiation emitted by a whole volume of atmosphere contained in the inverted cone received by the lowest cubic meter of air, not by the surface.

As we direct our radiometers towards the horizon, our radiometers detect thermal radiation of a volume of air of the lowest layer of air buoying over the surface.

The layer of atmosphere in contact with the surface, also known as boundary layer, emits more thermal radiation than upper layers because heat is being transferred from the surface to this layer of air by conduction, convection, and radiation. Above this layer heat is transferred towards even cooler layers of the atmosphere and towards the outer space.

Keeping this in mind, let us examine the results of the experiment.

We start on a nocturnal atmospheric temperature of 271.51 K. Remember that it is temperature, i.e. thermal energy content, of a vertical column of atmosphere up to 30km in height during nighttime.

The rate of radiative cooling of the surface is steady and our measurements show an initial power emitted by the surface of 308.2 W. This power emitted by the surface decreased progressively by 4.03 W each hour.

It means that after one hour, starting at 15:00 hrs UTC, the power emitted by the surface was 304.17 W, and the recorded thermal radiation of the atmosphere was 59.72 W. The change of temperature of the atmosphere was -2.46 K.

After two hours, the heat emitted from the surface was 300.14 W, and the change of temperature of the atmosphere was -2.52 K.

After three hours, the heat emitted from the surface was 296.11 W, and the change of temperature of the atmosphere was -2.59 K.

After four hours, the heat emitted from the surface was 292.08 W, and the change of temperature of the atmosphere was -2.68 K.

After five hours, the heat emitted from the surface was 288.05 W, and the change of temperature of the atmosphere was -2.62 K.

After six hours, the heat emitted from the surface was 284.02 W, and the change of temperature of the atmosphere was -2.98 K.

After seven hours, the heat emitted from the surface was 279.99 W, and the change of temperature of the atmosphere was -2.95.

The results above are shown in the following table, which includes emission of thermal radiation from soil, thermal radiation absorbed by the atmosphere, temperature caused by thermal radiation absorbed by the atmosphere and the difference between thermal radiation from soil and thermal radiation from atmosphere.

Remember that measurements of thermal radiation emitted

by the atmosphere include an inverted vertical conical column with radius of 30,000 meters, which is lesser than the range of measurement of our pyrometers, if and when the targeted radiating system offers a surface larger than the diameter of field of view of the device at maximum distance.

Notice on the table below these lines that the change of temperature of the atmosphere is progressive, i.e. it increases in time, while the loss of thermal radiation from the surface is steady and fixed, i.e. 4.03 W each hour, as well as the loss of thermal radiation from the atmosphere, which is about -2.2 W each hour.

Complete Dataset (Nighttime)

Time Interval	$Q_{rad\ soil}$ (W)	$Q_{rad\ atmos.}$ (W)	$T_{atmos.}$ (K)	$\Delta T_{atmos.}$ (K)	$dQ_{atmos-soil}$ (W)
0 h	308.20	61.93	271.51		-246.27
1 h	304.17	59.72	269.05	-2.46	-244.45
2 h	300.14	57.51	266.53	-2.52	-242.63
3 h	296.11	55.31	263.94	-2.59	-240.8
4 h	292.08	53.10	261.27	-2.68	-238.98
5 h	288.05	50.89	258.51	-2.76	-237.16
6 h	284.02	48.69	255.66	-2.84	-235.33
7 h	279.99	46.48	252.71	-2.95	-233.51

I plotted the dataset from the above table on the following graph. The blue line is for thermal radiation from soil; the red line is the thermal radiation from the atmosphere, and the green line is the difference between the thermal radiation from the surface and the thermal radiation from the atmosphere.

The underlying Principle is clearly illustrated given that the thermal radiation from the soil decreases in time, as well as thermal radiation from the atmosphere; conversely, the change of temperature of the atmosphere increases:

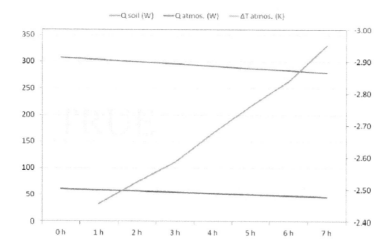

Graph 1: The Z-Underlying Principle

ΔT steadily increases while Qrad soil and Qrad atmos steadily decrease.

This only means that the temperature of the atmosphere decreases faster than the temperature of the soil and the temperature of the soil does not depend on thermal radiation from the atmosphere. Notice that the thermal radiation emitted by the surface is always higher than the thermal radiation emitted by the atmosphere.

Underlying Principle would not be possible if the atmosphere was radiating energy towards the surface and the surface would be absorbing it. The graph obtained from such unreal condition would be as follows.

Do not forget that the following graph depicts an unreal situation opposed to the second law of thermodynamics.

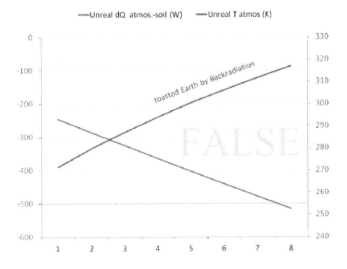

The formula to obtain the unreal thermal "backradiation" emitted by the atmosphere and absorbed by the soil:

$$Q' \text{ abs soil night} = (Q\text{soil} - 4.03 \text{ W}) + (Q\text{atmos} * 0.7)$$

Where Q' abs soil night is for thermal energy absorbed by the soil during nighttime, Qsoil is the measured thermal radiation emitted by soil, and Qatmos is the thermal radiation emitted by atmosphere. Luckily, this situation is unreal; otherwise, life on Earth would not be possible. Imagine an Earth at 300 °C! [175]

Under this unphysical scenario, the surface would emit thermal radiation which would be absorbed by the atmosphere, which would emit again towards the surface, which would emit more thermal radiation towards the atmosphere, which would absorb more energy and would radiate even more energy towards the surface, etcetera, etcetera, until toast the Earth.

Have you ever recorded an atmospheric temperature of 144°C on Earth? The assertion on an atmosphere radiating 342

---

[175] http://principia-scientific.org/publications/The_Model_Atmosphere.pdf

W/m^2 of thermal radiation towards the surface is unreal.

The question is: what the reason could be for people and some scientists with PhDs have been so easily deceived with this pseudoscience?

Answers and Conclusions

From this experiment with IR thermometers and radiometers, I have found that what we are really measuring, every time we point these devices towards a clear sky in an angle of 90° with respect to the surface, is a limited range of thermal radiation at wavelengths from 1 to 14 μm emitted by globules of air at high altitudes.

Along this experiment it has been demonstrated that radiometers record thermal radiation of floating globules of rarefied hot air at 6 to 30 km in altitude (corresponding to upper troposphere and stratosphere) that are transferring thermal radiation towards cooler volumes of air.

The field of view of radiometers draws a far extreme circle that is 5 km in diameter. It is an inverted conical shape whose apex ends on the lenses of the devices and base ends on any region of the upper atmosphere emitting thermal energy at wavelengths detectable by these devices.

Additionally, prevalence of thin cirri, which are emitting longwave and shortwave thermal radiation, constitutes a partial but efficient and constant obstacle to solar thermal radiation as well as a source of thermal energy that can be detected by radiometers and IR thermometers. As soon as we focus our radiometers or IR thermometers towards the sky in an angle of 90° with respect to the surface, we are actually measuring thermal radiation from cirri and cirrostrati at about 6 km in altitude, not any backradiation from the atmosphere.

Let me be a bit more explicit. The field of view of IR thermometers, radiometers, pyrgeometers, and pyrometers goes up, up, up, until it stumbles upon a lower density region at higher temperature than the surroundings that is absorbing, scattering, reflecting, and emitting solar thermal radiation. Radiometers and IR thermometers make an average of the globules of hot air and the thermal radiation from cirri into the whole trajectory of their fields of view.

I have found also that as we place radiometers and IR thermometers pointing sides at an angle of $0°$, that is when the field of view of the radiometer is parallel to surface, we are measuring thermal radiation of globules of hot air which wrap the cells of the device. It is thermal radiation emitted from the boundary layer between surface and atmosphere; the hottest or warmest globules that are almost to start buoying to upper altitudes are those which are in contact (in touch) with the very hot surface.

Resulting records would depend on the altitude of those globule (e.g. a globule radiating 60 W/m^2 would be at 30 km in altitude; globules at surface level, which start rising and are very hot because they are in contact with the hotter surface, would emit around 92 W/m^2, etc.). They merely detect the thermal radiation of relatively-small globules of hot air rising up.

Cirri and globules of hot air rising in the atmosphere are actually acting as vehicles to transport thermal radiation from the surface towards upper layers of the atmosphere, day and night (I have corroborated it during nighttime).

It is very clear from Thermodynamics and Stefan-Boltzmann Laws that heat is transferred exclusively from warmer surfaces towards cooler systems, never the opposite, and this experiment demonstrates it is applicable to climate system.

The disagreement between surface temperature caused by backradiation (which would be -91.35°C) and the actual temperature of surface (23.7°C), debunks the myths of a greenhouse effect by backradiation emitted by cooler greenhouse gases warming up a warmer surface.

Statistical Thermodynamics discredits very easily the argument of absorption of cool quantum/waves (lower frequency and longer wavelength than the absorbed quantum/waves) by warm mass particles.

We cannot take ad arbitrium electrons from highest energy microstates out to even higher energy microstates, from the mass particle, without breaking up the latter or without the occurrence of quantum tunneling, which has never been observed, detected, or produced in the atmosphere-surface system.

If we could produce quantum tunneling in our atmosphere, we actually could take absolute control of the planetary climate. We could warm up the poles and cool down the equator as easily as we can do it in lasers, without creating energy from nothing, but taking it from a region of the universe and placing it in another region.

If the surface were not radiating, the temperature of the atmosphere would be -72.2°C (less than Mars' atmospheric temperature at 1.5 meters above ground, which is -62°C in average). If an atmosphere would not exist, the temperature of Earth on daylight side would be ~120°C.

From observations and experimentation of nature, the total absorptance potential of the whole mixture of gases in the atmosphere is 0.2, and its total emittance potential is 0.201. These potentials include water vapor total absorptance and total emittance. As total emittance of sole water vapor is 0.65, it is quite clear that other gases in the atmosphere diminish the emittance and absorptance potentials of water vapor.

Is it not clear that the temperature of the atmosphere depends mostly on the surface temperature and not the opposite? The answer to the questions on the section "The Problem" is as follows:

Question: Does thermal radiation emitted by a cooler atmosphere warm up a warmer surface by backradiation?

Answer: No, thermal radiation emitted by the atmosphere does not warm up the warmer surface. This argument is unphysical because the thermal radiation emitted by the atmosphere is never higher than the thermal radiation emitted by the surface and it decreases in time in accordance to the thermal radiation emitted by the surface; additionally, the negative change of temperature of the atmosphere increases in time, contrary to what would happen if it were warming up the surface.

Question: What infrared thermometers, radiometers, pyrgeometers, and pyrometers are measuring as they are pointed up towards the sky?

Answer: Infrared thermometers, radiometers, pyrgeometers, and pyrometers are measuring thermal radiation limited by the range adjusted to 1-14 µm emitted from cirri and globules of air at different heights, which are rising vertically through the atmosphere.

Backradiation from a cooler atmosphere that warms up a warmer surface is a myth. It is not an irrefutable hypothesis because it is 100% discredited by correct experimentation.

Chapter 8—Seminal Sky Dragon Slayer Papers—Brehmer

From the dawn of exact knowledge to the present day, observation, experiment, and speculation have gone hand in hand; and, whenever science has halted or strayed from the right path, it has been, either because its votaries have been content with mere unverified or unverifiable speculation (and this is the commonest case, because observation and experiment are hard work, while speculation is amusing); or it has been, because the accumulation of details of observation has for a time excluded speculation.

—Thomas Henry Huxley

The Greenhouse Effect Explored— Is Water Vapor Feedback Positive or Negative?

A paper by Carl Brehmer.

Abstract

AN ESSENTIAL ELEMENT of the "greenhouse effect" hypothesis is the positive "water vapor feedback" hypothesis.

That is, if something causes an increase in the Earth's temperature this will cause an increase in the evaporation of water into water vapor. This new humidity will absorb more infrared radiation emitted from the Earth's surface. This increased absorption of infrared radiation is believed to warm the air even further. This makes the air able to hold more water vapor and result in even more evaporation, which increases the humidity even further and the cycle repeats.

This is called a "positive" feedback, since water vapor is believed to amplify atmospheric warming. Being curious about the truth of this hypothesis, I designed a simple experiment to study the effect of rising and falling levels of humidity on soil and air temperature and discovered that:

The addition of water to a climate system exerts a significant negative feedback against temperature changes night and day, water vapor has the same graphical relationship to temperature that insulin has to blood sugar and insulin is known to exert a strong negative feedback against blood sugar levels and...over the course of time the addition of water to a climate system causes a perceptible drop in the yearly mean temperature.

Materials

- Homemade Stevenson Screen with Temperature and Humidity Data Logger 4'10" off of the ground.
- Thermocouple attached to a Data Logger to acquire simultaneous soil surface temperatures.
- Internet records of yearly mean temperature and humidity

readings for several major cities in the world with contrasting climates.

- Computer spread sheet to compile data and create graphs.

Procedure—Part 1

Using 38 consecutive days of data harvested from the Stevenson Screen and thermocouple I calculated the mean dew point over that 38 day period and separated the days between those that fell above the mean, which I call "humid" days, and those that fell below the mean, which I call "arid" days.

I then graphed the mean temperature curve of the "arid" days against the mean temperature curve of the "humid" days to see what affect different levels of humidity had on the daily temperature curve, specifically looking for a positive feedback waveform, which we will discuss in more detail below.

Procedure—Part 2

Using two consecutive months of data harvested from the Stevenson Screen, I calculated the mean daily temperatures and graphed them against the mean daily dew point to see the relationship between temperature changes and the dew point, which, by the way, is an accurate reflection of the absolute humidity. Again, I was specifically looking for any indication of positive feedback.

Procedure—Part 3

I selected four sets of cities with the following criteria: a pronounced difference in humidity levels, about the same distance above the equator, receiving roughly the same amount of sunlight each day throughout the year and far enough inland to be unaffected by sea breezes.

With data harvested from the Internet, I compared the

temperature (adjusted for altitude) and the absolute humidity of four sets of "arid" vs. "humid" cities—looking for the effect of increased humidity on the temperatures of their respective climates to answer the question:

Does increasing the humidity cause a net increase in the air temperature as the 'greenhouse effect' hypothesis along with the "water vapor feedback" hypothesis says that it should?

Findings—Part 1

Affect of Humidity on Soil Temperatures

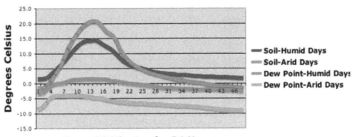

Every 30 Minutes for 24 Hours

An increase in the absolute humidity produced a strong negative feedback against day and night temperature changes.

It inhibited daytime warming and slowed nighttime cooling—as can be seen in the graph above which plots the mean temperatures of the "arid" days against the mean temperatures of the "humid" days.

Findings—Part 2

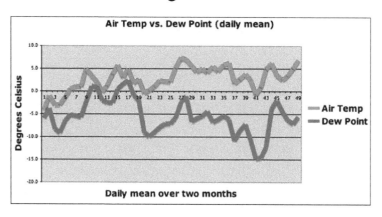

When plotting two month's of daily mean temperatures against daily mean dew points, as seen above, as the mean temperature rose and fell, there was a strong correlation between rising and falling dew points as well, although the change in the dew point lagged temperature changes by about a day.

This is the same relationship that rising and falling blood sugar has to rising and falling levels of insulin. The waveform of insulin also echoes changes in blood sugar levels while lagging behind the blood sugar level.

Since insulin is known to exert a strong negative feedback against rising blood sugar levels, this two-month long graph is consistent with humidity being a negative feedback against increasing temperatures.

What bolsters this idea is the fact that it rained near the beginning of this two-month period. As the soil dried out over time, the humidity levels trended downward while the temperature trended upward, which again is consistent with humidity being a negative feedback against increasing temperatures.

Findings—Part 3

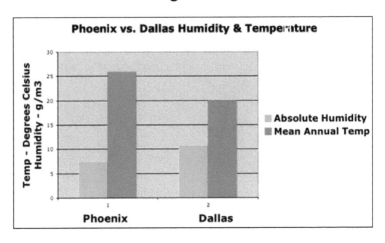

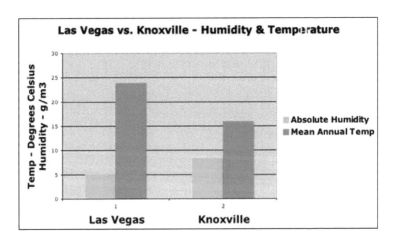

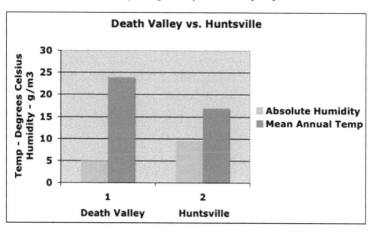

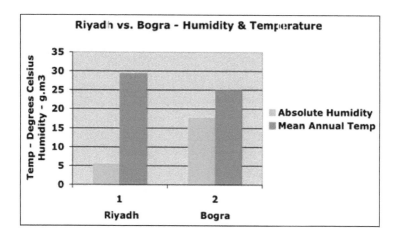

The four sets of cities used for my comparative study of arid and humid climates were: Phoenix vs. Dallas, Las Vegas vs. Knoxville, Death Valley vs. Huntsville and Riyadh, Saudi Arabia vs. Bogra, Bangladesh.

In all four cases, the more humid climate had a significantly cooler yearly mean temperature than the arid climate.

A Scientific Definition of Feedback

Let's discuss these findings. Before we can identify the signature characteristics of positive and negative feedback waveforms in the temperature record, we need an understanding of "feedback." The scientific definition of feedback is:

> *When the result of an initial process triggers changes in a second process that in turn influences the initial one. A positive feedback intensifies the original process, and a negative feedback reduces it.*[176]

To better understand the definition of feedback, let's look at some well-known examples of positive and negative feedback. The first example we will examine is the body's regulation of blood sugar levels through negative feedbacks exerted by the hormones insulin and glucagon.

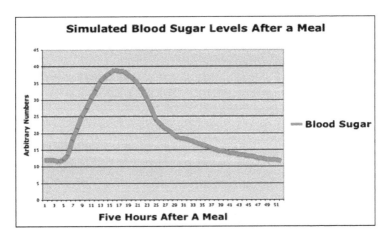

---

[176] Working Group I: The Scientific Basis, Appendix I—Glossary, http://www.ipcc.ch/ipccreports/tar/wg1/518.htm

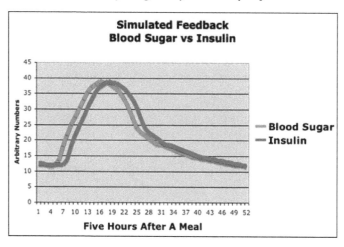

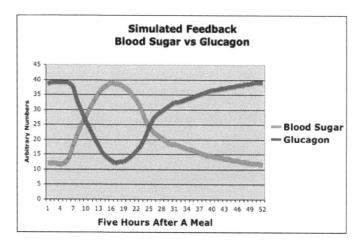

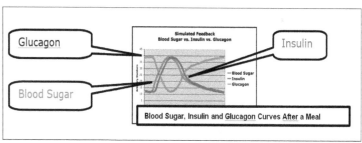

Blood Sugar, Insulin and Glucagon Curves After a Meal

This graph is a simulated curve of blood sugar levels for about five hours after a meal. Shortly after a meal is eaten, blood sugar begins to rise.

In response, the body releases insulin that lowers blood sugar.

Insulin's effect is called a negative feedback because it counteracts the rise in blood sugar seen after a meal. When the blood sugar begins to drop, the insulin level drops as well.

To keep the blood sugar from falling too far too fast and to maintain a basal level of blood sugar between meals, the body releases a second hormone called glucagon.

Its effect is the opposite of insulin.

It works to slow falling blood sugar.

Insulin slows rising blood sugars and glucagon slows falling blood sugars.

Though the action of glucagon opposes that of insulin, they are both negative feedbacks because they counteract changes in blood sugars—rather than amplify them. Again, if blood sugars increase, insulin kicks in to slow that increase.

If blood sugars decrease, glucagon kicks in to slow that decrease. As you can see the graphs above, a "second process" creates a negative feedback that can either be in-phase or out-of-phase with the "initial process."

What makes feedback positive or negative is not the direction of its force but whether or not it inhibits or amplifies the change that triggered it. In nature, negative feedbacks create stability while positive feedbacks create instability.

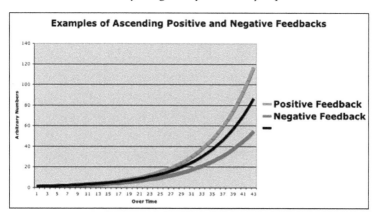

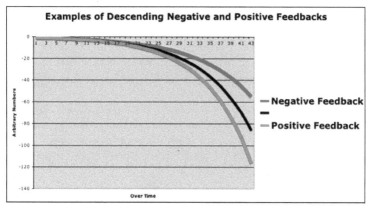

The two graphs above illustrate positive and negative feedbacks, one ascending and one descending. The positive feedbacks are in red and the negative feedbacks are in blue. As you can see, positive feedback amplifies the change while negative feedback attenuates the change—regardless of whether the direction of change is up or down.

If these graphs were temperature curves, then positive feedback could either cause greater warming or greater cooling, depending upon the time of day.

For example, it is said that "water vapor feedback" is positive because it is believed to amplify warming. If an increase in humidity were shown to amplify nighttime cooling, that would be positive feedback as well, because that would amplify the temperature change already occurring—cooling.

I only bring this up because ironically the most common example offered as proof that water vapor feedback is positive is the fact that humid nights cool more slowly than arid nights. This is actually a negative feedback against nighttime cooling. This is more than just a matter of semantics, because remember, in nature, negative feedbacks bring stability while positive feedbacks bring instability.

If we mislabel a negative feedback and call it positive feedback, we might be led to believe that the addition of humidity to a climate system will destabilize it.

Let's turn our focus to positive feedback for a minute. As you can see in the graph below, examples of positive feedback have a distinctly different look.

They have a signature exponential curve that usually ends abruptly because of a "terminating event."

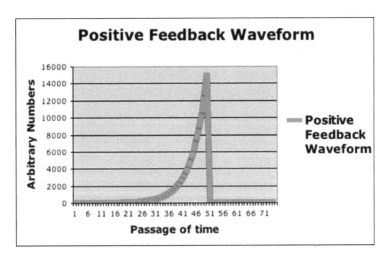

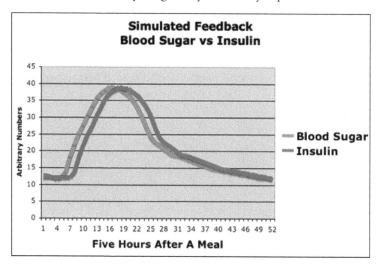

An example of positive feedback in nature can be seen in the labor pains of childbirth. Known as the *Ferguson Reflex*, each contraction stimulates a higher release of the hormone oxytocin, which increases the strength and frequency of the contractions. The "terminating event" is the birth of the child at which time contractions abruptly stop.

Another example of positive feedback is the squeal heard through a PA system when a microphone is placed near a speaker and sound from the speaker is picked up by the microphone and fed back through the amplifier. Everyone hears an abrupt loud squeal that terminates just as abruptly when the speakers blow, the microphone is moved away from the speaker or the amp is turned off. Another example of positive feedback is the growth in the debt of a company whose expenses are consistently greater than its receipts year after year. Its debt will grow exponentially until terminated by bankruptcy.

The signature trait of a positive feedback waveform is that it is very "spiked" compared to the rounded waveform seen in negative feedback.

Departing from this classical scientific definition of feedback contemporary literature defines positive water vapor feedback one-dimensionally and implies that positive water vapor feedback always results in a warmer temperatures. When you see a counter argument asserting that water vapor feedback is negative, the term is also used one-dimensionally and implies that negative water vapor feedback always results in cooler temperatures.

Again, positive feedback will only result in a warmer temperatures and negative feedback will only result in a cooler temperatures if the basal temperature is already trending warmer as it does every day from sunrise to mid afternoon.

If the basal temperature trends cooler—as it does predictably and repeatedly every night—then positive feedback would make the temperature even cooler and a negative feedback would result in a warmer temperature at the end of the night.

The Experiments—Part 1

Using this understanding of the scientific definition of feedback, let's take a look at the experimental results—starting with the study of the effect of humidity on the daily temperature curve.

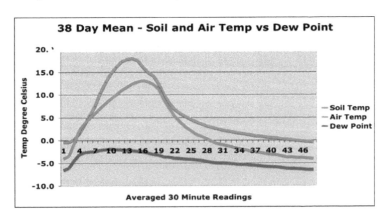

For 38 days I measured soil and air temperatures—along with the dew point—every 30 minutes, averaged these readings and graphed the daily temperature and dew point curves. The bottom, green line is the dew point, which is a good reflection of the absolute humidity. As you can, see the only time during the day that evaporation takes place and the absolute humidity increases is between sunrise and early afternoon.

If positive water vapor feedback results in higher temperatures, it happens during this period of the day, since an essential element in the positive water vapor feedback hypothesis is rising absolute humidity levels coupled with rising temperatures. For the rest of the day, both temperature and humidity decline. Positive feedback during that time would accentuate that rate of cooling.

The first thing that I did was find the 38 day mean dew point and divide the days up between those that fell above the mean—the "humid" days—and those who fell below the mean—the "arid" days. I then averaged their respective daily temperature curves and plotted these curves on the graphs below.

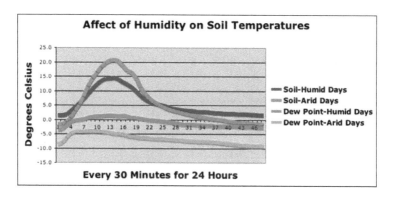

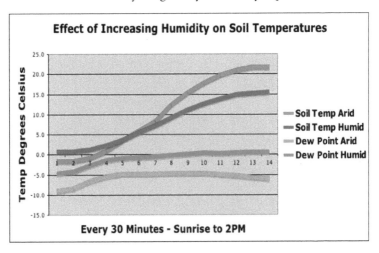

In the first graph, the red line is from the "arid" days, the blue line is from the "humid" days and the orange line is the average dew point curve from the "arid" days.

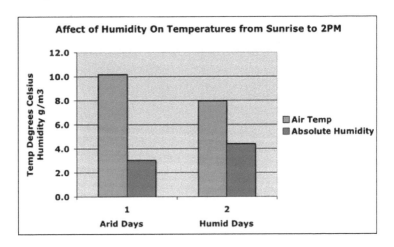

As stated above, since the positive "water vapor feedback" hypothesis requires an increasing absolute humidity coupled with a rising temperature and this only occurs daily between sunrise and early afternoon, I focused my attention on that period to see if the increased humidity on the "humid" days amplified the rate of temperature increase.

The red line is the soil temperature on the "arid" days and the blue line is the soil temperature on the "humid" days. The light blue line is the dew point on the "humid" days and the orange line is the dew point on the "arid" days.

Opposite from the positive water vapor feedback hypothesis, we see that as the humidity raises, the rate of soil warming decreases. This represents strong and pronounced negative feedback.

Again, as the humidity increases in the atmosphere, the rate of soil warming decreases during the period of the day when evaporation happens—thereby slowing evaporation.

If humidity exerted a positive feedback on soil temperatures, then the rate of soil warming from sunrise to early afternoon would increase as the humidity increases, but it doesn't; it decreases!

Here are the same readings in bar graph form. The two bars on the left are from the "arid" days and the two bars on the right are from the "humid" days. The red bars are mean temperatures and the blue bars are the mean absolute humidity. These are the averaged readings of temperature and absolute humidity from sunrise to 2PM.

As you can see, as the humidity increases the temperature decreases during the period of the day when evaporation occurs, during the only part of the day in which positive feedback would result in higher temperatures.

Again, this is clear and distinct negative feedback.

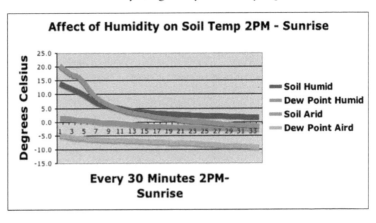

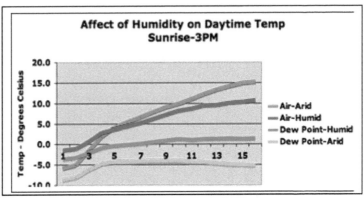

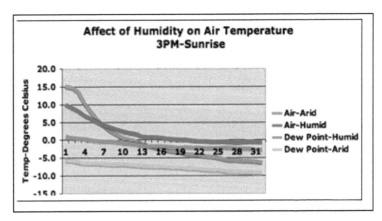

To complete our analysis of the affect of humidity on the daily temperature curve let's look at the rest of the day—from 3PM until sunrise the next morning. The blue line is the soil temperature on the "humid" days and the red line is the soil temperature on the "arid" days. The light blue line is the dew point on the "humid" days and the orange line is the dew point on the "arid" days. As you can see, an increase in the absolute humidity is accompanied by a delay in nighttime cooling. This, again, is negative feedback counteracting the more rapid cooling trend seen on "arid" days.

Those graphs were of soil temperatures. If we look at air temperatures we see the same negative feedback day and night.

Something needs to be clarified at this point. I do not assert that the negative feedbacks seen in the graphs are the effect of water vapor alone. Water vapor does not exist in isolation. Higher humidity in the air is accompanied by more cloud cover, which shades the Earth during the day and creates temperature inversions at night—slowing or stopping nighttime upward convection currents (an actual greenhouse effect.) More clouds also usually mean more rain or snow, which further cools the soil because such precipitation falls from an altitude where is it colder than the ground and cools the soil by direct contact. More humidity also usually means that there is more water in the soil, which has at least two affects on the temperature:

- More water is available to cool the soil through latent heat transfer, i.e., evaporation and...

- Increased water in the soil increases the specific heat of the soil, which will by itself dampen swings in diurnal temperatures seen in dry climates. These graphs manifest the net effect of all of those forces combined and produce a pronounced negative feedback against day and night temperature changes.

It is beyond the scope of this paper to sort out the contribution of each separate force to the net affect on temperature. I simply ask:

> *What affect does the addition of water to a climate system have on the overall temperature within that climate system?*

The "greenhouse effect" hypothesis combined with the "water vapor feedback" hypothesis asserts that the addition of water to a climate system should cause a marked increase in temperatures within that climate system since the addition of water brings with it increased humidity and water vapor is said to trap heat in the atmosphere.

As we have seen, the addition of water to a climate system, manifested by a higher absolute humidity, causes less warming during the day coupled with less cooling at night. However, we don't know—over time—whether these two opposing feedbacks cancel each other out or if one is dominant and swings the mean temperature higher or lower.

Let's expand our time frame to two months and look at daily mean temperatures vs. dew points over that period of time.

The Experiments—Part 2

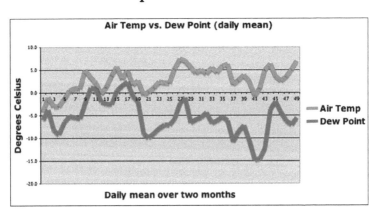

Here is a graph of the daily mean air temperatures vs. the daily mean dew points over a two-month period. The red curve is the daily mean temperature and the blue curve is the daily mean dew points, which again is an accurate reflection of absolute humidity. As you can see, as the temperature rose and fell the dew point rose and fell as well. Let me make a couple of comments about this graph.

a) First, although there is a strong correlation between the waveform shapes of these two trends, the temperature changes precede the dew point changes by about 24 hours—demonstrating that the temperature drives the humidity level as has been observed in other studies[177] and which is the first premise expressed within the "water vapor feedback" hypothesis. As the temperature goes up, more water is evaporated into water vapor and as the temperature goes down, more water vapor is condensed back into water.

b) Conventional wisdom asserts that this correlation between temperature and dew point increases and decreases proves that water vapor feedback is positive, yet we see the exact same pattern of correlation present in a negative feedback system. As already discussed, rising blood sugar levels are followed by rising insulin levels. Dropping blood sugar levels are followed by dropping insulin levels and insulin is known to exert a profound negative feedback against rising blood sugars. Therefore, this graph is consistent with water in a climate system exerting negative feedback against increasing temperatures.

c) It just so happens that there was precipitation near the beginning of this two-month period and, as you can see, as time passed and the soil dried out, the level of humidity in the air trended downward as the temperature of the air trended upward. The "rise and fall" correlation remained present. This is

---

[177] Wentz, F. J. and M. C. Schabel, 2000, *Precise Climate Monitoring Using Complementary Satellite Data Sets*, Nature, 403(6768), pps 414-416.

an inverse relationship and is, again, consistent with negative feedback—not positive feedback. The fact is, as the soil dries out, the general level of humidity drops and demonstrates an important reality. Water vapor feedback cannot exist where there is no water in the soil—such as the dry sand of an arid desert.

Next we will compare arid climates with humid climates and see if the presence of water in these respective climate systems has a warming or a cooling affect.

The Experiments—Part 3

I did this comparative study under the assumption that if water vapor traps heat in the atmosphere, then it will trap the heat in the location of the humidity. That is, the humidity present in Dallas, Texas does not trap heat in Phoenix, Arizona. Whatever heat is trapped in Phoenix will be the doing of the humidity present in Phoenix.

Let's start by comparing Phoenix to Dallas. They are about the same distance north of the equator and therefore receive about the same amount of sunlight every day. They are also inland far enough to not be affected by "sea breezes." Since Phoenix only receives about 7 inches of precipitation annually while Dallas receives about 35 inches, the air in Dallas is much more humid than the air in Phoenix. If the "greenhouse effect" hypothesis is true and the amount of heat the atmosphere traps increases as the humidity increases, then the mean annual temperature in humid Dallas should be much higher than the mean annual air temperature in arid Phoenix. Let's take a look.

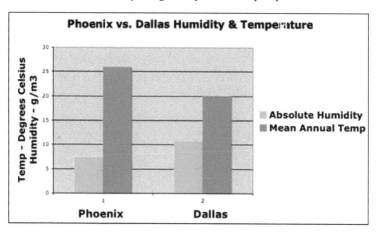

In this chart, the bars on the left are from Phoenix and the bars on the right are from Dallas. The blue bars are the yearly mean absolute humidity in grams per cubic meter. The red bars are the annual mean temperatures adjusted for altitude[178] in degrees Celsius. These numbers are from the National Weather Service. As you can see, though Dallas is significantly more humid than Phoenix, it is significantly cooler—on average—than Phoenix.

Next, let's compare Las Vegas, Nevada with Knoxville, Tennessee. Again, these cities are both about the same distance north of the equator and therefore receive about the same amount of sunlight every day. They are also both inland far enough to not be affected by "sea breezes."

Since Las Vegas only receives about 4.5 inches of precipitation annually while Knoxville receives about 48 inches, the air in Knoxville is much more humid than the air in Las Vegas. If the "greenhouse effect" hypothesis is true and the

---

[178] The International Standard Atmosphere published by The International Organization for Standardization (ISO), ISO 2533:1975 states that for every 1,000 meters that the altitude is lower the temperature raises 6.5 °C on average due to adiabatic heating. Based on that formula these numbers estimate what the annual mean temperature would be if both cities were at sea level.

amount of heat the atmosphere traps increases as the humidity increases, then the mean annual temperature in humid Knoxville should be much higher than the mean annual air temperature in arid Las Vegas.

Let's take a look.

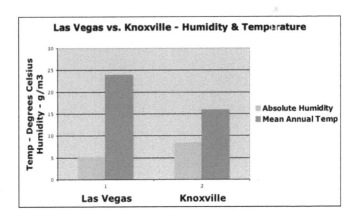

Again, in this chart the bars on the left are from Las Vegas and the bars on the right are from Knoxville. The blue bars are the absolute humidity in grams per cubic meter and the red bars are the mean annual temperatures adjusted for altitude in degrees Celsius. Again, these numbers are from the National Weather Service. As you can see, though Knoxville is significantly more humid than Las Vegas, it is significantly cooler—on average—than Las Vegas.

Let's take a look at Death Valley, California compared to Huntsville, Alabama. Again, these cities are both about the same distance north of the equator and therefore receive about the same amount of sunlight every day. They are also both inland far enough to not be affected by "sea breezes." Since Death Valley only receives about 2.4 inches of precipitation annually while Huntsville receives about 57 inches, the air in Huntsville is much more humid than the air in Death Valley. If the "greenhouse effect" hypothesis is true and the amount of heat that the atmosphere traps increases as the humidity increases then the mean annual temperature in humid Huntsville should be much higher than the mean annual air temperature in arid Death Valley. Let's take a look.

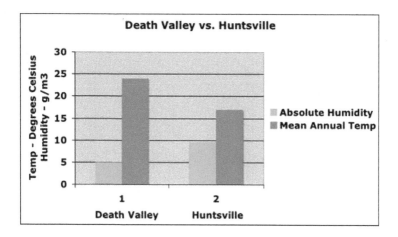

In this chart, the bars on the left are from Death Valley and the bars on the right are from Huntsville. The blue bars are the absolute humidity in grams per cubic meter and the red bars are the mean annual temperatures adjusted for altitude in degrees Celsius. As you can see, though Huntsville is significantly more humid than Death Valley, it is much cooler—on average—than Death Valley.

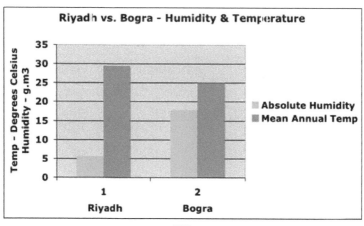

Let's look at an example from the international arena and compare Riyadh, Saudi Arabia with Bogra, Bangladesh. Again, these cities are both about the same distance north of the equator and therefore receive about the same amount of sunlight every day. They are also both inland far enough to not be affected by "sea breezes." Since Riyadh only receives about 3.7 inches of precipitation annually while Bogra receives about 63 inches, the air in Bogra is much more humid than the air in Riyadh. If the "greenhouse effect" hypothesis is true and the amount of heat the atmosphere traps increases as the humidity increases, then the mean annual temperature in humid Bogra should be much higher than the mean annual air temperature in arid Riyadh. Let's take a look.

In this chart, the bars on the left are from Riyadh and the bars on the right are from Bogra. The blue bars are the absolute humidity in grams per cubic meter and the red bars are the mean annual temperatures adjusted for altitude in degrees Celsius. As you can see, though Bogra is significantly more humid, it is noticeably cooler on average than Riyadh.

These observations might seem counter intuitive since we often perceive humid climates to be warmer than arid climates, but that is a sensory illusion. Since our bodies are water-cooled through perspiration, which is more efficient in low-humidity environments, people who move from Dallas to Phoenix or from Knoxville to Las Vegas think that they are moving to a cooler climate; but they are not. It just feels cooler.

Conclusion

What does this all mean?

Although it is true that warmer temperatures create higher humidity in climates where there is water in the soil to evaporate, that greater humidity does not lead to even more warming.

Quite the contrary.

As we have seen, the presence of water in a climate system exerts negative feedback on temperatures both day and night, which stabilizes the wide diurnal swings in temperature seen in arid climates and, over time, causes humid climates to be some what cooler on average than arid climates.

In this sense, water acts as the Earth's thermostat and not its heater. The observations made in this paper also falsify any notion that there could ever be runaway global warming driven by positive water vapor feedback where the oceans evaporate into the atmosphere and all life on Earth perishes.

Why?

Because "water feedback" is negative feedback and if it were going to happen it already would have.

These empirical observations do not contradict various climates changing around the world and continuing to vary over time, but rather demonstrates the presence of water on our planet acts as a stabilizing force, exerting negative feedback against temperature change—up or down.

What Do You Think?

Can the biosphere tolerate high humidity? Would an increase in the Earth's absolute humidity be "catastrophic"? Remember, we are not urged to fear the hypothetical 1°C global warming a doubling of carbon dioxide levels alone might cause. Rather, we are told to fear the resulting positive feedback—the increase in global humidity a little global warming would cause.

The fact is, the real-world change that water vapor makes within a climate system is to cause life within the local biosphere to explode. How insular must one's view of the biosphere be if one does not know that the number and diversity of species within a climate system are directly proportional to the amount of humidity in the air? How brainwashed must one be to support proposed international agreements and global carbon taxation schemes whose intent is to limit humidity in the atmosphere and thereby prevent the expansion of rainforests and preserve the integrity of deserts?

It is true what they say; the most potent greenhouse gas—water vapor—does change the climate profoundly. It changes it from a desert to a forest. It has a veritable "greenhouse effect" in that it promotes the growth of lush greenery—as does an actual greenhouse.

Where water vapor is scarce and humidity is low, life is scarce and there is no greenery.

Why?

Because, in addition to sunshine and carbon dioxide, water is necessary for photosynthesis. When and where there is an absence of photosynthesis, there is an absence of biological life. Today, elementary school children are being taught to fear "high humidity."

Elementary school teachers can incorporate [the danger of high humidity] lesson plans into their science curriculum in a number of ways.[179]

---

[179] https://education.cu-portland.edu/blog/classroom-resources/3-sites-that-offer-elementary-climate-change-lesson-plans/

Here is what you can do.

Whenever you hear the phase "climate change" think "high humidity" because that's the climate change they want you to fear.

Do you fear high humidity?

I don't.

I welcome it because I know that when the humidity goes up lush, green vegetation is soon to follow.

Chapter 9—Seminal Sky Dragon Slayer Papers—Tamarkin & Bromley

Those who have knowledge don't predict.
Those who do predict don't have knowledge.
—Lao Tzu

Definable Effects of Manmade Carbon Dioxide

CARBON DIOXIDE IS the "gas of life" providing the carbon on which all plant and animal life on Earth is based.

The IPCC and the anthropogenic climate change community have asserted that carbon dioxide (CO_2) is a pollutant because it drives global warming or climate change.

Computer models have been generated based on the unproven "Radiated Greenhouse Gas Emissions" theory which predicts catastrophic changes in the Earth's climate leading to much future death and destruction.

No demonstrable, empirical evidence of this theory is available. No signs of anthropogenic climate change have been discovered. Yet the climate alarmist's community convinced elected leaders and policy makers to implement proposed solutions to prevent this hypothetical destruction. The proposed solution is the vast reduction of energy leading to enormous worldwide population reduction under the control of a single socialist worldwide government. Furthermore, governments are implementing significant taxes on carbon dioxide. The IPCC and global warming community assert that mankind is responsible for a 33% increase in total atmospheric carbon dioxide concentration over the last forty years.

However, a mathematical analysis shows that the human produced carbon dioxide concentrations are so low as to be unmeasurable and there is no correlation to the increases in carbon dioxide and man's burning of fossil fuels. Plant life thrives on increased levels of carbon dioxide which in turn provides increased food production for animals and mankind. Satellite records show a significant "greening" of the Earth in terms of increased plant life.

All human lifeforms on Earth—plant and animal—are carbon-based. Carbon is a key component of all known life on Earth, representing approximately 45-50% of all dry biomass. Complex molecules are made up of carbon bonded with other elements, especially oxygen and hydrogen and frequently also with nitrogen, phosphorus and sulfur. Carbon dioxide or CO_2 is a naturally occurring compound consisting of carbon and oxygen atoms and is the gas of life. Carbon is exceedingly abundant on Earth.

Research by Rice University Earth scientists suggests that virtually all of the Earth's life-giving carbon came from a collision about 4.4 billion years ago between Earth and an embryonic planet similar to Mercury.[180]

The most abundant element in the human body is oxygen, making up about 65% of the weight of each person.[181] Carbon is

---

[180] http://astrobiology.com/2016/09/where-did-carbon-come-from-for-life-on-earth.html

[181] https://www.thoughtco.com/chemical-composition-of-the-human-body-603995

the second most abundant element, making up 18% of the body. Although you have more hydrogen atoms than any other type of element, the mass of a hydrogen atom is so much less than that of the other elements that its abundance comes in third, at 10% by mass.[182]

Animals get carbon from eating plants as well as other animals who obtain carbon from plants. There are no carbon-based vitamins or food supplements. Plants obtain virtually all their carbon from the air.

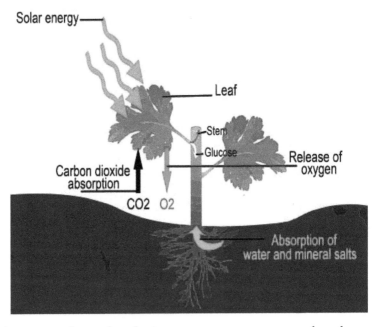

Air is mostly made of nitrogen, oxygen, argon, and carbon dioxide. Plants absorb carbon dioxide from the air. This carbon makes up most of the building materials that plants use to build new leaves, stems, and roots.[183] The oxygen used to build glucose

---

[182] https://www.thoughtco.com/atomic-mass-and-mass-number-606105
[183] https://askabiologist.asu.edu/recipe-plant-growth

molecules is also from carbon dioxide. Energy to fuel the chemical reactions comes from sunlight and the process is referred to as photosynthesis.

Yet the IPCC, UN, many government-funded laboratories and universities and various other political bodies say carbon dioxide is a pollutant. In fact, the United States Environmental Protection Agency included carbon dioxide in its 2015 Endangerment Ruling.

Why?

So government agencies could impose taxes on carbon dioxide. An example was the attempt to require all households to deploy carbon dioxide monitors so that the homeowners could be taxed for the CO_2 they generated from the use of natural gas and a derivative of electricity use. Even U.S. housing corporations Fannie Mae and Freddie Mac would have potentially benefited from these taxes and developed plans to implement enforcement.[184]

Why would these international and even U.S. governmental organizations embrace the deceptive and fraudulent concept of Anthropogenic Global Warming now conveniently called climate change?

- To impose burdensome taxes on something all people use: energy.

- To advance a socialist, one-world government.

- To force a worldwide order-of-magnitude population reduction over the next few hundred years through the total elimination of inexpensive abundant energy required to sustain agricultural, transportation and advanced human lifestyles.

---

[184] https://greatclimatedebate.com/congressional-letter-to-fannie-mae-regarding-their-patent-on-residential-emissions-trading/

Anthropogenic Global Warming (AGW), now called climate change because the world is not warming, originated at the 1975 "The Atmosphere: Endangered and Endangering" conference, organized by anthropologist Margaret Mead, and Paul Erlich, author of *The Population Bomb.*

In the early 1980s, "The Club of Rome" embraced the empirically unprovable Radiated Greenhouse Gas Emissions hypothesis as a means to scare people into believing abundant inexpensive energy must be restricted because it creates catastrophic global warming.[185] It has not and does not. Forty years of lower troposphere average global temperature readings show the Earth's temperature has gone up and down by slightly less than ± 0.75°C.

Water vapor comprises 95% of all 'greenhouse gases.' Carbon Dioxide is a trace gas. Manmade CO_2 can only be responsible for 0.117% of any warming from all combined 'greenhouse gas' including water vapor. Most of the recent increases in atmospheric CO_2 concentration come from gasification of the oceans which is a function of temperature. Cold water dissolves more CO_2 than warm water. Temperature increases always precede CO_2 increases with a significant lag. The amount of "warming" enabled by manmade CO_2 is so low it is virtually unmeasurable.

A comparison of the atmospheric CO_2 concentrations from 1979 to 2018 shows no Pearson Correlation to temperature.

However, there is strong correlation to decreases in temperature caused by volcanic activity and increases in temperature caused by El Niño events, as shown in the chart below.

---

[185] https://greatclimatedebate.com/prosecutorial-abstract/

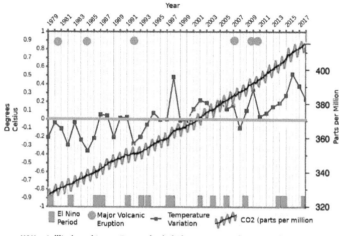

UAH satellite-based Lower Tropospheric (LT) temperature dataset and atmospheric concentration of Carbon Dioxide;
1979 to present

The Earth is over 4.6 billion years old. It has had an atmosphere for over 4.4 billion years. The composition of the atmosphere has changed many times due to natural causes and local climates have varied periodically over periods measured in thousands of years.

However, it is unreasonable to study climate records for 200 years and conclude man has an effect. Two hundred years is only 4.5×10^{-8} of the Earth's age.

What tools have the climate alarmists used to convince a mostly scientifically illiterate world population?

- Popular media stating that increased carbon dioxide levels result in increased temperatures while the fact of the matter is that increases in temperatures lead to increased carbon dioxide concentrations as evidenced by the well understood paleogenic records.

- Popular media claims that today's carbon dioxide levels are at a record high, while in fact over paleogenic time frames today's records at near record lows.

- Popular media making false claims about extreme weather events and sea level rise without full disclosure and explanation of the facts.

- Manipulated data sets of temperature records and poor reporting stations both on land and at sea.[186]

- False claims that the science is settled and 97% of scientists agree that additional CO_2 contributed by man is increasing the global average temperature. The media never mentions things like the 31,487 American scientists…9,029 of which have doctorate degrees…who signed a petition urging the U.S. government to reject the Kyoto AGW agreement.[187]

- Use of computer models based on the false theories of greenhouse gases and temperature sensitivity with the intent to sell a catastrophic future based on events forecasted tens of years out, predicated on unproven theories and causal behaviors.

We produced a chart showing the Mauna Loa, H.W. Keeling CO_2 data and a forty year average global temperature based on the UAH6 satellite data base.[188] There has been a 33% increase in atmospheric CO_2 from 1971 to present however there is there is no causal statistical correlation between CO_2 and temperature changes.

Although the IPCC and others claim that the recent 33% increase in atmospheric CO_2 is totally anthropogenic, that is manmade due to burning fossil fuels, there is no correlation between the CO_2 concentration levels and the rapidly increasing use of fossil fuels over the last 40 years.

---

[186] https://greatclimatedebate.com/erasing-americas-hot-past/

[187] http://www.petitionproject.org/

[188] https://greatclimatedebate.com/yearly-temperature-variation-and-atmospheric-co2-levels-1979-2018/

However, when we overlaid a forty-year timeline of El Nino events on the same chart there is a pronounced correlation to temperature increases and specific El Nino events.

Next, we compared annual decreases in temperature with major volcanic eruptions producing very significant amounts of volcanic ash dissipated into the upper atmosphere. Again, there was a distinct correlation to decreases in annual average global temperature.

Now we have on one simple to understand chart the correlation of average annual global temperature and natural events causing annual increases and decreases in annual average global temperature.

The Earth has a natural built in thermostat and the dwell of that thermostat maintains a remarkably consistent average annual global temperature given the fact that the Earth's heater, the Sun, is 93 million miles from the Earth. Over the last 40 years, the annual average global temperature has had a ±0.75°C variation.

To further aid the scientifically lay population in the understanding of climate science and natural variations we have produced an extremely detailed climate tutorial.[189]

The combined worldwide consumer and taxpayer burden of the Climate Industrial Complex including that of the related Big Green Energy Scheme is over USD $2 trillion annually.[190]

Simple math can be used to calculate the rate of change of one variable versus another variable. The rate of change of one variable versus another is known as its slope or velocity, also known as its first derivative.[191] The change in atmospheric carbon dioxide (CO_2) concentration over a period of time is the slope of

---

[189] https://greatclimatedebate.com/tutorial-anthropogenic-global-warming-agw/

[190] https://greatclimatedebate.com/funding-climate-industrial-complex/

191

https://www.mathwarehouse.com/calculus/derivatives/what-is-meaning-of-first-order-derivative.php

CO$_2$ concentration, or the first derivative of CO$_2$ concentration with respect to time. The change of slope with respect to time is the second derivative, also known as acceleration. We can use this simple math to calculate the change of atmospheric CO$_2$ concentration versus time, that is, the slope or 1st derivative of CO$_2$ concentration.

And, we can also calculate the change in slope of CO$_2$ concentration versus time, that is, the second derivative of CO$_2$ concentration with respect to time, or the acceleration of CO$_2$ concentration. This simple math is the basis of this chapter.

Decades ago, Professor Keeling set up his laboratory on the Big Island of Hawaii at 11,000 feet altitude on the side of Mauna Loa. The instruments in this laboratory have been measuring atmospheric CO$_2$ concentration since then. These measurements show atmospheric CO$_2$ concentration has been steadily increasing since the instruments on Mauna Loa were installed.

In other words, the laboratory provides us with the slope of atmospheric CO$_2$ concentration, which is also known as the first derivative of atmospheric CO$_2$ concentration with respect to time.[192] Since CO$_2$ is generally accepted to be a well-mixed gas in air, the Mauna Loa data is generally accepted to represent the global average atmospheric CO$_2$ concentration. Here is the graph from the Keeling Laboratory on Mauna Loa.

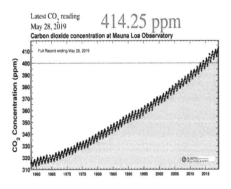

---

[192] https://sealevel.info/co2.html

In the data files underlying the above graphic, we have the raw date to calculate the change of atmospheric CO_2 concentration over time (the slope or first derivative) as well as the rate of change of slope over time (the second derivative with respect to time.)

In the graphic and raw data, we can see the increase and decrease in CO_2 levels due to seasonal changes. This seasonal change appears as jagged shark's teeth on the consistently upward sloping CO_2 concentration. In the spring and summer, when plants are growing and oceans are warming, CO_2 concentration increases slightly. In winter, when plants lose their leaves and algae die, and oceans cool, CO_2 concentration decreases slightly. The instruments in the lab on Mauna Loa and the Keeling graph are sensitive enough to record these relatively minor seasonal CO_2 concentration changes within the overall data and graph of changing CO_2 concentration over time. In other words, we can see the second derivative of CO_2 concentration, the change in slope with respect to time, in the graphic.[193]

We know from other sources CO_2 concentration was increasing long before data collection began at the Mauna Loa Keeling lab. But, we do not need that information for the purpose of this short paper.

The Keeling graph reports 414 CO_2 molecules per 1,000,000 molecules of air in the Earth's atmosphere, or 414PPM, or 0.0414%. PPM is only one of several different possible measures of concentration. The chemical composition of air consists of nitrogen, oxygen, argon, water vapor and various trace gases as well as various aerosols held in suspension.[194] CO_2 is one of those trace molecules. Nitrogen comprises 78% of the gases in the atmosphere while Oxygen comprises 21% and Argon comprises 0.93%. Water vapor concentration in air is

---

193

https://www.ugrad.math.ubc.ca/coursedoc/math100/notes/apps/se cond-deriv.html

[194] https://www.space.com/17683-earth-atmosphere.html

highly variable, from less than 1% to 4%. CO_2, methane, ozone and the other gas molecules in air are known as trace molecules and all of these trace molecules taken together make up less than 1% of the molecules in a volume of air. A cubic meter volume of air at sea level is 99.9% empty space. Air is not dense compared to any liquid such as water where molecules are so closely packed together that they are in physical contact and can share electrons and conduct heat among them.

The 414PPM, or 0.0414% concentration of CO_2 in air, represents the net sum of all CO_2 absorption and desorption events on Earth. It is the sum of trillions of events which are occurring every second.

For example, the oceans in the far north and in the far south are absorbing CO_2 because cold water absorbs and holds more CO_2 than warm water, like a cold soda pop keeping its CO_2 bubbles. Another example is the absorption of enormous amounts of CO_2 from the air by all green plants. All green plants use CO_2 from the air along with water and sunlight in a process called photosynthesis which converts CO_2 into carbohydrate molecules.

Sugars are a group of common carbohydrate molecules. Carbohydrate molecules are the building blocks for all plant cells. Animals, insects, fish, humans, all life on Earth is based on carbohydrate molecules in cells which are made by green plants from carbon, water and sunlight. Animals, insects, fish etc. eat plants, then those plants are in turn eaten by other animals, insects, fish, humans and so on in a continuous process called the food chain.

Another example of an enormous and ongoing change in CO_2 contributing to the net atmospheric CO_2 concentration is methane (CH_4) emissions. Methane is continuously emitted by warm water, just as is CO_2, and is continuously absorbed by cold water, just as is CO_2. About 50 to 60 times more CO_2 molecules are dissolved in the water of the Earth's oceans compared to the Earth's air. This ratio, expressed as a partition co-efficient, is determined by Henry's Law.[195] It is a constant of nature. It's neither a theory nor a hypothesis; it is a scientific law that is more proven and far better understood than gravity. Henry's Law determines the ratio partition of a gas between liquid water and the gas above the liquid water.

Henry's Law is dependent on the pressure of the gas, the temperature of the gas and water, and to a minor extent, the minerals like salt in the water. Since air pressure at sea level is nearly constant, the primary determinant of the amount of CO_2 in air is the temperature of ocean water. Oceans are like your soda pop. If the soda pop is cold, then the CO_2 bubbles stay in the pop. If the soda pop warms, the pop loses its CO_2 bubbles. As mentioned, determined by Henry's Law, there is 50 to 60 times more CO_2 in the oceans than in the atmosphere.

Warm ocean water emits huge amounts of CO_2 and methane which contribute to the net atmospheric CO_2 concentration reported in the Keeling Mauna Loa data. The largest source (by orders of magnitude) of CO_2 and methane in the air is the emission of these molecules by warm water in oceans and soils. CO_2 and methane are absorbed back into cold water in amounts also determined by Henry's Law, which also is a component of the net atmospheric CO_2 concentration reported in the Keeling Mauna Loa data.[196]

Chemists know that methane (CH_4) released into the open air at the average temperature and air pressure at sea level converts spontaneously (oxidizes) to CO_2 and H_2O when in the presence of a gaseous molecule such chlorine. On average, a CH_4 molecule in air will be oxidized to yield a CO_2 molecule and a H_2O molecule within 8 years, a natural process occurring continuously.

Chlorine is found naturally near the surface of warm salty ocean water. Oceans cover more than 70% of the Earth's surface.

---

[195] https://www.sciencedirect.com/topics/earth-and-planetary-sciences/henry-law
[196] https://sealevel.info/co2.html

Like CO_2, most methane is emitted from warm ocean water. Secondly, methane is emitted from the natural breakdown of plant material in soil. In other words, methane emitted by warm ocean water and soil is also a huge source of CO_2 in the Earth's atmosphere and is a component of the net atmospheric CO_2 concentration reported in the Keeling Mauna Loa data.

Thus, the slope (or first derivative) of net atmospheric CO_2 concentration which we see in the above Keeling curve is determined mostly by Henry's Law which is determined mostly by the temperature of the oceans. The warming oceans since the end of the last ice age are the dominant source of net atmospheric CO_2 concentration.

Summarizing so far, we have a huge amount of absorption of CO_2 by nature and a huge amount of emission of CO_2 by nature. The net sum of all these absorption and emission events appears as the upward sloping line of the net atmospheric CO_2 concentration as measured by the instruments on Mauna Loa and displayed in the graphic above.

Now we must address human-produced CO_2. Most human-produced CO_2 results from burning methane, propane, butane, gasoline, kerosene, jet fuels, oil, and coal. We commonly lump these together and call them fossil fuels. An additional major source of human-produced CO_2 is the production of cement.[197]

Government agencies, academia and industry scientists estimate that CO_2 emissions from humans burning fossil fuels increased by 300% (approximately 15% per year) since the year 2000.[198] Measured in millions of tons of CO_2 or carbon, this appears to be a large amount and a large increase. It is calculated based on the CO_2 emitted by burning an amount of fossil fuel. It is not a measurement of CO_2 in the atmosphere. Statistically or visibly examining the slope (first derivative) or examining the rate of change of slope (second derivative) of net atmospheric

---

[197] https://greatclimatedebate.com/global-co2-emissions-from-cement-production/

[198] https://cdiac.ess-dive.lbl.gov/trends/emis/glo_2010.html

CO_2 concentration in the Keeling data, this apparently large amount of human-produced CO_2 since 2000 is not detectable as a change in the first or second derivative. There are no 'shark's teeth' or other peaks or anomalies caused by the surge in human CO_2 emissions; there are no detectable changes in first or second derivative due to the emission of this apparently large amount of human-produced CO_2 which has been emitted into the atmosphere in the relatively short period of time since year 2000.

The emissions of human-produced CO_2 are so tiny compared to the net atmospheric CO_2 concentration that the human-produced emissions cannot be measured or detected as a change in net atmospheric CO_2 concentration, nor a change in the rate of change of net atmospheric CO_2 concentration. In science and statistics, we say that the human-produced CO_2 is statistically insignificant with regard to the net atmospheric CO_2 concentration. The human contribution of CO_2 to the net CO_2 flux cannot be differentiated from random noise in the measurement of the very much larger net atmospheric CO_2 concentration.

Therefore, human-produced CO_2 has no measurable effect on our environment or on Earth's temperature or on global warming or on global cooling.

Accordingly, it logically follows that humans could not change the planet's temperature by either increasing or decreasing the amount of CO_2 in the air. If humans stopped using all fossil fuels and even stopped breathing, there would be no detectable change in the net CO_2 concentration in the air. The planet will warm, or the planet will cool, or the planet's temperature will be flat as an average, climate will change, but in any case, human-produced CO_2 does not significantly contribute. It is very important to understand that point.

Therefore, everything else regarding anthropogenic "greenhouse gases" and so-called anthropogenic global warming or anthropogenic climate change is a purely academic subject. Interesting to some people, but none the less an academic subject. Hundreds of computer models have been developed costing many millions of dollars to calculate "greenhouse" warming due to anthropogenic CO_2 (including the burning of fossil fuels, the volume of cow flatulence, the eating of meat, etc.), but all of these are purely academic subjects for discussion and study. They have no measurable effect on the Earth's climate.

Professor Dr. Donald J. Easterbrook BSc, MSc, Ph.D. Prof Emeritus Geology, Western Washington University pointed out in 2015 that "CO_2 is not the "greenhouse effect." AGW CO_2 is adding 0.0000000006342 watts/m² (joules/second.) This is a calculation only. There is no method to actually measure such a small amount of energy. "Water Vapor is 90-95% of the "greenhouse effect."

Regarding methane (CH_4) as a "greenhouse gas," on a molecule by molecule comparison between CO_2 and CH_4, CH_4 absorbs about 80 times more infrared radiation during a 20-year period than CO_2.[199] But, on the other hand, CO_2 concentration is two orders of magnitude more than CH_4 concentration. And, the reason for this, as explained earlier, is that the methane spontaneously oxidizes to CO_2 and H_2O in the open air. The amount of infrared absorption by a gas is determined by Beer's Law, which specifies that amount of infrared radiation absorbed is linearly proportional to the concentration of the gas.[200] Thus, CO_2 absorbs far more infrared radiation than CH_4, and water vapour—which is about 100 times higher concentration than CO_2—absorbs far more infrared radiation than CO_2. Obviously, humans have no means to control water vapor.

---

[199] https://greatclimatedebate.com/water-vapor-rules-the-greenhouse-system/

[200] https://chem.libretexts.org/Bookshelves/Physical_and_Theoretical_Chemistry_Textbook_Maps/Supplemental_Modules_(Physical_and_T heoretical_Chemistry)/Spectroscopy/Electronic_Spectroscopy/Electr onic_Spectroscopy_Basics/The_Beer-Lambert_Law

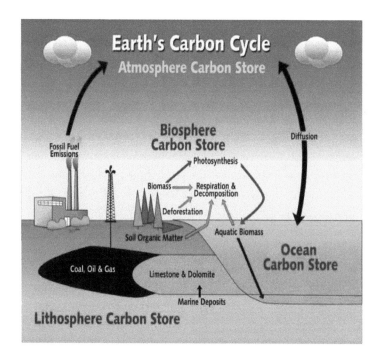

Another part of the Earth's carbon cycle is worth mentioning again. The slope of net atmospheric CO_2 concentration in the air has been consistent since the end of the last ice age. Net atmospheric CO_2 concentration has been increasing. Henry's Law says that 50 to 60 times more CO_2 is dissolved in the oceans than in the air. Logically that implies that the amount of CO_2 in the oceans is now and has been decreasing since the end of the last ice age. So, what happens to the CO_2 that is dissolved in the oceans?

This is a major part of the Earth's carbon cycle. CO_2 dissolved in water is a weak acid. This weak acid reacts with calcium (for example but also other minerals,) which is dissolved in ocean water. There is far more calcium on the Earth and dissolved in the oceans than the total amount carbon in all its forms on the Earth. There is enough calcium in ocean water to chemically combine with all of the carbon that exists on the Earth. Aquatic chemists describe this as oceans being an infinite sink for carbon. This weakly acidic form of carbon dioxide in water combines with calcium in water to form limestone, also known as calcium carbonate, or $CaCO_3$.

Limestone is a solid which settles in water to become sediment on the floor of oceans and seas. Over years of sedimentation, the limestone is compressed by more and more sediment and becomes rock, or it could be incorporated by mollusks and small sea life into their shells and skeletons.

Humans harvest limestone to make buildings and floors. We also burn limestone at high temperature, which is how cement is produced. Burning of limestone to produce cement releases CO_2 back into the atmosphere where once again it can be absorbed by plants to start the carbon cycle again. The other way limestone releases CO_2 back into the air is by the high heat from volcanoes, fissures in the Earth and similar tectonic events.

There are perhaps thousands of these events continually occurring on land and on the ocean floor, a process which has been occurring continuously for billions of years. The CO_2 emitted from tectonic heating of limestone contributes to the net atmospheric CO_2 concentration we see in the Keeling Mauna Loa data. These tectonic processes are orders of magnitude larger than anything humans could do.[201]

In another part of the carbon cycle, enormous amounts of methane (CH_4) are formed on the continental shelves in the ocean in a chemical complex with water and a mineral. It is slurry similar to mud, which, if you bring it to the surface, can be lit with a match. The amount of CH_4 in this slurry and silt on the floor of the oceans is far larger than the total amount of oil ever discovered, perhaps larger by three orders of magnitude.

Where does it come from?

---

[201] https://study.com/academy/lesson/order-of-magnitude-definition-examples.html

This methane is the product of slow and continuous degradation of the carbohydrate molecules in the cells of every living thing. When the cells die and are digested down through the food chain by one animal, insect, fish, human, bacteria after another, when it is rotted, then methane remains. When the molecular bonds in the carbohydrate polymer molecule are broken, the eventual result is methane and water. Rain and rivers eventually carry that CH_4 into the oceans, or else it is emitted into the air and oxidized to CO_2 as previously described. This degradation process and the food chain described earlier are part of what is known as the Earth's carbon cycle.

The slurry complex is known as methane clathrate or methane hydrate. In places around the world there are pools of clathrates that are kilometers thick or slowly flowing down the walls of canyons in the oceans.

Near the boundaries of continents and oceanic plates, deep under the oceans, are subduction zones where the plates of ocean floor meet the continents and are pressed (subducted) beneath the continental shelves.

Clathrate slurries of methane are subducted beneath the continents along with the oceanic plate. In a very slow process taking millions of years but occurring continuously for billions of years, methane under heat, pressure and containment is reformed into longer and more complex hydrocarbons. The CH_4 forms bonds with other CH_4 and larger hydrocarbon molecules are created. This is the reason we will continue to find more gas and oil and the reason we find gas and oil miles beneath the continents and ocean floor where life has never existed.

The movement of the oceanic plates and continents has been as is today creating oil from the continuously dying and rotting cells of living matter, the slow and continuous breakdown of carbohydrate molecules that were originally created by plants absorbing CO_2 from the air.

In summary, the human contribution to the net atmospheric CO_2 concentration and to the temperature of the Earth is trivial and statistically insignificant; negligible and of academic interest only.

How insignificant?

As an example, let's say that the Earth was cooling, and humans decided to warm the oceans in order to warm the air. Water is denser than air, so water retains heat better than air. The heat content of the oceans is about 3 orders of magnitude greater than the atmosphere, 5.6×10^{24} compared to 5×10^{21} Joules/degree Kelvin.

If we calculate or look up on a website the total power output of all of the power facilities of all kinds on the Earth, and then assume we will use all of that power to heat the oceans and do nothing else with that power, it would take about 10,000 years to raise the temperature of the oceans by a mere 1°C. That is how insignificant the human contribution would be.

However, working to make engines better and fossil fuels burn as efficiently as possible will make our lives more pleasant. But it is not CO_2 that is dirty, or polluting. As explained above, CO_2 is plant food and necessary for life on this planet. More CO_2 is better. But inefficiently or partially burned fossil fuels release hydrocarbons like benzenes into the air which are not good; this is true air pollution.

Reducing real hydrocarbon pollution from inefficient fuel mixtures and inefficient engines is the engineering and chemistry challenge for humans. Attempts and costs to remove or reduce human-produced CO_2 are wasted effort and money.

Another real problem is plastics that have been designed to be non-bio-degradable or non-recyclable. They are ugly to look at, problematic garbage, and destructive for sea life, birds, insects, etc.

Ultimately, these poorly designed plastic products are harmful to the environment and delay the carbon cycle. But these materials too will eventually break down over long periods of time and release CO_2 into the air so that it can feed plants. Bio-degradable plastics are sensible.

As we are discussing the purely academic subject of AGW, there are a few other points worth noting.

Antarctica and Greenland are currently accumulating ice mass, not losing ice mass. The peninsula of Antarctica that points north toward Argentina has been warming due to sub-ice and sub-sea volcanic activity.

That area has been losing ice on land and sea, but in the last few years, overall the Antarctica continent a net increase of ice on land is observed. The ice mass gained on land exceeds the ice mass lost on land. The ice mass on land is increasing and becoming thicker. The weight of that ice is causing an increase in glacial calving at the coastlines. And all of this is also observed in Greenland.

Once again, we come back to slope. The rate of change in sea level (i.e. the slope) has not changed. That is, the second derivative of sea level has not changed.

Sea level has been increasing (i.e., the slope or first derivative has been positive) since the end of the last ice age; at that time sea level was perhaps 400 feet below today's sea level. However, if ice continues to accumulate on land, or if ice mass begins to decrease on land, then we will see a change in the slope of sea levels, (i.e. a change in second derivative of sea level with respect to time.) So far, there has been no detectable change in slope of sea level. Sea level has been very slowly rising.

Ice floating in the oceans or floating in lakes, so called sea ice, does not affect sea level.

Multiple studies by NASA and others show that the Earth is becoming greener as the net atmospheric CO_2 concentration has increased. Many science studies, and databases of studies, show that more CO_2 and more warming increases the growth of green plants in forests, in grains and other foods, etc.

See the graphic below.

The human contribution is trivial. But we can all hope that CO_2 continues to increase and that temperatures stay flat or once again begin a slow warming trend. Average global temperature has been essentially flat (zero slope) for about 20 years now.

The *only* way carbon gets into plants and thus into animals, insects, fish, humans etc. is when the plants absorb CO_2 from the air for photosynthesis.

When plants use CO_2 to make carbohydrate molecules, they produce oxygen as a by-product. Humans and most other non-plant life survive on the oxygen which is produced as a by-product of plant photosynthesis. Higher net atmospheric CO_2 concentration results in more plant growth. Lower CO_2 concentration results less plant growth, which also implies less food and a less green Earth.

We now have over 35 years of Landsat satellite imagery showing that a positive (increasing) slope of atmospheric CO_2 concentration is greening our planet.

Plant life is flourishing.

Could one hope for anything more promising than this? Quite the opposite of what the world's climate alarmists contend *should* be happening to Earth's vegetation, rising atmospheric CO2 enrichment is proving to be a tremendous *biospheric benefit*, overpowering the many real and negative influences that society and nature have inflicted upon it over the past three decades, as shown in the figure below.

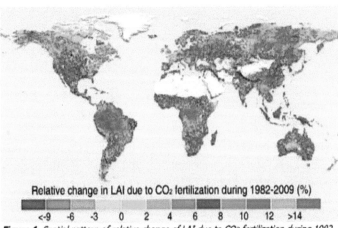

Relative change in LAI due to CO₂ fertilization during 1982-2009 (%)

<9   -6   -3   0   2   4   6   8   10   12   >14

Figure 1. *Spatial pattern of relative change of LAI due to CO2 fertilization during 1982 to 2009. The relative change of LAI in each pixel is derived from the ratio of the increment of LAI driven by elevated atmospheric CO2 to the 28-year average value of LAI simulated by model ensemble mean under scenario S1. Source: Figure S12, supplementary information from Zhu et al. (2016)*

Finally, satellites measuring infrared radiation emitted from the Earth's upper atmosphere into outer space are reporting that infrared radiation from Earth to outer space is currently decreasing (i.e. the slope or first derivative is negative.) That means that the Earth is receiving less energy from the Sun and is therefore emitting less energy into outer space.

In other words, the Earth is presently cooling. It may take years before we perceive or measure this cooling down on Earth's surface due to the insulating effect of the oceans and atmosphere. The oceans especially act as an enormous insulator, far more than the atmosphere, delaying radiation of energy from the surface back into outer space.

Once again, the impact of human activity on climate change, while purely academic, is interesting to study, but, as you can see from the information provided above, the actions of humans with regard to CO_2 emissions will have no measurable impact on global warming or global cooling.

Probably the most significant thing we can do to improve our environment is to plant more forests and stop cutting rainforests.

References

Professor Murray Salby, What is really Behind the Increase of Atmospheric CO_2? [202]
Professor Jamal Munshi, Responsiveness of Atmospheric CO_2 Emissions: A Note[203]
Wolfgang Knorr, Is the Airborne Fraction of Anthropogenic CO_2 Emissions Increasing? [204]

---

[202] https://greatclimatedebate.com/what-is-really-behind-the-increase-of-atmospheric-co2/

[203] https://greatclimatedebate.com/responsiveness-of-atmospheric-co2-to-anthropogenic-emissions-a-note/

[204] https://greatclimatedebate.com/is-the-airborne-fraction-of-anthropogenic-co-2-emissions-increasing/

Chapter 10—2018 and Beyond, Victory Lap

Doubt is not a pleasant condition, but certainty is absurd.
—Voltaire

IT HAS BEEN many years since the publication of *Slaying the Sky Dragon: Death of the Greenhouse Gas Theory*; long years in which old friends have passed away and new ones have come into the fold.

2018 marked thirty years since Dr. James Hansen and UK Prime Minister, Margaret Thatcher, put concerns about greenhouse gases and man-made global warming onto the global political map.

Looking back to 1988, we now see that NASA, the world's most prestigious space agency, peopled by the brightest and best scientists, was hijacked for nefarious purposes.

Hansen's presentation to the U.S. Congressional committee was a masterful political stunt. It succeeded in persuading policymakers, but more importantly, the general public, that NASA was endorsing his claim of *"99 percent certainty"* that carbon dioxide was our climate's control knob and human emissions had taken us close to a catastrophic *tipping point.*

This book, our members and our principles of association scorn such appeals to authority to dress up party political points scoring. In truth, the original Slayers were adamant their message was about the science, not the politics. Indeed, founding member, Dr. Martin Hertzberg was a lifelong Democrat. John O'Sullivan, who first brought the group together, never voted for any political party other than for the British Labour Party. Others, who shall remain nameless, also don't fit the stereotype given to us.

Whatever our various political differences we were as one in the shock we felt when reading many of the emails of government climate 'scientists' exposed in the Climategate scandal.[205] For example, Dr. Phil Jones, Britain's most senior government climate scientist, head the of the Climate Research Unit, University of East Anglia, even admitted in an intercepted e-mail that much of the historic temperature data was fake. Jones revealed to his clique of international government researchers that the sea surface temperature data in the Southern Hemisphere temperature record are mostly made up.

Tom,
   The issue Ray alludes to is that in addition to the issue
of many more drifters providing measurements over the last
5-10 years, the measurements are coming in from places where
we didn't have much ship data in the past. For much of the SH
between 40 and 60S the normals are mostly made up as there is
very little ship data there.
   Whatever causes the divergence in your plot it is down to
the ocean.
   You could try doing an additional plot. Download from
the CRU web site the series for SH land. It doesn't matter if
is from CRUTEM3 or CRUTEM3v (the former would be better). If that
still has the divergence, then it is the oceans causing the
problem. What you're seeing is too rapid to be real.
Cheers
Phil

---

[205] http://www.lavoisier.com.au/articles/greenhouse-science/climate-change/climategate-emails.pdf

Jones was exposed, like many of his colleagues, as a crook. These were (and still are) practitioners of post-normal science. Dr. Tim Ball's exceptional, best-selling book, *The Deliberate Corruption of Climate Science* exposes in detail how post-normal science is a veneer for using subject opinion-determined consensus to override the objective, empirically-focused traditional scientific method that served humanity so well since the time of Sir Isaac Newton.

Our shared belief is that adherence to the traditional scientific method, as extolled by Karl Popper, is the right way—the only way—to proceed in the pursuit of discerning what is fact or fiction in the climate debate.

Please be assured, most of us were formerly believers in man-made global warming. Our skepticism and climate realism has *grown* not abated over time.

Certainly, none of us would have foreseen a decade ago that we would eventually be united in our conviction that all the available empirical evidence would show that carbon dioxide can only cool, never warm anything.

Beyond doubt, the trend of thinking in the peer-reviewed literature has shifted dramatically toward the Slayer position. We see now many studies using empirical evidence that is affirming a lowered expectation of any climate impact from CO_2.

Too many honest scientists were sucked into Hansen's game. Among them was Spencer R. Weart, director of the Center for the History of Physics of the American Institute of Physics. Weart is pre-eminent among establishment science historians in splashing gloss. Weart's book, *The Discovery of Global Warming* is compulsory reading for modern students in this field.

Weart plugged Hansen's comparison of Mars and Venus with Earth, asserting life as being very fragile and vulnerable to any climate shifts. Weart writes:

In the 1960s and 1970s, observations of Mars and

Venus showed that planets that seemed much like the Earth could have frightfully different atmospheres. The greenhouse effect had made Venus a furnace, while lack of atmosphere had locked Mars in a deep freeze.[206]

That passage and its unwitting or intended deception leads the reader to assume that the greenhouse gas theory was dominant, at the very least from the 1960s and 1970s.

But as we showed herein, the important Charney report of 1979 omitted any mention of the term. So, if we believe settled science has settled nomenclature, then Weart does his readers a disservice by such obfuscation.

Worse still, Like Venus, Mars has an atmosphere with about 960,000PPM CO_2 (96%). And yet the planet's average temperature is -55°C.

The difference between the average temperature on Venus (462°C), Earth (15°C), and Mars (-55°C) has everything to do with atmospheric pressure, or density, not on CO_2 concentration (96%, 0.04%, and 96% respectively).

If the greenhouse hypothesis worked as assumed, Mars would not be -55°C. In addition to atmospheric pressure, distance from the Sun also plays a significant role in the planetary temperature.

Also, in line with the Slayers on the role of adiabatic[207] pressure on climate on all such planets are Drs. John Robertson and George Chilingar, professors of geology and environmental (petroleum) engineering. They have authored 12 textbooks, 70 books, and 575 scientific papers between them. Both are verifiable experts in heat transfer physics.

---

[206]

http://www.hup.harvard.edu/catalog.php?isbn=9780674031890&content=reviews

[207] adiabatic: the constant decline in temperature of an air parcel as it rises in the atmosphere due to pressure drop and gas expansion

Robertson and Chilingar affirm adiabatic pressure is perfectly capable of explaining the variances in temperatures on planets like Earth, Mars, and Venus using each planet's atmospheric pressure gradient without reliance on the traditional greenhouse effect theory that assigns a governing role to carbon dioxide.[208]

The determinative role of atmospheric pressure in planetary temperatures has also been asserted by Dr. Oleg Sorokhtin of the Russian Academy of Sciences. Though not outright rejecting the GHE these scientists call it the adiabatic theory of greenhouse effect.[209]

Nonetheless, these scientists put the dampers on any radiative-driven control by carbon dioxide as Sorokin et al find:

> *According to the adiabatic theory of greenhouse effect (see below), besides the Sun's radiation, the main determining factors of the Earth's climate are the Earth's atmospheric pressure and its composition. The denser the atmosphere (i.e., the higher the atmospheric pressure), the warmer the climate.*[210]

As Florides and Christodoulides find:

> *...the average surface temperature of the Earth is determined by the solar constant, the precession angle of the planet, the mass (pressure) of the atmosphere, and the specific heat of the*

---

[208] https://www.wiley.com/en-gb/Environmental+Aspects+of+Oil+and+Gas+Production-p-9781119117377)

[209] See: Sorokhtin et al., 2007; Florides and Christodoulides (2009).

[210] http://www.ask-force.org/web/Global-Warming/Sorokhtin-Evolution-Earths-Global-Climate-2009.pdf

atmospheric mixture of gases.[211]

In 2017, adding to the peer-reviewed literature asserting carbon dioxide's innocence came a group of Italian scientists with a study asserting that climate models "are very likely flawed" in the face of no global warming trend this century.

The Italian scientists concluded that:

> *The [greenhouse gas] theory might even require a deep re-examination.*[212]

All this despite atmospheric levels of CO_2 smashing through the 400PPM when climate alarmists had spent years warning us at 350PPM was the level at which a "tipping point" would be crossed.[213]

We know that CO_2 in the past reached about 8,000PPM. If pre-industrial levels of carbon dioxide were about 250PPM, then 8,000PPM represents 5 doublings of CO_2.

If there is a positive water feedback loop, then we would have seen runaway global warming when levels of carbon dioxide were at around 6,000 to 8,000PPM.

At all measured time scales (both paleo and yearly), carbon dioxide lags temperature change.[214] All of this strongly supports the view that CO_2 is a response not a driver of temperature

---

[211]

https://www.researchgate.net/publication/23226792_Global_warming_and_carbon_Dioxide_through_sciences

[212] *Natural Climate Variability, Part 2: Interpretation of the post 2000 Temperature Standstill*, Scafetta, Mirandola & Bianchini, International Journal of Heat and Technology, Vol. 35, Special Issue 1, September 2017, pp. S18-S26

[213] https://350.org/science/

[214] https://www2.meteo.uni-bonn.de/bibliothek/Flohn_Publikationen/K287-K320_1981-1985/K299.pdf

change.

The long and protracted battle for control of the minds of people has involved trillions of dollars to prop up a narrative relying on junk greenhouse gas science to foster large-scale changes in society. Thomas Kuhn defined these changes, called paradigm shifts, as "a fundamental change in approach or underlying assumptions."

The greenhouse effect is a theoretical conceptualization. It has never been observed. It's never been proven. The only reason anyone believes it is necessary is because of the argument from authority combined with unphysical mathematical gymnastics.

The new paradigm shift relies on objective, empirical data. It shall be viewed through the lens of science comporting with the Popperian principles of verification by replicability, openness and above all, falsifiability.

But today, the changes point in the opposite direction of what was intended. On the back of free and global access to information on the Internet we have enjoyed a renaissance; the free and global open exchange of scientific analysis and ideas beyond the gatekeeping of mainstream journals.

It works well in other fields of debate. Like or loathe him, Donald J. Trump cleverly used online social media. He tapped into a palpable universal disconnect of the public with those establishment 'experts' who, for too long, controlled the prevailing paradigm.

As in politics, so it has come to pass in science. The common core is an anti-establishment shift (not 'left' versus 'right' politics). It stems from past failures (institutional corruption and incompetence).

Citizen scientists, retired academics, applied scientists and engineers in their thousands rallied together in the blogosphere to be the intelligentsia of deplorables overthrowing a rotten and complacent (government) scientific establishment serving only government's own ends.

National academies had sold us out. Mainstream journals,

too. Alternative bodies for independent thinkers is the only solution to preserve objective, open science.

We are one such emergent body, Principia Scientific International, growing far beyond a blog into a physical entity, a legally-incorporated registered company with a London office. Hopefully, others will follow suit.

We oppose post-normal science and look to the guidance of traditionalists in the field such as British philosopher G. E. Moore. His 1903 book *Principia Ethica* is a stark warning for our time; it speaks to the dangers of the 'appeal to nature' and the indeterminate construct of moralism; thus, objective science is best served searching for truth rather than 'goodness.'

The message has been getting through. A paradigm shift is underway in the very halls of academic excellence. Myles Allen, a geosystem scientist at the University of Oxford conceded the retreat from the post-normal nightmare:

> *We haven't seen that rapid acceleration in warming after 2000 that we see in the models. We haven't seen that in the observations.*[215]

In a video produced by PragerU, eminent Princeton University physicist William Happer had this to say about greenhouse gas-obsessed climate models:

> *And I know they don't work. They haven't worked in the past. They don't work now. And it's hard to imagine when, if ever, they'll work in the foreseeable future.*[216]

---

[215] https://www.thetimes.co.uk/edition/news/we-were-wrong-worst-effects-of-climate-change-can-be-avoided-say-scientists-k9p5hg5l0

[216] https://www.prageru.com/videos/can-climate-models-predict-climate-change

Happer astutely recognises these are mathematical models based on fudged numbers. As was pointed out in the peer-reviewed paper of Dr. Gerhard Gerlich of the Institute of Mathematical Physics at the Technical University Carolo-Wilhelmina, Germany and Dr. Ralf D. Tscheuschner in 2007:

> *Mathematically, even within the most simplified models you cannot predict anything, because all these ones crudely approximate non-linear partial differential equations with unknown boundary conditions. There is simply no physical foundation of the computer models with and without CO_2.*[217]

Now a final dose of physical reality: Cato Institute climate scientists Patrick Michaels and Chip Knappenberger found that real-world warming has been on the low end of model predictions for the last six decades,[218] and a more recent study published in the journal Nature Geoscience found a similar trend.

Kenneth Richard has collated the evidence from the scientific literature (over 30 peer-reviewed papers) documenting some of the regions of the world where there has been no detectable warming trend during the period that anthropogenic carbon dioxide emissions have been claimed to have dominated climate changes (generally since the mid-20th century).[219]

Richard reports:

> *As the scientists indicate, large portions of the Pacific, Atlantic, Indian, and Southern Oceans have*

---

[217] https://arxiv.org/abs/0707.1161

[218] http://dailycaller.com/2015/12/28/climate-models-have-been-wrong-about-global-warming-for-six-decades/

[219] http://notrickszone.com/2016/08/15/abundant-scientific-evidence-that-global-warming-is-a-made-up-concept/?utm_source=twitterfeed&utm_medium=twitter#sthash.SJW8Gh1t.dpuf

been cooling in recent decades. There is also scientific documentation of recent ($20^{th}/21^{st}$ century) cooling (or no long-term warming trend) in the southeastern U.S., Northern Europe, Antarctica, China, Canada/Canadian Arctic, Western South America (Chile), South Africa, Greenland, Iceland, Antarctica, and the Arctic. One has to wonder how and from where a large net "global warming" signal could have been obtained when there has been so much regional cooling.

Among the cited papers are: Riser et al., 2016; Wunsch and Heimbach, 2014; Dong and Zhou, 2014; Robson et al., 2016; Fan et al., 2014; Purich et al., 2016; Rogers, 2013; Chattopadhyay and Edwards, 2016; Christy and McNider, 2016; Esper et al., 2012; Murray and Heggie, 2016; Divine et al., 2011; Turner et al., 2016; Altnau et al., 2015; Sinclair et al., 2012; Doran et al., 2002; Yuan et al., 2015; de Jong et al., 2013; Zhu et al., 2016; Wang et al., 2016; Holzer et al., 2015; Genarretti et al., 2014; Pitman and Smith, 2012; Zinke et al., 2014; Andres, 2016; Chylek et al., 2004; Hanna and Cappelen, 2003; Dahl-Jensen et al., 1998; Box et al., 2009; Hanna et al., 2004; Kahl et al., 1993; Hanhijärvi et al., 2013; Zhang et al., 2015.

About 80% of the contiguous U.S., Europe and much of Asia, including parts of the Arctic (Eastern Siberia), cooled during the 1990-2015 period. These cooling regions may encompass approximately one-third of the top half of the globe.

Despite global warming, recent winters in the Northeastern United States (US), Europe and especially in Asia were anomalously cold. Some mid-latitude regions like Central Asia and eastern Siberia even show a downward temperature trend in winter over the past decades.[220]

The Southern Ocean surrounding Antarctica and extending into the South Pacific has been cooling since 1979:

> *Observed Southern Ocean changes over recent decades include a surface freshening (Durack and Wijffels 2010; Durack et al. 2012; de Lavergne et al. 2014), surface cooling (Fan et al. 2014; Marshall et al. 2014; Armour et al. 2016; Purich et al. 2016a) and circumpolar increase in Antarctic sea ice (Cavalieri and Parkinson 2008; Comiso and Nishio 2008; Parkinson and Cavalieri 2012). ... The majority of CMIP5 models do not simulate a surface cooling and increase in sea ice, as seen in observations.*[221]

Such richness in the scientific evidence, freely shared, fuels this new-found pragmatism.

In 2012 even the powerful science journal *Nature* was cottoning on that there was a real problem in the science saying the... "...research is riddled with systematic errors." [222]

The same year, NOAA's extreme weather expert, Martin Hoerling, slammed James Hansen:

> *The Hansen piece is policy more than it is science, to be sure, and one can read it for the former. But facts should, and do, matter to some...he [Hansen] writes from passion and not reason.*[223]

---

[220] Cohen et al. 2014a; McCusker et al. 2016

[221] Purich et al., 2018

[222] https://www.nature.com/news/beware-the-creeping-cracks-of-bias-1.10600?nc=1370467662440

[223] https://dotearth.blogs.nytimes.com/2012/05/11/another-view-on-extreme-weather-in-a-warming-climate/

17 new scientific papers have followed suit to put reason above passion and thrown further doubt on the CO_2 radiative greenhouse effect, as Kenneth Richard demonstrates.[224]

Particularly impressive are Nikolov and Zeller in a 2017 paper. They beautifully affirm Slayer science by inter alia showing...

> ...*surface heating can accurately be predicted over a broad range of conditions using only two forcing variables: top-of-the-atmosphere solar irradiance and total surface atmospheric pressure... The hypothesis that a freely convective atmosphere could retain (trap) radiant heat due its opacity has remained undisputed since its introduction in the early 1800s even though it was based on a theoretical conjecture that has never been proven experimentally.*[225]

Therefore the heat-trapping hypothesis remains just that; a hypothesis, with no evidence to support it.

The other peer-reviewed, published papers in the same vein are: Allmendinger, 2017; Blaauw, 2017; Huang et al., 2017; Viterito, 2017; Hertzberg et al., 2017; Song, Wang & Tang, 2016; Manheimer, 2016; Hertzberg and Schreuder, 2016; Mikhailovich et al., 2016; Vares et al., 2016; Easterbrook, 2016; Chemke et al., 2016; Haine, 2016; Ellis and Palmer, 2016; Evans, 2016; Gervais, 2016.

As Dr. Tim Ball says, the only trend in the literature now is distinctly headed towards zero for climate sensitivity to carbon

---

[224] http://notrickszone.com/2017/06/08/17-new-scientific-papers-dispute-co2-greenhouse-effect-as-primary-explanation-for-climate-change/#sthash.JrxiNXy5.dpbs

[225] https://www.omicsonline.org/open-access/new-insights-on-the-physical-nature-of-the-atmospheric-greenhouse-effect-deduced-from-an-empirical-planetary-temperature-model.pdf

dioxide.

So, why has it gone so wrong for 'climate sensitivity' to carbon dioxide?

True believers will tell you Climate Sensitivity (CS) is real and measurable in Nature and that there exists a carbon dioxide/temperature logarithmic relationship (CO_2/Temp log).

We are then glibly told that "for each doubling of CO_2 in the atmosphere our planet's temperature will increase by [you fill the blank] degrees."

So, you would think such a 'formula' had been derived in a laboratory, with simulated conditions to that of the atmosphere, because such an experiment would be impossible to perform in the real atmosphere.

But here is the first problem for GHE believers. Our atmosphere is an open system and every laboratory a closed system, so how can any such CS formula devised in a lab have any validity? Well, it can't. It's that simple.

Dr. Ball says:

> *The concept of climate sensitivity was first derived, as with so much done on climate, to overcome a perception problem not a scientific one. Who did the actual calculations of climate sensitivity is not documented to my knowledge. The earliest paper I have is the 1984 paper by James Hansen and Takahashi referenced in this paper.*[226]

Dr. Ball tells us that the need for climate sensitivity began back in the early days of attacks on cattle as the source of methane causing warming.

It was triggered by animal rights people and promoted by a

226

http://www.columbia.edu/~jeh1/mailings/2012/20120508_Climat eSensitivity.pdf campaign and book, *Beyond Beef*, by Jeremy Rifkin, a long-time provocateur and promoter of misinformation.

The bias was disclosed in the failure to mention the 250 million cows in India or the replacement of buffalo with cows in North America among other factors that don't produce any foodstuff, but that's another story.

The problem with blaming methane (CH_4), as they are trying to do again, is that it is a "greenhouse gas" but at 0,00017% of the total atmosphere and 0.36% of the main three, water vapor (H_2O) (95%) and carbon dioxide (CO_2) (4%) by volume.

So, methane and later CO_2 are minuscule amounts that the public naturally said seem insignificant. That term, by volume was quickly challenged by the claim that methane and CO_2 were small by volume but much more important by effectiveness (remember our earlier analogy using the potency of cyanide?)

This idea later became sensitivity, but there was never agreement on the amount. The dominant usage was that methane (CH_4) was twenty times more effective than CO_2 which was 6 times more effective than (H_2O).

Joe Postma:

> *They arbitrarily drew a straight line from the temperature at the end of the little ice age, to today's temperature, and said that the increase in temperature must be from the increase in carbon dioxide during that time.*
>
> *So, it is just an assumption, which they then treat as fact, and insert into the climate models.*
>
> *The models are always wrong because the increase in temperature since the little ice age is NOT due to the increase in carbon dioxide from the period. The little ice age ended for other reason and we went back to more normal temperatures.*

We hope this helps our readers. If nothing else it will confirm that the issue is political not scientific, which is why it is difficult to track original sources.

Remember, zero sensitivity validates the null hypothesis. The greenhouse gas dragon is thus slain.

Hansen's exploitation of the authority and prestige of NASA to cover up the shambles of his fudged pseudo-science at the Goddard Institute of Space Science (GISS) in Manhattan took a severe blow when his former colleagues blew the whistle.

Dr. Duane Thresher recently gave us a unique insight into the mindset of his former colleagues and how they operated. He reveals:

> *While I was at NASA GISS, we used to make fun of the physicists/mathematicians at the National Bomb Labs for getting into climate modeling.*

Urging skeptics to "follow the money," Thresher exposed how billions were wasted to make it appear the models were produced by teams of experts deftly applying the very best supercomputers money could buy.

The reality contradicted that façade. Dr. Thresher recalls:

> *For my master's in atmospheric science, I was at the University of Arizona. My advisor was Dr. Robert Dickinson, a climate big shot at the time from the National Center for Atmospheric Research (NCAR). He could really haul in the grant money.*
>
> *They got a supercomputer, a "mini" but still very expensive. Supercomputers need to be cooled. They put the supercomputer in the supply closet off the terminal room and shut the door. It crashed frequently due to overheating. They opened the door and put a fan on the floor in the doorway. It crashed less frequently.*

It has been of immense satisfaction to watch, month by month, another paper here, a study there, each undermining a travesty of a 'climate consensus' that has stymied real progress in this infant field for three decades.

There should be no place in science for trickery, showmanship and political passion. Science demands cool heads and rationality. Recently, Russian scientists (more dispassionate and rational than Hansen et al.) have also declared the GHE dead.

In essence, as long as there is a free and unfettered sharing of ideas and information online, there is every chance what is objectively right will prevail over falsehoods and misconceptions.

The momentum is ours.

Chapter 11—Principia Scientific International

To kill an error is as good a service as, and sometimes even better than, the establishing of a new truth or fact.
—Charles Darwin

PSI Core Values

OUR TEAM OF writers are unpaid, receive no financial inducements, favors or promises for creating this work. As a large group of independents we hold diverse political opinions—of the left, center and the right—but have determined our work will be free of party politics.

Please read our Mission statement.[227] Principia Scientific International represents transparency and truth; we shun the vagaries of political advocacy and choose not to subordinate ourselves to the moralizing pre-determinism of discredited 'post normal' science.

The essence of genuine scientific inquiry shall exemplify the

---

[227]   https://principia-scientific.org/psi-mission-statement/

sui generis, or the abiding maxim that goodness is indefinable and exists in science only insofar as the pursuit of truth ought to be our abiding goal.

Our members feel a moral duty to preserve the traditional methods of open scientific inquiry free from persecution, ridicule and censure.

New Renaissance of the Traditional Scientific Method

The Association is indebted for its name to Sir Isaac Newton's *Principia Mathematica* that signaled the modern legacy of the English Scientific Method, often shortened to just the traditional Scientific Method.

But also we give thanks to British philosopher G. E. Moore and his 1903 book *Principia Ethica* that cautioned us as to the dangers of the 'appeal to nature' and the indeterminate construct of moralism; thus objective science is best served searching for truth rather than 'goodness.'

Sir Isaac Newton (1642-1727)

Reclaiming a Scientific Legacy

Over the past three decades there has grown a widespread perception of increased corporate and governmental meddling in science; disenfranchised specialists have sought to be heard in the one forum not yet entirely constrained by the gatekeeping mentality of self-serving politicians, media and publishing outlets: the Internet.

With the Internet as our main, but not exclusive, medium of operation we strive to redress the balance and by our strength in numbers, advance the work of science authors and advocates seeking to distribute important new ideas/theories untainted by subjective ideology. To achieve our goals it is essential for us to seek to form a large, international subscriber-based association whereby those of talent and merit, in this cause may receive this association's technical, financial and moral support.

Donate and Support Open and Principled Science

Other than purchasing this book, please consider helping PSI's non-political mission to advance the traditional scientific method by making a donation at our website: principia-scientific.org. The widest public awareness and support is desperately needed if science is not to become an ever more exploited tool for the cynical manipulation of public perception in the furtherance of unprincipled and dystopian government and corporate ends.

Our Main Functions

PSI aims to promote best scientific practice in the community; to defend the interests of the members, to educate specialists and non-specialists about new theories and refinements in best practice; to disseminate amongst our members, domestically and internationally, news and views for the betterment of their knowledge and performance.

Our specific objectives include:

- Promoting the broadest possible dissemination of impartial science information untainted by politics or corporate interest in as many languages and to as many nations as possible.

- Advancing independent, non-affiliated scientific discoveries unencumbered by political ideology or corporate financial interest.

- Providing impartial scientific advice and evidence to international policymakers, news outlets and the general public

- Being a cost effective ebook publishing service to our members at preferential rates for their personal and career advancement.

- Offering financial support either by grant or loan, to authors in science who we believe have potential to advance the association's core values.

- Discouraging inappropriate or unconscionable scientific methods by exposing them where they are proven to exist.

- Publicizing our successes via the Internet and mainstream media as appropriate (including television, books, radio, film).

> *A man may imagine things that are false, but he can only understand things that are true, for if the things be false, the apprehension of them is not understanding.*
> —*Sir Isaac Newton*